Over the Fells

With best wishes

Bob Orrell

By the Same Author

Saddle Tramp in the Lake District

Saddle Tramp in the Highlands

Saddle Tramp on the Isle of Man

Lakeland Monuments

Around and About Emmerdale

The Best Guide to Ravenglass

Amulet - a charm restored and sailed to the Western Isles

The History of Harrison and Hetherington Ltd, Carlisle.

Blowout

Over The Fells

by

Bob Orrell

Bob Orrell Publications

Bob Orrell Publications
Ain House Cottage, Irton,
Holmbrook, Cumbria CA19 1XA

ISBN   1 872880 07 X

Copyright © 2003 Bob Orrell
www.boborrell.co.uk
First published in UK by
Oxford University Press 1984

British Library Cataloguing in Publication Data
available.

Photographs by Bob Orrell
Cover design by Louis Mackay

Printed in Kent
by JRDigital Print Services Ltd
Produced by Author Publishing Ltd

To

Thor and Sammy

Acknowledgements

The author is extremely grateful to the following suppliers, who generously provided equipment for the journey:-

Field & Trek, Brentwood	sleeping bags, stoves water carrier, billies, compass
George Fisher, Keswick	Waterproof suits
Fjallraven, Harrogate	Kanken rucksacks
G T Hawkins, Northampton	Climbing boots
P D Hendren, Whitehaven	Photographic equipment
Marilyn Hutchcroft, Ennerdale	Handspun Herdwick sweaters
R Saunders Ltd, Chigwell	Saunders Base Camp tent

Introduction to the 2003 Edition

When Oxford University Press first asked me to write this book for youngsters almost two decades ago, I wanted it to be a true story of actual events rather than a novel, and I hope that you will enjoy reading about the journey I made with Abi and Philip, Thor and Sammy as much as we enjoyed making it. A revived interest in the book has enabled me to publish this new paperback edition, and I am pleased to include many photographs taken during the journey that were not in the first edition.

This book is for young people and I have often been asked, "Would we need to be experienced mountaineers to follow your route?" Even without a pony to carry camping gear and provisions the route would make a wonderful walking/camping holiday and you would return from it with a knowledge of the real Lake District you will not find in a tourist brochure.

The first essential is to have someone in charge of the party who is experienced in mountain travel and, provided that you have the proper clothing and footwear and you keep a careful eye on the weather, there is enormous enjoyment to be had from traversing places like the high-level path by Napes Needle on Great Gable or bivouacing for the night on Striding Edge, Helvellyn. The Lake District is there to be enjoyed, but enjoy it safely.

Bob Orrell
Eskdale, 2003

Over the Fells

- - - - - Route Taken

Workington

Bassenthwaite

Keswick
Loweswater
Derwentwater

Whitehaven
Crummock
Water

Thirlmere
Ullswater

Buttermere
Patterdale

Ennerdale
Water
Gillerthwaite

Grasmere
Ambleside

Wastwater

Coniston
Hawkshead
Windermere

Ravenglass
Bowness
Coniston
Water

N
W — E
S

Barrow in Furness

map by Jean Thompson

Chapter One

'This is a funny looking saddle,' exclaimed Philip, lifting the pack-saddle off the floor, 'where do you sit?'

'It's not for sitting on,' I said, 'it's a pack-saddle and it's only used for carrying things like boxes and bags. We're going to carry our camping equipment on it.'

'But what are all these straps for?' asked Abi, trying to sort out a tangle of harness.

'I can show you better tomorrow when we load Thor,' I said. 'It looks complicated, but it's quite easy to understand. Just stack it on the table for now. I want to check if anything is missing.'

The summer holiday was with us at last and for Philip and Abi it was to be a holiday with a difference. They had spent a lot of their spare time helping to look after my ponies and their parents had said I could take them with me on a journey through the Lake District.

At first my suggestion of a walking tour was greeted with groans and excuses.

'We live in the Lake District and can see it every day,' grumbled Abi. 'In any case, I can't possibly carry a rucksack, it makes by back ache.'

'I think I've sprained my ankle playing football,' said Philip, limping round the room. 'Look, it's swelling.' He waved his leg in the air, but before I could examine it he had hurriedly pulled his boots on.

'Oh well, we'll not bother then,' I said casually. 'It's just that I thought we might take Thor with us as a pack-pony to carry the tent and equipment.'

The response was electric.

'Take Thor as a pack-pony!' cried Abi. 'What a marvellous idea. I don't mind walking as long as I don't have to carry a heavy rucksack.'

Philip's eyes shone with excitement. 'I've always wanted to really explore the Lake District. We could follow the old smugglers' trails and try to find their caves.'

There was a mad scramble to find a map and spread it out on the kitchen table. 'We're here,' I said, pointing to a dot that marked my small farm at Gillerthwaite in the middle of Ennerdale Forest. 'We could follow the pack-horse route through the forest then climb over the fells by the passes and then, if you want to go along the smugglers' paths we could work our way to the coast at Ravenglass. We could go over the fells again to Coniston and across Lake Windermere by the ferry to the eastern fells at Kentmere and eventually make our way back to Ennerdale. What do you think of that?'

'It sounds fabulous,' said Philip, following the route on the map with his finger.

'How far will we have to walk each day?' asked Abi, cautiously.

'Oh, I think seven or eight miles a day will be enough,' I said. 'A lot depends on the weather, but we can always find a place to camp if you feel you're too tired to go on.'

Making a list of things we needed for the journey was great fun and the day before we were due to set off the kitchen floor was littered with the pack-saddle and harness, plastic bags bulging with breakfast cereal, packets of soup, dried potatoes, apples, oranges, cheese, sugar, lemonade crystals, chocolate, margarine, biscuits, matches and a first aid kit. Then there were sleeping-bags, foam rubber mattresses, a tent, knives, forks, spoons, cups, plates, pans and a paraffin stove. Abi had packed enough spare clothes for an expedition to the North Pole instead of two weeks in the Lake District.

'You can't possibly take all this, Abi,' I said, staggering under the weight of a bag full of what she insisted were 'essentials'.

'It's full of bath salts and tins of talcum powder to make her smell nice,' said Philip mischievously, 'all girls are like that.'

'No they're not,' retorted Abi, 'at least I'm not. I just like to be clean that's all.'

'You've got a tin of talcum powder in your bag, I've seen it,' taunted Philip. Abi went red and started to reply, but I interrupted. 'Would you two stop arguing, we've got a lot to do before morning. You can take one change of clothes each, two pairs of socks, a sweater, a towel and soap, a tooth-brush and paste and your waterproofs. And that's all, otherwise poor old Thor will be bow-legged before we've gone a mile.'

I picked up Philip's bag and felt the weight. 'What on earth have you got in here, a suit of armour?'

'It's only a book or two and a few comics to read when we're in the tent,' he muttered. Before I could put the bag down the seams burst with the strain and out poured six *Beanos*, five *Dandys*, four Enid Blyton books, a book about fishing in the Lake District, *How to Identify Birds*, *Know your Trees*, a book of ghost stories and *Swallows and Amazons*.

'Goodness me,' I gasped, 'he's a travelling library.'

Abi howled with laughter at the sight of the pile of books and comics on the floor. 'A bit heavier than a tin of talcum powder, aren't they Philip?' she teased between fits of the giggles. Philip bit his lip and looked downcast for a moment or two, but fortunately he saw the funny side of it and a broad grin spread over his face. 'Well, how much weight can Thor carry?' he asked.

'It depends on the type of country he has to walk over,' I said, 'but when we've loaded all our equipment on to him it will weigh about thirty-five kilograms, which is quite enough for any pony to carry over the fells.'

When the last item was packed into the three canvas bags which were to be tied to the pack-saddle and each bag carefully weighed with a small spring balance, we sat round the lounge fire and discussed our route.

'I think we'll have an easy day to start with,' I said, spreading the map on the carpet. 'We'll go through the forest and over Black Sail Pass to Wasdale and ask permission to camp at a farm. It's only a few miles and it will do nicely to loosen our muscles up. I'm going to give you a notebook and pen and I want you to keep a diary describing what we do each day. If we follow the tracks the smugglers used to take you'll have plenty to write about. I'd like you to list the birds we see along the way and also wild flowers and places of interest.'

Philip coughed. It was a signal he was about to ask a question. 'What is it now?' I asked, faking a yawn. 'If you're going to ask me can you take a giant telescope so that you can look at the stars, the answer is definitely no.'

'Er no, it wasn't that,' he said with a grin. 'Please can I take my fishing-rod, it's only short and I'll carry it on my rucksack.'

'He says he'll catch fish for us every day,' smirked Abi, 'but I'm glad we're taking food with us or we might get very hungry while we wait for a fish to jump on to his hook.'

Philip put his tongue out at her and, sliding the fishing-rod out of its narrow canvas bag, handed it to me. It was a nice little fibreglass boat rod in two sections, each about forty-five centimetres long and, together with a small spinning reel, it was an ideal rod to take on a camping holiday.

'It's a super rod,' I said, passing it back to him, 'but what are you going to catch with it?'

He picked up the copy of *Where to Fish in the Lake District* from the floor. 'If you'll let me take this,' he said eagerly, 'it tells you which tarns and rivers have fish in them, and if we camped by them I bet I could get a trout for breakfast.'

'All right, it's a bargain,' I said, 'you can take the rod and the book and we'll stop as often as we can.'

Abi was not convinced. 'I bet we have to buy a packet of fish fingers,' she grumbled.

Philip grabbed a sock and flung it at her.

'You rotten thing, what did you do that for?' she yelled.

'It's one way of telling you to put a sock in it!' said Philip, chuckling at his own joke.

I intervened before it developed into a full-scale battle. 'We have to be up early in the morning, so save your energy for the walk tomorrow. Off you go to bed. Breakfast is at eight o'clock sharp.'

Chapter Two

Early the following morning the sun rose slowly over the long ridge of Red Pike and High Stile, which forms a high barrier on the northern side of the Ennerdale valley. As it climbed higher into the pale blue sky, rays of golden light caught the tops of the peaks and painted them first a bright pink, then a deep red. The warm glow crept steadily down the rocky fellside and chased dark shadows between the rows of spruce trees in the silent forest.

'Isn't it beautiful?' exclaimed Abi. She was leaning on the yard gate with her chin cupped in her hands, staring spellbound at the view.

'Fantastic,' spluttered Philip, as he staggered across the yard, weighed down by the heavy canvas bags. At least it sounded like 'fantastic', but the word was lost. He was carrying his fishing-rod in his teeth at the same time. Dropping the bags on to the ground, he collapsed on top of them. 'Phew,' he exclaimed, mopping his forehead with his sleeve, 'if it's hot this early, what's it going to be like later on.'

'Hotter,' giggled Abi.

'All right, clever,' retorted Philip, 'stop day-dreaming and come and help me to carry the bags out, we're leaving soon.'

'Coming,' called Abi slowly, and continued to stare into space over the gate. Philip waited for a second or two, but she ignored him. 'Girls!' he snorted and stamped back to the house.

After breakfast, Thor was brought up from his field and given a thorough grooming with a stiff brush. Of all the ponies on my farm, Thor is my favourite. He is a typical fell pony, black, with short stumpy legs, a large friendly face and a long mane and tail. He much prefers eating and sleeping to anything else and has to be coaxed into action with lumps of mint cake. He is slow when going downhill and painfully slow when going uphill. He is frightened of tractors, absolutely hates anything that flaps in the wind and is positively terrified of mice. But he does like apples and boiled sweets, people who give him titbits and anyone who is prepared to spend hours untangling knots in his mane.

'Why do we have to do this?' Abi panted with the effort of pulling the grooming brush along Thor's broad back. 'He looks clean enough to me.'

'Well look at it this way,' I replied, 'if you got out of bed in the morning and went out for the day without having had a wash or combed your hair, you'd probably feel very grubby and uncomfortable. It's just the same with a pony. Besides, you have to make sure his hair and skin are clean before you put a saddle on him, otherwise he'll become very sore.'

Philip dumped the pack-saddle and harness on a bench by the barn door and looked puzzled. 'I still can't understand what all these buckles and straps are for,' he said. I lifted the pack-saddle and placed it on Thor's back. 'Well, imagine a load fastened to the saddle. As long as Thor is walking along a flat path the saddle will stay in the middle of his back. But if we were climbing a steep path the saddle would slide down his back and fall off, so a wide piece of leather called a breast-strap is fastened round his chest. And if Thor were going downhill the saddle would slide over his head, so to hold it back straps called breeching fit round his back legs under his tail. If everything fits properly a pack-pony can go up and down hill all day without the pack falling off.'

With the pack-saddle and harness carefully placed in position, the bags crammed with equipment were tied on to the saddle with rope, one on each side and one resting across the top. A quick check was made to see that the load was well balanced and we were ready to start. To hold our waterproof suits, notebooks, maps and bars of chocolate for lunch, we each carried a small rucksack.

Sensing we were about to leave, my Border collie, Sammy, went wild with excitement and rushed about barking furiously. Philip laughed, 'He wants to come with us, can we take him?'

Ready to leave — the start of the journey at Gillerthwaite

Sammy dropped a stick at my feet and looked up with large, brown eyes, begging me to say yes.

'Well all right,' I said, 'on condition that you'll look after him and keep him on a lead when we go through farms and villages.'

Philip raced back to the house to fill a bag with dog food. 'I'll look after him, I promise,' he shouted.

Abi untied Thor's lead rope from the post. 'Can I lead him through the forest?' she asked.

'All right,' I replied, 'but walk to one side of him or he might stand on your heels.'

Abi pulled gently on the rope and Thor lumbered through the gate on to the wide forest track. We were on our way. Abi leading Thor, Philip and I a few metres behind, and Sammy racing in front to find a stick. There was hardly a cloud in the sky and it was very hot as we plodded slowly along between the rows of tall spruce trees. After an hour or so I called a halt and we rested in the shade of a huge heap of logs stacked by the side of the track and let Thor nibble at the few blades of grass growing out of the bank.

'Does all this wood go to make paper?' asked Philip, sucking noisily on an orange.

'Most of it,' I replied, 'although these long, thick tree trunks which we're sitting on will be sawn into boards and lengths of timber for building houses. If you look at the thin end of each log you'll see that it's marked with numbers. The one next to you is marked six point three and fifteen; it simply means that the log is six point three metres long and it is fifteen centimetres in diameter at its narrowest end. From those figures a forester can tell how much money the log is worth.'

'That's a good idea,' said Philip. 'I'm going to look for the biggest log in the forest as we are walking along.'

Descending Black Sail Pass into Wasdale

We continued for over four miles, following the track as it climbed steadily upwards through the trees towards Great Gable blocking the head of the valley. At times the track went right along the edge of a gorge and we looked down a tremendous drop to the River Liza, thundering and crashing over the rocks below. At a point where there was a wide gap in the trees, Philip suddenly stopped, open-mouthed. 'Hey, look at Pillar

Rock,' he called, pointing upwards. Abi and I joined him and we looked up through the trees. A vast, rocky pinnacle towered above the forest, filling the whole skyline like a huge church spire. The sun was shining on it and every rock face and grassy ledge stood out, crystal clear.

'Gosh!' exclaimed Abi. 'I've never seen it so clear. I wish we could climb it.'

'Well, we might one day, but one step at a time. We've got this journey to do first. Let's move on.'

At the edge of the forest we joined an old pack-horse track and followed it for a mile or so to Black Sail Youth Hostel, one of the remotest hostels in the Lake District. Many years ago it was a shepherds' hut, where they lived during the summer months, looking after their sheep on the high pastures, but it was eventually taken over by the Youth Hostels Association. The Warden was out when we knocked, but the door was open and, full of curiosity, Abi and Philip had a quick look inside. Sammy sneaked round the back to see if there might be a bone lying about, but he came back looking very disappointed. All around the hostel the scenery was magnificent, with tremendous peaks and towering crags in every direction. From the hostel door we could see Black Sail Pass very clearly, zigzagging up to a ridge between Kirk Fell and Pillar.

'Have we got to go up there?' Abi couldn't believe it. 'It looks far too steep to take a pony. Can't we go round?'

Philip bit his lip and looked worried, but said nothing.

'Don't worry,' I said, 'it's not as bad as it looks. Hundreds of pack-ponies used to go over the Pass in the old days, carrying wool from the farms, and smugglers came this way too, with ponies carrying barrels of rum and whisky, so I think old Thor will climb it without much trouble.'

I took Thor's rope and led the way along a narrow path from the Youth Hostel to a wooden bridge crossing the River Liza. Thor snorted and refused to step on the bridge at first, but we fed him with lumps of Kendal Mint Cake and he was so busy chewing he forgot to be frightened and walked across without hesitating. From the bridge the path climbed easily at first, then steepened as we reached the foot of the Pass. It was still incredibly hot and sweat poured off us with the exertion of climbing only a short distance. We rested briefly, then started the long slog up a very rocky path winding up the fell. Years of heavy rain had washed the surface away and Thor had to clamber up tricky patches of rock right on the edge of a long drop into the beck below. Philip and Abi watched anxiously as he slipped and skidded, sparks flying from his iron shoes, but they need not have worried; Thor was a native pony of the Lake District and used to rough ground. As we climbed higher, Black Sail Youth Hostel shrank to the size of a doll's house, far below, and we had a marvellous view right down Ennerdale. Abi was wheezing like a leaking balloon by the time we reached the half-way mark and Philip's face was the colour of a beetroot.

'Shall we give Thor a rest?' I said, when we reached a wide ledge.

'Oh yes please,' croaked Abi, 'I'm dying for a drink.'

'Me too,' whispered Philip hoarsely, and sank against a boulder.

Luckily we were not far away from a small beck and we filled our cups with ice-cold water mixed with orange crystals. It was absolutely delicious. Thor slurped his ration out of a soup bowl, but Sammy decided the best way to cool off was to jump in the water instead of drinking it and he wallowed and splashed like a baby seal. For once we did not mind when he shook himself and sprayed us with a cold shower.

At the top of the Pass we rested again and basked in a refreshing breeze blowing inland from the coast. The first section of the long descent into Mosedale was extremely steep and loose and I had to guide Thor down it very slowly to prevent him from slipping over the edge. All was going well when suddenly one of the straps on the breeching snapped under the strain and the loaded pack-saddle slid down on to Thor's neck. He tried to lift his head but the weight of the packs held it down and he began to panic. Abi grabbed one side of the saddle and Philip the other, while I tried to push it along Thor's back, but it was too heavy. Slowly the weight began to drag him towards the edge of the path and a steep drop, and although we pulled desperately, trying to hold him back, it was pulling us as well. Thor had almost reached the edge when I managed to release the girth straps and the pack-saddle thumped on to the rocks. Abi heaved on Thor's lead rope and pulled him to safety while Philip jumped on the pack-saddle to stop it rolling down the fell.

'That was a close thing. Are you two all right?' I asked anxiously. But they were none the worse for the fright and a piece of chocolate kept Thor happy while we struggled to strap the saddle on to his back and lash the bags into place. Lower down the fell the path improved and we made good progress down a long series of zigzags to Mosedale and followed a good path to Row Head Farm. Mr Naylor, the farmer, said he did not allow camping on his land, but when he saw we had a pony with us he said we could stay for one night and showed us a small paddock with plenty of grass.

'I hope that dog is safe with sheep,' he grunted, looking at Sammy.

'Yes,' I said, 'he's very well trained, he's a working sheep-dog.'

'Is he now,' he said, fondling Sammy's ear and opening his mouth to look at his teeth. 'He's not very old, but he's certainly a handsome fellow.'

Sammy looked pleased and licked his hand to show he wanted to be friends.

We pitched the tent in the corner of the paddock and, having turned Thor loose and stowed all the gear in the tent, we walked through the fields to the Wastwater Hotel to quench our thirst with glasses of iced Coca Cola. We were ravenously hungry when we returned and hurriedly prepared a meal of beef chow mein followed by a mug of Oxo. Sammy crunched his dog food then lay down in a corner of the tent and fell fast asleep.

Walking at a steady pace it had taken us until 6 o'clock to reach Row Head Farm and now, as the evening advanced, dark shadows were creeping over the head of the valley. We sat in the grass outside the tent and watched the last rays of the setting sun flicker across the craggy face of Great Gable.

'Look at that. It's like a searchlight,' said Abi excitedly, as a ray of light swept down Great Hell Gate Screes and lit up the vast rock buttress of Eagles Nest Ridge. Philip dived into the tent for my binoculars and managed to scan the crag before the light faded.

'What did you see?' I asked as he pushed the binoculars back into their case.

'I thought I saw something that looked like a huge spike of rock at the bottom of the crag, but I'm not sure.'

'It's a spike of rock all right,' I said. 'It's the most

Thor stumbles into a bog near Burnmoor Tarn

famous spike of rock in the country. It's called Napes
Needle and it's very impressive when you're standing
close to it. It's about thirty metres high.'

'I'd love to see it,' said Abi. 'Can we climb up to it
tomorrow?'

'We can if you really want to,' I said, 'but it's quite a
slog to reach it and it means asking the farmer if we can
stay another night. What about you Philip, do you want
to climb up to the Needle?'

'Oh yes please,' he said without hesitation, 'I've always wanted to try rock scrambling and I could make a sketch of it in my notebook.'

'All right then,' I said, 'you get into your sleeping-bags and I'll go and ask the farmer if we can stay another night.'

When I returned, ten minutes later, they were both fast asleep.

The next morning the lovely blue sky had vanished and thick cloud hung over the fell tops. It was still very warm though and we ate our breakfast by the edge of a beck that flowed past our campsite. By nine o'clock we had washed up, tidied the tent, checked the paddock gate to make sure Thor could not get out and, with Sammy on a lead and rucksacks well filled with choco-late bars, apples, cameras and films, we set off through the farmyard and joined a well-trodden path leading towards Great Gable. For the first half mile or so the path was easy but, crossing a wooden foot-bridge, we reached the foot of Great Gable and started up an incred-ibly steep path leading across scree to the base of the crags. We had already climbed quite a way up the fellside, but to reach the Needle we were faced with a difficult scramble over loose boulders and stones.

'I hope you've got a good head for heights,' I called, working my way along a particularly nasty section of the path, only wide enough for a boot and with a sheer drop to the valley below. 'Make sure you've got a firm grip and you'll be all right.' I let Sammy off his lead and he ran off in front of us.

Abi edged her way slowly across, followed by Phi-lip, and we scrambled up to the safety of a broad, grassy ledge below a wide expanse of grey rock.

'I can't see Napes Needle,' said Philip, staring at the

crags in front of us.

'Be patient,' I said, 'we're not quite there. This is the start of Eagles Nest Ridge, the Needle is just round the corner.'

A wall of rock barred our way and forced us to descend a rib of loose stones and heather to the foot of a broad gully and there we saw it. High in the gully, carved by nature out of solid rock and standing vertically, like the head of a gigantic spear, was Napes Needle. Forgetting the danger of the drop below us, Abi and Philip stared, wide-eyed at the sight of this unique rock.

'Has it ever been climbed?' said Philip.

'Oh yes, hundreds of times', I replied, 'but it was a chap called Haskett-Smith climbed it first, nearly a hundred years ago. What makes it particularly difficult is that there is no easy way off the top and you have to be an experienced rock climber before you can tackle it.'

We climbed the gully to the foot of the Needle and stared at the smooth walls. 'Well, now you've come all this way to see it, would you like to climb a little way up it?'

'Can we?' they chorused in amazement.

'There's a ledge about seven metres up,' I said, 'it's quite safe and the climbing is easy.'

'Oh great,' shouted Abi and swarmed up like a monkey. Philip's legs were shorter than Abi's and he could not reach some holds, but by standing on my shoulders he managed to get a grip and heave himself up to join her. Sammy was determined not to be left behind and tried to jump up to the ledge, but I made him guard the rucksacks and he whimpered with frustration as we climbed the rock and left him behind.

Two young rock climbers, festooned with rope, scrambled up behind us and prepared to climb a ridge

Abi and Philip on Napes Needle

close to the Needle.

'I think I would like to be a rock climber,' said Abi as the climbers sorted out their ropes and equipment.

'I wouldn't,' said Philip, 'this is quite high enough for me.'

We watched the climbers work their way up the steep ridge, protecting each other with the ropes as they went, until, with a wave, they disappeared out of sight over the top of the crag.

Sammy was overjoyed to see us when we climbed down the Needle to the gully and retrieved our rucksacks and he raced ahead as we followed a high path right across the face of Great Gable to an old pony track at Sty Head. It was late in the afternoon, but it was still very hot and we lay in the heather by the edge of a tumbling beck and drank mug after mug of cool water laced with lemonade crystals. From our vantage point we could pick out the route of the pony track winding its way down the fellside to cross Lingmell Beck by a ford, then making almost straight for the inn at Wasdale Head.

'Did the smugglers use this pass as well as Black Sail?' asked Abi.

'Yes,' I said, 'it was used a great deal. In fact, in its day this was part of the main route from the port of Ravenglass to Keswick. They used to smuggle all sorts of things, but because the Sty Head route drops down into Borrowdale it was used for smuggling something rather unusual and I bet you can't guess what it was.'

'I know. Home-made whisky,' said Philip.

'No. I'll give you a clue: it's used in pencils.'

'In pencils,' said Abi, disbelievingly. 'What would they want to smuggle pencils for?'

'Well they didn't actually smuggle pencils,' I said, 'but the black lead inside them. There used to be a black lead mine at Seathwaite in Borrowdale a long time ago and, in those days, black lead, or "wad" as the locals called it, was nearly as valuable as gold. The owners used to have armed guards patrolling near the mine, but they weren't clever enough to beat the smugglers. They used to take it to Ravenglass and exchange it for brandy and French lace smuggled in from the Isle of Man.

'It would be fun to follow the same path as the smugglers when we set off tomorrow,' said Philip, busily writing about black lead in his notebook.

'And go to Ravenglass, to see where they landed their ships,' added Abi.

'Well we will, if the weather keeps fine,' I said. 'We'll go over Burnmoor and down Mitredale to Ravenglass. But come on,' I jumped to my feet, 'Sammy is getting impatient. Let's go back to the camp-site.'

It was nearly seven o'clock when we reached the tent and we were tired and weary. Thor was stretched out in the grass, fast asleep, but he woke up with a snort when he heard us and trotted over to see if there was any Kendal Mint Cake to spare. We were ravenously hungry and feasted on fried sausages mixed with instant potatoes and baked beans; it looked revolting but tasted marvellous. As darkness approached, huge black clouds drifted down from the fell tops and drove all the warmth out of the air.

'It looks as if there's a storm brewing,' I said, as I looked through the tent door and watched Kirk Fell and Great Gable being slowly swallowed up by the cloud. 'I think we ought to pile stones round the edge of the tent and on the tent pegs in case there's a gale in the night.'

Abi and Philip were in their sleeping-bags and were very reluctant to leave them, but when I pointed out that to spend a few minutes gathering stones would be much better than having to climb out in the middle of the night to hunt for missing tent-pegs, they were out in a flash and carrying stones from the beck.

Chapter Three

During the night there was an occasional rumble of thunder, but when daylight came the sun appeared from behind the clouds and bathed the valley in a warm glow. After breakfast we dragged everything out of the tent and carefully packed the holdalls, weighing them to make sure they would balance evenly on Thor's back. At nine o'clock we left the field and called at the farmhouse to thank Mr Naylor for allowing us to camp. He had been up early gathering sheep and the yard echoed with a constant baaing and bleating as ewes looked for lost lambs among the seething mass of woolly bodies. We stopped to watch the men as they grabbed a struggling sheep then, holding it firmly between their knees, skilfully removed the fleece with electric shears. A dab of red marking fluid was brushed on its side and it was released into a pen, looking very embarrassed about being made to stand around without any clothes on. Sammy whimpered with excitement and longed to leap in and show how he could gather sheep and keep them in order, but Philip kept him on a tight lead.

Abi led Thor through the yard of the Wastwater Hotel then, by way of a shallow ford, over Lingmell Beck to the National Trust's campsite on the edge of Wastwater. Almost every tent seemed to have a radio blaring away and the noise made Thor very nervous.

'Keep a good grip on his rope, Abi,' I warned.

'Thank goodness we didn't have to camp here,' she said. 'We wouldn't have been able to listen to the birds or the sheep or anything.'

Sammy growled his disapproval and kept close to my heels. It was a relief to leave the noisy campsite behind and join a track slanting across the fellside above Wasdale Head Hall Farm. The surface of Wastwater was like a mirror and as we climbed higher the view was absolutely breathtaking. Wasdale Head was laid out below us like a relief model in a geography class. Green meadowland was divided into squares, rectangles and circles by the grey stone walls. Tiny cattle and sheep grazed close to the miniature farmhouses and model cars stood in rows in front of the white painted inn. Only the high fells that enclosed the head of the valley in the shape of a horseshoe were as tall as we were and we could see over the bristly ridge of Yewbarrow to Red Pike and the long, flat summit of Pillar. Close to Pillar was Kirk Fell, looking for all the world like a circular pyramid with a pointed top. Even our old friend Great Gable had lost its rugged appearance and looked like an upturned pudding basin decorated with pebbles. While we rested we spent a few minutes practising map reading and Abi became quite excited when she discovered that we were on the lower slopes of Scafell.

'It's a pity we can't go to the top, then I could boast that I've climbed the highest mountain in England.'

'Well you'd be wrong,' I said. 'Scafell Pike is the highest.'

'But I always thought Scafell and Scafell Pike were the same,' said Philip.

'So do a lot of people,' I said, 'but if you look at the map you'll see that although they stand next door to each other, they are separate summits.'

"It's not as easy as it looks at sheep dog trials"
Helping to gather sheep at Hagg End Farm

'So they are,' said Abi, kneeling over the map spread on the grass. 'Scafell Pike is nine hundred and seventy-seven metres and Scafell is nine hundred and sixty-four metres. Oh well,' she went on, 'I don't care, it's just as nice being on the second highest.'

Thor had found a juicy patch of bleaberries while we were studying the map and refused to leave when we wanted to set off again, but a prod on his rump and the promise of a lump of mint cake when we reached the top spurred him on. The angle of the track eased off on the crest of the ridge and ahead was the bleak expanse of Burnmoor. Abi led the way, guided by cairns of stones placed at intervals among the banks of slimy peat. The track was difficult to find at times, but eventually we reached hard, dry ground and from the top of a little hillock we looked down on the glittering waters of Burnmoor Tarn. Philip hurriedly produced *Where to Fish in the Lake District* from his rucksack and thumbed through the pages.

'Listen to this,' he said, and read from the book in an urgent voice, as if he had discovered some top secret information. '"Burnmoor Tarn contains a variety of freshwater fish including Brown Trout."' He thrust the book back in his rucksack. 'Can we stop while I fish for a bit?' he pleaded. 'I bet there's some real whoppers in there and I might get one or two for tea'

'All right then,' I said. 'You agreed that if I let you bring a fishing-rod you would provide us with fresh fish, so now you've got a chance to prove it.'

'Oh, no, surely we're not going to waste time fishing,' cried Abi, 'he never catches anything.'

'I do so,' said Philip, huffily. 'I've caught lots and I'll catch one or two here, you'll see.'

'Humph!' said Abi.

When we reached the tarn I slackened Thor's girth strap and let him graze on the few patches of grass by the water's edge. Philip quickly assembled his fishing-rod and reel and tied on a few hooks and a bright orange float. Sammy sat beside him, head cocked on one side, fascinated by this new game.

"It would be quicker if I jumped in and caught one"
Sammy watches Philip fishing

'Stand back, I'm going to cast,' hissed Philip, 'and you mustn't make a noise.'

We ducked as the line swished round our heads and watched the float sail through the air and land with a plop in the water. In a flash Sammy realized what the orange thing was. Of course, it was a ball! With a loud yelp he plunged into the tarn and, grasping the float in his teeth, swam back to the bank and dropped it at Philip's feet, shaking himself vigorously and spraying icy water all over us. Philip was absolutely furious.

'Sammy, you great stupid idiot,' he yelled, 'you've frightened all the fish away now. Go and lie down.'

Poor Sammy slunk away and cowered in the heather licking his paws. Philip angrily sorted out the tangle of line and float and, placing fresh bait on the hooks, he cast the line again. For over an hour he tried several different places around the tarn, but without success. He was terribly upset and hardly spoke as he unscrewed his rod and put it in the canvas bag. 'That book is a lot of rubbish,' he muttered, swinging his rucksack on to his shoulders and stamping off along the track.

For once Abi realized he was in no mood for jokes and tried to cheer him up. 'Never mind, you'll be able to fish in the sea when we reach Ravenglass,' she said comfortingly. Philip perked up at the idea.

'Great,' he exclaimed, his face breaking into a big grin. 'I might land a salmon.' He patted Sammy's head, 'Sorry I shouted at you, Sammy.' Sammy wagged his tail and bounded away to find a stick for Philip to throw for him.

Leaving the wide pony track, we followed an easy path west, by the deserted house of Burnmoor Lodge, then across open moorland to descend steeply into the wooded valley of Mitredale. Most of the cloud cleared from the sky and it was very hot. We stopped briefly to drink from the ice-cold water of Black Gill, then pressed on through Low Place Farm to join a surfaced road leading to Irton Road Station on the Ravenglass and Eskdale miniature railway. A train arrived while we were crossing a humpbacked bridge over the line and the hissing and clanking of the steam engine gave Thor such a fright he ran off up the lane. When we eventually caught up with him he was standing in a field up to his knees in buttercups, chewing happily with a herd of cows. He was very reluctant to leave his new friends and Abi had to heave on his rope before she could lead the way through a mass of prickly gorse bushes to a good path leading to Muncaster Fell and Ravenglass.

Compared with the fells around Wasdale, Muncaster Fell is not very high, but the view from it is one of the best in the Lake District. From the summit, not only can you see many Lakeland peaks, but also the hills of Southern Scotland and the Cumbrian coast from St Bees Head, round in a wide curve, to a large fell called Black Combe, above the town of Millom. If the weather is particularly clear you can see well beyond Black Combe to Morecambe Bay and the Lancashire coast.

'Is that the Isle of Man?' called Abi, standing on top of the summit cairn and pointing to what looked like a huge, upturned boat lying on the surface of the blue Irish Sea.

'Yes, you're quite right,' I said. 'That's the summit of Snaefell sticking up in the middle.'

'Isn't that where those fish called kippers come from?' asked Philip. He seemed able to think of nothing but fish.

'Well a kipper isn't exactly a fish itself,' I explained. 'It's a herring that's been opened out and smoked over a wood fire. Because the Isle of Man fishing fleet catches a lot of herring, the islanders have built up a kipper smoking industry and they send them all over the country.'

'We have them for tea sometimes,' said Abi. 'They taste delicious, but I wish they'd take the bones out.'

We dropped down from the summit and continued along the path, carefully avoiding patches of oozy peat and sphagnum moss.

'What on earth's that?' said Abi, pulling Thor to a halt and staring at a large slab of rock resting on two smaller boulders at the side of the track. Philip dashed ahead to get a closer look.

'It's got letters and figures on it,' he shouted. 'Do you think it was a place where Druids used to sacrifice human beings?'

'Ugh! I hope not,' said Abi. 'The thought gives me the creeps.'

'Look at these marks on top of the rock. I'll bet they were made by the points of swords when they were pushed through girls being sacrificed,' said Philip fiendishly.

'Stop it, you bloodthirsty little horror,' squealed Abi, backing away from the rock and looking as though she was about to run all the way to Ravenglass.

'Ignore him Abi,' I said. 'He's got a vivid imagination, but he couldn't be further from the truth. You've only got to look at the date carved on the rock to realize that.'

Abi peered cautiously at the rock. 'Ross's Camp 1883,' she read out. 'Was it an army camp?' she asked.

'No,' I replied, 'though there's an interesting little story behind it. Ross was the estate manager for Lord Muncaster of Muncaster Castle at Ravenglass and he liked the view from here so much he had a wooden chalet built so that he and his family could stay for several days. Why he brought this huge stone here no one really knows, but a farmer friend of mine in Eskdale told me that it used to be in the yard of Hinning House Farm, that's the farm below us,' I said, pointing to a whitewashed farmhouse in the valley. 'My friend's grandfather lived at the farm and he said that Mr Ross hired a team of six Clydesdale horses and hauled the stone to the site of his chalet and a stonemason carved his name and the date on it.'

We set off again and dropped down the fell to the tiny village of Ravenglass where we camped for the night in a field near the beach. While Abi and I erected the tent, Philip hunted for worms on a smelly dung heap by a ruined barn.

'I've got some beauties,' he shouted, brandishing a squirming heap in a plastic bag. 'There's bound to be plenty of fish in the sea. I'll be back shortly.' And clutching his fishing-rod, he dashed down the lane to the beach. He was away about half an hour and when he returned he was clutching a large fish.

'Goodness me, Abi,' I said, jumping to my feet, 'he's caught one already. It's fish for dinner tonight.'

Philip dropped the fish on a plate, but far from being excited about his catch, he was surprisingly silent.

'What's wrong?' I asked. 'Are you worn out with the effort of landing the monster?'

'No,' he muttered, turning red in the face.

'What then?' I persisted.

'Er, well, I didn't actually catch it,' he confessed ruefully. 'The tide was out, so I swapped my bag of worms for the fish with a man working on a boat.'

We looked at him in amazement, then burst into fits of laughter.

'That's brilliant,' cried Abi. 'I would never have thought of that.'

No meal of fish and potatoes ever tasted as good as dinner that night and all for the price of a bag of worms!

Chapter Four

It was a flock of herring-gulls arguing over the skeleton of our fish that woke us early the next morning. They were perched on top of a wall and made the most awful din, squabbling and swooping at each other in an attempt to fly off with the fish bones.

'Go away, you noisy brutes. Shoo, shoo!' shouted Abi, crawling through the tent door and waving her sweater at them. They rose in a cloud of flapping wings and flew away over the village. 'What a gorgeous morning,' called Abi. 'Come and look at the sea.'

Philip and I pulled on our boots and scrambled out of the tent. The grass was still wet with the morning dew and we kicked up clouds of spray as we ran across the field to the shingle beach. Abi was right, it really was a beautiful day. The tide was coming in fast and the wavelets breaking on the beach flashed and sparkled in the bright morning sun. Ravenglass is a natural harbour formed by three rivers, the Esk, the Mite and the Irt, joining together in front of the village and flowing out in a narrow estuary to the Irish sea. On either side of the estuary are miles and miles of golden sand dunes that are the home of black-headed gulls and colonies of oyster catchers. Many other birds and animals live on the sand dunes but not a solitary thing moved as we stood staring at the deep blue sea and listening to the sound of the advancing tide as it swirled around our boots.

"Have you any mint cake to spare?"

'What a smashing place for smugglers to land their boats,' said Philip. 'I wonder if there are still rum barrels and other things hidden in the sand dunes. I wish we could explore them.'

'Well it's quite possible that some stuff might have been buried and forgotten,' I said, 'but there's not much chance of finding anything. In any case, the smugglers would only leave their cargo in the sand dunes until it was safe to bring it into the village. Come on, I'll show you one of the houses where they used to hide it.'

We walked along the beach to the edge of the village street and stopped at the rear of an old house which had a flight of stone steps leading up from the beach, but ending mysteriously at a blank wall.

'This house used to be called the Ship Inn,' I said, 'and according to some old tales, was a favourite smugglers' hide-out. Some say the Customs men forced the landlord to brick up the door at the top of the steps to stop smugglers sneaking in during darkness.'

'Gosh, it must have been really exciting being a smuggler,' said Philip. 'Did they ever get caught?'

'I suppose they must have done at times,' I replied, 'but they had very fast sailing-ships and they knew every inch of the coast.'

We left the old Ship Inn and spent an hour or so wandering round the picturesque cottages in the village's only street, before loading Thor and setting off through the grounds of Muncaster Castle, heading for Eskdale. It was fiendishly hot once we left the shelter of the tall trees around the castle and climbed the steep fellside. In many places the path was overgrown with thick bracken, almost as tall as Thor, and it took ages to force our way through it.

'It's hard to believe this was once a Roman road,' I panted, smashing down the bracken with a heavy stick and heaving fallen branches to one side. 'It was the Romans who first discovered Ravenglass and then cut this road through to Eskdale to build a fort on Hardknott Pass, but they would have a job getting through it nowadays.'

I dragged a heavy tree trunk to one side and the worst was over. The path descended steeply through Chapels Wood and on the way passed close to an attractive stone tower. We stopped to look inside. Sammy had exhausted himself chasing rabbits, so we left him with Thor, dozing under the shade of the trees.

'Was it a watch-tower of some sort?' asked Abi. 'It's got slits all the way round to fire arrows out of.'

'It looks as if it was part of a castle at some time,' said Philip, peering inside the door, 'but there's no sign of any steps leading to the top.'

'Well, it's got quite an interesting history behind it,' I said, 'but it wasn't a watch-tower or part of a castle. It was built as a monument to King Henry VI, who was

King of England in the fifteenth century. You might not have covered the Wars of the Roses in your history lessons at school yet, but it was a long conflict between King Henry, who was from Lancashire and whose emblem was a red rose, and the Duke of York, whose emblem was a white rose. In a battle at Hexham, in Northumberland, King Henry was beaten, but managed to escape and hide in the hills. The story goes that two shepherds were working with their sheep in the field where we are standing now, when a man appeared and asked the way to Muncaster Castle. He was covered in mud and absolutely worn out. The shepherds took him to the castle and the Lord of the Manor, Sir John Pennington, discovered that the traveller was King Henry himself. He stayed at the castle for a few days and when he left, the King gave Sir John a small glass bowl and said the Penningtons would always have good luck, provided the bowl was never broken. The bowl is still in the castle today and the Penningtons built this tower to mark the spot where the shepherds found the King.'

'What a lovely story,' said Abi, 'but what happened to King Henry after he left the castle?'

'Ah well, it's rather a sad ending,' I said. 'He reached Lancashire safely, but he was betrayed and captured and eventually died in the Tower of London.'

'That's awful,' said Abi, 'and after all he'd been through, too. Let's leave him some flowers.' And flinging her rucksack on the ground, she gathered a bunch of foxgloves, field daisies and buttercups. 'There you are King,' she said quietly, placing the flowers on a ledge inside the tower, 'that's from us.'

Below the tower the path joined a wide track and we followed its winding course up Eskdale until it joined a surfaced road by the King George IV Inn. It was so hot hardly a word was spoken as we trudged along the hard,

Monument to King Henry VI in Chapels Wood, Ravenglass

dusty track, and the sight of the inn was like a mirage in a desert.

'Please could we stop and buy a glass of orange?' said Philip hoarsely. 'My tongue feels like a piece of leather.'

'Mine too,' said Abi. 'I could drink a whole lake.'

I bought four large glasses of orange squash, one for

each of us and one to share between Thor and Sammy. Feeling a lot better, we rejoined the old Roman road at Forge Bridge and followed it through lush, green meadows, along the edge of the River Esk, to the welcome shade of Scots pine and oak trees in Dalegarth Wood. Thor's hooves and our boots scarcely made a sound on the carpet of soft soil and leaves and there was an almost eerie silence as we threaded our way between the shadowy trees.

'Isn't it spooky,' said Abi with a shiver. 'I'm glad I'm not on my own. I get the feeling that robbers are going to ambush us at any minute.'

'Oh, you're safe enough these days,' I laughed, 'though it might have been different a hundred years or so ago, when pack-ponies came this way, loaded with all sorts of valuable goods. An old man in Ravenglass once told me that his great-grandfather used to bring a lot of cattle this way too. Ships brought them to Ravenglass from Scotland and the Isle of Man and drovers took them over the fells to the market at Kendal. It was a long, hard walk for the cattle and to stop their feet being damaged on the rough ground a blacksmith used to shoe them, just like a horse.'

After a mile or so the dark canopy of leaves and branches thinned out and the sun streamed through shimmering silver birch and bright green larch trees. On we went, passing Dalegarth Hall, with its peculiar round chimneys, and winding in and out of woods and meadows, until eventually we reached Penny Hill Farm, near the head of the Eskdale valley. The farmer's wife was very friendly and helpful and obtained permission from the owner of a nearby estate for us to camp in a small field by the edge of the River Esk. We were so hot and dusty we flung our boots and socks into the grass and raced down the field to soak our feet in the cool water. Sammy dived straight in and swam round, barking excitedly to us to join him. Thor rolled contentedly in the grass for a minute or two then ambled after us and stood in the river, sucking noisily at the water and blowing it through his teeth like a great black hippopotamus. When the tent was pitched and the equipment neatly stowed away under the flysheet, I rummaged through the food bag.

'What would you like for dinner?' I asked.

'Ugh, I can't bear the thought of food,' said Abi. 'It's far too hot to eat. All I want is a cold drink.'

'I'm not hungry either,' murmured Philip, stretched out in the grass. 'Let's mix a panful of water and orange crystals.'

'You've got to eat something, we've got a long way to go tomorrow. How about sardines?' I held up a tin.

'Ooh, no thanks,' said Abi, pulling a face.

'I don't like sardines,' said Philip. 'If we've got to eat I'll just have a few biscuits and a piece of cheese.'

The evening meal was a very sparse affair, but the heat certainly did not affect Sammy's appetite. He pulled his bag of dog food from under the tent and sat by it wagging his tail until I poured a heap on to the grass.

When the sun went down in the evening, we sat on a little hillock above the campsite and watched the fells change colour and the trees lose their shape as dusk settled over the valley. Beautiful though it was, there were very obvious signs of a change in the weather.

'Look at the fells,' called Philip, 'it's so clear you can almost see every rock.'

'It's nice to look at,' I said, 'but it could mean the end of the sunny days. Look at the clouds forming.'

High in the sky a strange bank of cloud, broken up like huge, flat snowflakes was creeping in from the west.

'It's a sure sign of a change in the weather when you

can see a long way and that type of cloud comes across the sky. We'd best make sure everything is under cover.'

'Does that mean we're in for a storm?' asked Philip, fearfully.

'Oh no,' I smiled, 'nothing as drastic as that, but make sure your waterproofs are easy to get at when we set off tomorrow.'

It was so hot and humid during the night it was impossible to sleep and by eight o'clock the next morning we were dressed, packed and ready to leave. The weather was still fine, but the cloud that was creeping in when we went to bed had now completely covered the sky and had turned from fleecy white to a threatening grey. A few spots of rain thudded on to our backs as we followed the bridle-way through Penny Hill Farm towards the bulk of Harter Fell. At the foot of the fell a great wooded chasm carries Spothow Gill, a normally placid beck that splashes its way over a rocky bed to join the river Esk. During heavy rain though, the beck swells to a mad, raging torrent, which over the years has ploughed through rocks and boulders and swept away the ford where, at one time, the packmen and cattle drovers were able to cross without difficulty. Nowhere could we find a crossing place for Thor and we floundered around in chest high bracken until we found what appeared to be a path leading down to the road at Wha House Bridge. We eagerly followed it only to find our way barred by a single strand of wire.

'Don't touch it,' I yelled, as Philip and Abi walked forward, 'it's an electric fence.'

They both jumped back in horror.

'We might have been electrocuted,' gasped Abi, 'they ought to be banned.'

'Oh it won't hurt you,' I laughed. 'It works off a battery and the idea is to give cows a slight shock to stop them from straying. Come and help me to move it.'

We gingerly untied the string holding the wire to a tree and, while I held it to one side, Abi led Thor through the gap and Philip scurried after them leaving me to retie the string. Heavy drops of rain bounced off the leaves of the trees as we reached Wha House Bridge and the surfaced road leading to Hardknott Pass. We were heading for an old pack-horse track which starts at the foot of Hardknott Pass and traverses diagonally across Harter Fell to Dunnerdale. By the time we reached it the drops had become a downpour and we scrambled into our waterproof coats and trousers and pushed on up the steep track, panting with the effort of trying to keep up with Thor. There were many stops to get our breath back before we reached the top, but eventually the worst was over and we sat on a rock and looked down through the sweeping rain to the glistening valley below. On the move again, the wide track ended in a sea of bog, but a thin path led us safely through to the edge of Dunnerdale Forest.

It was still very warm, despite the rain, and conditions were perfect for that nasty little brute the midge to come out and look for breakfast. In the Lake District, the midge lives in boggy ground and damp woods, not in ones or twos, or in tens, or even hundreds, but in thousands. They delight in annoying humans and when they saw us arrive at the edge of the forest they descended in a huge cloud and crawled over our faces, into our ears and hair, noses, mouths, up our sleeves and down our shirts, until there was hardly an atom of skin that was not covered in red blotches. No amount of arm waving would dislodge them, but fortunately they hate the dark and finally we managed to escape from the little pests by plunging deep into the forest. An hour of tripping over hidden roots and falling into holes full of water and black slimy peat brought us to the edge of the forest and an isolated farm at Grassguards, perched high on the fellside above Dunnerdale. The rain was pouring down like a monsoon and the air had turned very chilly.

'Could you drink a mug of soup?' I shouted, as we slipped and slithered down through the trees to a gate.

'Oh yes, please,' shivered Abi. 'But where can we shelter from the rain?'

'We'll find a big tree with lots of branches. I'll go on ahead. Philip, follow me with Thor, will you.'

Quite close to the farm I found a huge Sitka spruce and soon we were huddled together under the branches with a pan of soup bubbling on the stove. Sammy curled up between us and went to sleep and to keep Thor happy, Abi gave him a packet of biscuits. As we sipped our soup and stared at the rain bending the branches of the smaller trees around us, Philip started laughing to himself.

'Isn't it silly,' he giggled. 'Only yesterday it was so hot we couldn't eat and now we're shivering with cold and having hot soup.'

'Well, that's typical of the weather in the Lake District,' I said, 'and it's one of the reasons why so many people get lost on the fells. They look so easy to climb when the sun is shining, but in mist and rain they can become very dangerous.'

'I think I prefer the woods to the fells,' said Abi. 'You can shelter from the sun if it's too hot and sit under the trees and have soup if it's raining.'

Thor was dozing peacefully under another tree when I tied the bag containing the food and stove back on to the pack-saddle and he was rather grumpy about having to move on again. We tempted him with a large piece of

"A watched pot never boils" Sheltering from the rain in Dunnerdale

mint cake and he crunched it loudly as we descended a steep, rocky path to Dunnerdale, to a series of large stepping-stones crossing the wide River Duddon. A wire rope stretched above the stepping-stones provided added safety and Abi and Philip skipped across while I coaxed the reluctant Thor to wade into the water. We were glad when the rain eased to a drizzle. Just above the river we joined a motor road when I let Thor graze while we ate chocolate and studied the map, looking for a place to camp.

'How are you both feeling?' I asked.

'A bit tired,' said Philip, 'but I'll go on for a while yet.'

'Me too,' said Abi, 'although if we could find somewhere to camp I'd like to change into dry clothes, the rain has seeped through my anorak.'

'All right,' I said, 'we'll stop the night in Dunnerdale

and tomorrow we'll go over the Walna Scar road; it's a very old pack-horse track leading from Dunnerdale to Coniston. The map shows a farm called Long House at the foot of the Walna Scar and it will be a good point to start from. Let's ask if we can camp there.'

It took several minutes of loud knocking on the farmhouse door before heavy bolts were drawn back and the farmer's wife stood on the threshold.

'Would it be possible to camp on your land for the night and graze our pony?' I enquired.

'I'm very sorry,' the farmer's wife replied, 'I'd like to help you, but the owner of the farm will not allow us to take campers. You could try further down the valley, though I'm not sure if they would take your pony.'

It was a dreadful let-down, but there was nothing we could do but apologize for troubling her and lead Thor back up the farm track to the road. Abi and Philip looked very miserable and weary and to add to our problems a strong wind sprang up and drove vicious gusts of rain on to us.

'We've got two alternatives,' I said, as we crouched in the shelter of a wall discussing what to do. 'We can walk down the valley to another farm, but if they won't take Thor we're really stuck. On the other hand we're right at the foot of Walna Scar now and if you're game we can carry on over the top to the old mine workings at Torver, where we can camp on the fellside. I'd better warn you though, it's a fairly tough walk and the weather is getting worse. What do you say?'

To my astonishment they never hesitated.

'Let's carry on. We're thoroughly wet now,' said Abi, 'so we can't get much wetter.'

'I'd rather continue than risk being turned away from another farm,' said Philip.

'That's very brave of you,' I said. 'We'll wait until

this squall blows over then we'll set off.'

When the wind died down I checked Thor's girth and the packs and led the way to the foot of the Pass. Years of rain, snow and frost had long since gouged away the original surface of the track and we alternated between walking along a rocky trench and wading ankle deep in mud. At times it was very strenuous and our bodies were soon steaming with the effort of having to lift our mud caked boots high enough to continue walking. Half-way up the fell the track passed through a gate in the wall and I was leading Thor towards it when Philip shouted, 'Look behind you! We're in for it now.'

I glanced over my shoulder to see an enormous black cloud tearing towards us, spreading out across the sky and plunging the valley into darkness.

'Quick,' I bellowed, 'get through the gate and behind the wall.'

We ran as fast as our mud caked clothing would allow and collapsed behind the wall in the nick of time. With a roar like an express train, the wind hit the wall, bringing with it torrential rain that churned the track into a sea of mud within seconds. Stinging hailstones lashed through gaps in the wall and thudded into our anoraks like bullets. Sammy flattened himself against us, whimpering with fright as the wind howled and screamed overhead. Thor was terrified and tried to run away, but I kept a firm grip on his rope and pulled his head behind the wall. It was an incredibly nasty squall, yet as quickly as it came, it went, raging across the fell towards Coniston. Within minutes the wind had dropped and the heavy rain died away to a drizzle.

'Wow,' said Philip, shaking the white layer of hailstones off his coat, 'I hope we don't get caught in another one of those while we're climbing the Pass.'

'So do I,' said Abi. 'That was really scary.'

Leaving the shelter of the wall, we trudged slowly on up the track. Looking down on Dunnerdale, the scene was breath-taking. A weak sun had somehow managed to squeeze its face through the cloud and the valley shone like silver as shafts of bright light swept across the saturated fields and swollen becks. Then, as if someone had turned off a light switch, the valley was plunged into semi-darkness again as another belt of advancing cloud swallowed up the sun.

'That cloud looks as if it's heading this way,' I warned. 'Fasten your coats securely and tie the cords of your hoods to stop the ends from hitting you in the face.'

We were only a short distance from the top of the Pass when the squall caught up with us and a sudden gust of wind bowled Philip completely over. He quickly scrambled to his feet and hung on to the pack-saddle. All the way to the summit of the Pass we were battered and buffeted by the wind and rain and as we squelched past the summit cairn the wind increased to gale force. But we were safely over. The wind realized it had lost its battle and, with a final blast that blew my woolly hat off my head, it retreated to Dunnerdale and left us in peace to look down on a sunlit valley, as if we had crossed into another world. On the Coniston side of the Pass the track had been so badly washed out it was impossible for Thor to walk on it and, at times, I had to lead him down steep heather. Far below I could see the tempting expanse of grass where I hoped to camp, but it never seemed to draw any nearer as we made long detours to avoid nasty drops. It took ages before the final awkward section of path was over and the last slippery slope was behind us. We had made it. With a tremendous sigh of relief we pitched camp close to a fast flowing beck and dived inside the tent for a huge dinner of soup and corned beef, followed by biscuits and jam.

Camping in open country with a pony is always a problem. Unless they are fenced in, most ponies will wander in search of food and can often be a very long way from the campsite the following morning. To prevent Thor from wandering when we pitched camp, I fastened hobbles to his front legs. These are simply two broad leather straps joined together by a short chain which, when fastened round a pony's front legs, allow it to move very slowly and prevent it from straying. At least that is what hobbles are supposed to do, but it is amazing how a clever pony can devise ways of escaping. When we started our dinner Thor was grazing happily by the tent, but by the time we had finished he was nowhere to be seen.

'He's disappeared,' said Abi, having searched the area around the tent in a wide circle.

'Rubbish,' I retorted irritably. 'How can a great oaf like Thor disappear? He's probably asleep in the long bracken. Have another look.'

Philip joined Abi and they set off to search a jumble of old buildings near the campsite. Taking binoculars, I climbed a nearby hill and scanned the horizon, but there was no sign of life. Suddenly a familiar whinny rang out over the fellside and Thor appeared from behind a wall, shooting along in a series of great leaps. He had discovered a way of moving forward even with the hobbles and he was on his way back to Ennerdale.

'Catch him,' I yelled, and Abi raced through the bracken and grabbed his headcollar while he was taking a breather.

'Thor, I'm ashamed of you,' I scolded when Abi and Philip brought him back to the campsite. 'You've had an easy time so far and in another week or so we'll be home. We're doing this journey and we need your help.' He stood with his ears back, listening to me, but I am sure he would have run away again given the chance. To make it difficult for him to escape, I tied a piece of rope between his headcollar and the hobbles to prevent him from lifting his head and leaping forward. He tried a few times but eventually gave up and, sinking into the bracken, he fell fast asleep.

During the evening the sky darkened ominously and thunder clouds growled at each other as they swirled around the dark crags above our campsite. A fierce wind whined through the bracken, flapping the canvas of the flysheet and straining the guylines. It was a sure sign of an approaching storm and, piling rocks on to the tent-pegs, we snuggled deep into our down sleeping-bags to escape from it. Sammy sensed something wrong and burrowed under my sweater, leaving only the tip of his tail peeping out of a sleeve. The first spots of rain thumped against the tent about midnight and within seconds a heavy downpour was battering the canvas as if we had camped underneath a waterfall. All night the storm raged with squall after squall doing its best to tear the tent to pieces. We could not sleep and we lay with sleeping-bags pulled over our heads listening to the wind approaching first with a slight whisper as it swished across the fellside, increasing to a moan as the rain squall gathered speed, then finally a screaming roar as it reached us with full fury. Abi and Philip were worried that the tent might blow down, but when I convinced them it was made to withstand storms, we passed the long night playing spelling games.

Chapter Five

The first streaks of dawn broke through the clouds at around five o'clock in the morning and I unzipped the tent door and looked out. It was an incredible sight. Water was cascading off every fellside and huge water-falls poured down the crags, sending boulders and debris crashing in watery avalanches through the bracken. By eight o'clock the rain and wind had died away and the air was so warm we were able to eat breakfast outside the tent. There was no sign of Thor and for a horrible moment I thought he had run away again, but Philip found him sheltering under an over-hang of rock. Thunder was still rumbling round the fell tops and, anxious to be on our way before another storm caught us, we dragged all the gear out of the tent, only to have to hurl it all back in again and dive after it when a heavy shower poured out of the sky without warning. It cleared away after ten minutes or so and we clambered out to strike camp and load Thor.

We joined a broad, stony track and followed it round the base of a large, straggling fell, until it merged with a surfaced road that dropped steeply to the village of Coniston. It began to rain heavily as we approached the village main street and we stopped in the doorway of a hotel to put on our waterproofs. Thor decided he liked the look of a large plant inside the hotel and gave the guests a dreadful fright by clattering up the stone steps and pushing the door open.

'A horse', gulped the manager, hardly able to believe his eyes. Then recovering quickly, he shouted, 'There's a horse standing on my new carpet, get it out, get it out!'

A burly porter strode across the hallway, but by this time I had a firm grip on Thor's lead rope and heaved him out of the hotel and down the road. The street was crammed with visitors and cars and we threaded our way carefully through them to the safety of a small patch of grass by the village car-park. An 'Ice Cream' sign attracted Philip's attention and he dashed across to a shop and returned with four large cornets. Quite a crowd of amused onlookers gathered when Thor started to eat his cornet. He is a terrible show-off and makes all sorts of funny noises when he eats ice cream.

In the centre of the patch of grass there was a stone monument with a plaque and Abi and Philip wandered over to look at it.

Donald Campbell's Monument, Coniston

'"In memory of Donald Campbell C.B.E.,"' read Abi, '"who died on January 4th 1967 while attempting to raise his own world water speed record on Coniston Water."'

'I've never heard of Donald Campbell,' said Philip, 'who was he?'

'Oh, he was famous for attempting speed records in cars and boats,' I said. 'His boats and cars were always called *Bluebird* and, in fact, he reached over 400 miles an hour in his car.'

'Golly!' exclaimed Philip. 'That's faster than some aeroplanes. What speed did he do in his boat?'

'Well when he came to attempt to break the water speed record on Coniston in November 1966, he already held the world record at over 276 miles per hour and he wanted to try for 300. On the day mentioned on the plaque, January 4th, 1967, he tried early in the morning and reached 297 miles per hour and decided to have another run and see if he could go over 300. There were a lot of people watching and I was there myself, standing on top of a hill above the lake. I saw the boat speed down to the lower end of the lake and then turn and rest for a few minutes. Then with a tremendous roar of its engines, it started off again, but when it reached about half-way up the lake I saw it fly into the air and crash down on the water and sink.'

'How terrible,' said Abi. 'Did they manage to find it?'

'Yes, they found the wreckage of the boat in very deep water and a little doll he carried with him as a mascot was floating on the surface, but although they searched for weeks, they never found Donald Campbell's body.'

Abi and Philip hardly spoke a word after we left the monument and splashed through the rain towards

Hawkshead. Even when I suggested stopping for hot soup they showed little enthusiasm.

'Look,' I said after a long silence, 'there's no point in brooding about Donald Campbell. He knew what risks he was taking and I'm sure he would have no regrets.'

'Do you think so?' said a whispered voice from deep inside an anorak hood.

'I'm sure of it, so stop upsetting yourselves and let's shelter in the wood ahead of us and make a pan of soup.'

It was rather uncomfortable sitting in the rain, heating soup on the paraffin stove, but it was worth the effort. We felt a lot warmer when we set off again to climb the long hill out of Coniston. The narrow road was very busy with cars and as each one whizzed by we were sprayed with small stones and icy water. To make matters worse the rain came down in such torrents we could hardly see ahead of us, but we stumbled on until we reached the top of the hill and escaped into a lay-by. We ached in every bone, but the rain had not finished with us yet. It brought a strong wind along to help it and we were blown down the last few miles to Hawkshead with such force we were almost running.

On the edge of the village a car stopped and a friend of mine, Jean Crosbie, climbed out to talk to us. She insisted that instead of camping we should spend the night at her house and she would dry our wet clothes. It was an offer not to be refused and we pushed on through the rain to Sykeside, an old farmhouse hidden in a wood not far from the edge of Lake Windermere. Jean and her husband, David, were waiting for us with a meal and a huge log fire roaring in the sitting-room. The driving rain had seeped into our anoraks through zip-fasteners and we were soaked to the skin. Jean rummaged through her cupboards and lent us an assortment of shirts and trousers while our wet clothes were spread out to dry in the kitchen. It was absolute bliss to relax in dry clothes and bask in the warmth.

The rain cleared away completely during the night and early next morning the rays of the sun streamed through the windows and promised a fine day. Feeling refreshed with all our clothes dry, we thanked the Crosbies and set off in warm sunshine to walk a mile or so to High Wray and the start of a wide track running between plantations of tall trees on the shores of Lake Windermere. What a contrast to the previous day; the sky was blue and all around us the aroma of pine and spruce and peaty soil hung in the warm air.

'We haven't used our wild flower identification book since we started our journey,' I said, 'let's see if you can identify a few flowers on the side of the track. What about these tall red plants here?'

Abi rummaged through her rucksack and brought out the small *Oxford Book of Wild Flowers* and she and Philip stood in front of the plant and attempted to identify it.

'I can never understand these books,' grumbled Philip. 'It's full of pictures but where do you start looking?'

Abi was busy reading the introduction. 'It says here that the flower drawings are divided into colour sections so if we look at red flowers we'll probably find it.' She thumbed through the pages. 'Oh dear, there are dozens of red flowers, it will take ages.'

'Hey, stop there,' said Philip, peering over her shoulder, 'that looks like it.'

Abi turned back a page or two, '"Rosebay willowherb,"' she read, 'yes, that's it. We've found it.'

Inspired with the success of identifying the first plant, they hunted along the hedgerow and discovered herb robert, bistort, dog rose and speedwell and argued over several more. Thor rather spoilt the fun by eating

"I wonder what this is called?"

the flowers as soon as they were identified so we put the book away and continued through the wood.

'Can we stop for a while so I can fish?' pleaded Philip, as the winding path took us close to the water's edge. I had almost forgotten he was still carrying his fishing-rod.

'All right,' I said. 'We'll stop for an hour and have a picnic. Is it worth getting the frying-pan out?'

Philip went red in the face, but ignored the taunt and, emptying his fishing tackle on to the ground, started to fit it together while Abi and I unloaded Thor and tethered him to a tree on a long rope. It was a perfect day for fishing, but Philip's chances of catching anything were spoilt by an inconsiderate family in a speedboat, who kept zooming up and down, sending a tremendous wash up the beach. No self-respecting fish could be expected to tolerate treatment of that sort and they all swam off to another part of the lake. At least I imagine that is what happened because, even after an hour of patiently casting his stale crust of brown bread into the water, not a solitary fish was tempted to nibble at it.

'When I grow up I'm going to ban speedboats,' said Philip threateningly, thrusting his fishing-rod into its bag. 'Some people just don't care.'

'Never mind,' I said, attempting to cheer him up, 'let's go for a swim.'

At the word 'swim', Sammy raced down to the lake and jumped in before we had time to take our boots off. Abi said she would paddle instead of going in for a swim.

'You're frightened of showing your skinny legs,' jeered Philip splashing water at her.

'No I'm not,' she snapped, 'and if you really want to know, I've got quite nice legs. It's just that it's too hot for swimming.'

But Philip was not listening, he was racing Sammy to an abandoned ball floating on the water. The sun had climbed high into the sky and it was such a delight to sink into the cool water and escape from the sweltering heat. It was mid afternoon before we loaded Thor and continued on our way along a thickly wooded shore-line at the foot of the steep scar of Claife Heights.

'What a super place to camp,' said Abi, gazing long-ingly at a lush, green meadow reaching down to the lake edge.

'It looks tempting in daylight,' I said, 'but I don't think you'd be very keen to stay at night; it's haunted by a ghost called the "Crier of Claife".'

'Ugh,' shivered Abi, 'I can't bear the thought of meeting a ghost, let's move on.'

'They don't scare me,' boasted Philip. 'What sort of ghost is it?'

'Well, that's the weirdest part of the story,' I said, 'because no one who has met it has lived to describe it. It all started on a stormy night a few hundred years ago. Just a little way ahead of where we are now is the ferry which carries cars and passengers across the narrowest part of the lake, but in those days the ferry was a rowing-boat and anyone wanting to cross had to shout for the boatman. Well, on this particular night, there was a terrible storm raging and the boat was tied up on the other side of the lake by the ferry house and the boatman was sitting by his fireside feeling sure that no one would want to cross on such an awful night. Just about midnight, he was preparing to go to bed when he heard a voice shouting from the other side for the boat. He wasn't keen to row across in such rough conditions, but it sounded as though the person needed help, so he pushed his boat into the water and set off. He was away a long time and when he returned he was alone and whatever he had seen was so horrifying he was struck dumb with fright and died a few days later. From that time, whenever the weather was stormy on the lake, shouts and screams could be heard coming from Claife Heights.'

For once Philip was lost for words. He had listened to the story with wide eyes and his mouth open.

'Gosh,' he gulped, glancing nervously at the shadowy woods, 'perhaps we ought to get going. I'm sure Thor is keen to reach a farm,' and grabbing the lead rope he led the way along the track to the ferry.

The modern car ferry, which hauls itself back and forward across Lake Windermere on wire ropes, was unloading on the opposite side when we arrived and it meant a wait of twenty minutes or so. We were ravenously hungry and joined the queue in front of a mobile snack-bar and tucked into hamburgers, ice cream and coke. When the ferry arrived the ferryman very kindly held the cars back until Thor was wedged safely in a corner of the deck and, though he snorted with fear at first, he soon calmed down when he found he was the centre of attention, with children crowding round to pat his nose and feed him biscuits and sweets. The ferry chugged across the lake and grounded gently on the opposite bank where we joined a slow moving crocodile of vehicles as it crawled along the narrow road leading from the ferry. At a T-junction the cars turned off towards the town of Windermere, leaving us to plod slowly up a long hill and escape into a quiet lane overhung with shady sycamores and bordered with scented hawthorns and hedgerows of red campion. We were dripping with sweat and longing for a cool drink by the time we reached an isolated farm at Hagg End where I asked if we could camp for the night. A girl called

'All at sea' On the Windermere Ferry

Tanya, who helped to run the farm, showed us to a patch of soft grass in the shade of a wall, and we were so tired within half an hour we had pitched the tent and were fast asleep inside it.

The next day was as beautiful as any day could be. Early in the morning a white mist hung over the field where we camped, but as the sun rose higher it warmed the air and the mist vanished, revealing a pale blue sky and a marvellous view over bright green meadows to purple fells in the distance. Tanya came to ask if Abi and Philip would like to learn to milk a cow and we all went with her to the byre where Daisy, a fat brown and white Ayrshire, was already chomping through her breakfast. Tanya sat on an old three-legged stool and slid a bucket under Daisy's bulging udder.

'Now, milking is quite easy if you think about it,' said Tanya. 'Those four teats are full of milk and to get it to flow into the bucket you have to squeeze them firmly, not pull down on them.' She demonstrated by gripping a teat between her thumb and forefinger and squeezing. A jet of milk squirted into the bucket. 'To do it properly, you sit right up to the cow, grip the bucket between your ankles and tilt it slightly. Then using both hands, grip the two teats nearest to you and squeeze alternately, like a pumping action.' She demonstrated and a continuous stream of milk frothed into the bucket.

'Doesn't it hurt her?' asked Abi.

'Not if you do it right, and Daisy would soon let you know if she wasn't happy. Come and try it.'

Abi sat on the stool and nervously gripped a teat with one hand. She squeezed several times, but nothing happened. Daisy stopped eating and turned her head to see who the unfamiliar hand belonged to.

'Try again,' said Tanya, 'but this time move your

hand higher up and if you press you'll feel the milk flowing.'

Abi squeezed and this time a few drops of milk splattered into the bucket. She tried again and within minutes was milking with both hands, as if she had been doing it all her life. When Philip tried he never quite mastered the technique, but he managed to get a pint or so before Daisy bellowed a warning that if he did not squeeze more gently she would kick him into the yard. To be on the safe side Tanya finished milking her and took the full pail into the house to filter it through a special sieve. Then there were calves to feed, byres to muck out, eggs to collect and a whole host of other jobs to be done every day, no matter what the weather was like. Sammy was overjoyed when a flock of sheep had to be moved from one field to another and he wriggled through the grass on his stomach to show Tanya's dogs that he, too, was a real sheepdog and not just a pet. It was late in the morning before the last tasks were finished and, reeking strongly of cow dung and sheep, we waved our thanks to Tanya and were off down the farm lane towards the hamlet of Ings and a pony track that would take us over the fells to Kentmere.

It was another hot day and Thor sweated so much the pack-saddle kept slipping to one side and threatening to fall off. It was infuriating to have to adjust it every ten or fifteen minutes and eventually we rested and let Thor dry off in the sun. There was no hurry, it was only a short distance from Ings to Kentmere and we lazed in the heather by the edge of a beck and drank lashings of ice-cold water. Abi found an attractive clump of flowers growing in the ruin of an old building and with the help of our flower book we identified them as great hairy willow herb. With the pack-saddle

Approaching Kentmere Hall Farm, Kentmere

buckled into position again on Thor's broad back, we continued along a dusty track with a superb view over the Kentmere valley to the high fells and the Nan Bield Pass, which we planned to climb the next day. Philip borrowed my binoculars and scanned the route over the Pass.

'It looks steep,' he said, 'I hope Thor will be able to climb it.'

'You needn't worry about that,' I replied, 'as long as the weather is good, he'll bound up it like a sheep.'

Dropping gently down to the valley, we reached the end of the track in the yard of Kentmere Hall Farm and stopped to admire the old building.

'Was it a castle at one time?' asked Abi, busily making a sketch of a square tower attached to the farmhouse for her notebook.

'Well, not exactly a castle, it was just a tower the owner of the land and his family could take refuge in when the Scots came into Cumbria to raid farms and drive the cattle back over the Border. Eventually, when the raids stopped, farmhouses were built and there's an interesting tale about Kentmere Hall. Most old farmhouses have a huge wooden beam above the fireplace which supports the floors above and when they were building this farm the beam was so heavy not even ten men could lift it. While they were struggling with it a man called Hugh Hird, from Troutbeck, the valley on the other side of the fell, came to see if he could help. He was called the "Troutbeck Giant" because of his size and he just picked up the beam on his own and placed it in position on the walls. The beam was about ten metres long and if you think about it, that's the length of a bus.'

Philip paced out ten metres along the track while Abi made a sketch of Hugh Hird holding the beam above his head.

We were given permission to camp in a field close by the River Kent and as soon as Thor was unloaded we changed into swimsuits and plunged into a deep pool. At first the cold water took our breath away, but we spent the afternoon having great fun sliding down a waterfall and diving under the water. Sammy had a whale of a time diving in to retrieve sticks and racing round to slide down the waterfall. When we tried to lie in the sun to dry off, he shook water all over us until we were forced to join him in the pool again. The swim gave us an enormous appetite and for dinner we had large helpings of mashed potatoes and sausages, followed by cheese, biscuits and fruit cake. When the pans and plates were washed and put away, I spread the map out to decide on the next day's route.

'We've got a tough day ahead of us tomorrow,' I said, 'so we'll have to make an early start. We've got about ten or twelve miles to cover, which may not sound much, but it will involve a lot of fairly strenuous climbing before we reach the summit of High Street. As you can see from the map, it's eight hundred and twenty-eight metres high and quite a long walk to reach it. On the top we follow the summit ridge and then descend by way of the Knott and Satura Crag to Angle Tarn, then down to Side Farm in Patterdale. If we half fill the water-carrier we can either drink the water or make soup, depending on what the weather is like. I'd like to leave here by nine o'clock at the latest, so I suggest we have an early night.'

There was a rush to spread out mattresses and sleeping-bags and, although we lay and watched the sunset through the open tent door, we were all fast asleep before the sun finally slid down behind the fells and darkness settled over the peaceful valley.

Chapter Six

The following morning a heavy dew clung to the branches of the trees and hedgerows as we led Thor through the field gate and on to the road, but when we climbed above the hamlet of Kentmere the sun had already dried the grass. It was a glorious morning, fresh and clear, and the view was delightful, with green pastures and wooded slopes spreading out on either side of the valley and reaching up to the sharp ridges and peaks of the high fells. Walking on soft, springy turf was a welcome change from the hard, dusty surfaces we had experienced and we were constantly stopping to identify wild flowers. There was bright yellow tormentil, sweet smelling wild thyme and delicate blue harebells, but the best find was clumps of tall yellow plants called monkey flower, growing in wet ground by the edge of a beck. Kentmere seemed to be a naturalists' paradise and at every bend we discovered new plants or stopped to watch crows feeding on a dead sheep, or kestrels hovering above the stone walls, waiting patiently for a shrew to scurry through the grass. From a safe branch in a high tree, a buzzard watched warily as we approached and, not quite sure what to make of us, flapped its powerful wings and glided away across the valley.

The climb up Nan Bield Pass was steep and rough at first where the original path had been washed away and Thor had great difficulty keeping his feet on the loose shale and clay that crumbled under his weight. Higher up, the angle eased off, but the path had been cut across the side of a steep fell and we looked down an almost sheer drop into Kentmere Reservoir directly below us. Treading very carefully, we continued along the path to the foot of a high crag. It was a final barrier between us and the summit of the Pass and we stopped to rest and check the ropes holding the packs.

'Pull the breast strap a bit tighter,' I called. 'We must make sure the pack-saddle doesn't slip back or we'll be in trouble.'

Philip adjusted the thick leather strap and with a gentle pull on Thor's lead rope, Abi led him round the boulders, up the narrow path that climbed the precipice in a series of zigzags. There was no opportunity to stare at the view as the path was very badly washed away in places and one slip would have sent Thor crashing down to the rocks below. We puffed and panted our way slowly towards the top and suddenly the climbing was over. Harter Fell towered above us on our right and stretching away to our left was a peak with the peculiar name of Mardale Ill Bell.

'What a relief,' gasped Abi, sinking down on a pile of rocks, 'I could do with a drink of water.'

'Me too,' said Philip, sucking in lungfuls of air. 'Can we have some now or do we have to wait until we reach the top of High Street?'

'Well, I've got a little surprise for you,' I said with a grin. 'I knew you'd be thirsty after this climb so I filled an extra water container. It's in my rucksack.'

'Oh great,' whooped Philip. 'I've got a packet of lemonade crystals somewhere.'

He filled our mugs, poured a bowl of water for Thor and Sammy, and we lay back against the boulders and sipped the cool lemonade. It tasted delicious. The sun was very hot and I had closed my eyes to rest them from the glare when a few spots of water landed on my face. Thinking it was either Abi or Philip playing a joke, I said, 'I shall get very cross with the person who is throwing water at me.'

'We're not throwing water at you,' said Philip, 'it's raining.'

'It's what?' I cried, leaping to my feet.

'It's raining,' repeated Philip. 'Look at that cloud.'

I could hardly believe my eyes. One minute the sun had been beating down from a clear sky and now a large black cloud had appeared from nowhere. Almost before we could pull on our waterproofs, the spots of rain increased to a frenzied downpour that had Thor snorting with fear and pulling madly at the rope tethering him to a rock. I quickly untied him and we pushed on up the ridge towards Mardale Ill Bell, almost blinded by the force of the rain, but there was not an atom of shelter anywhere. We staggered on and reached a cairn marking the top of Mardale Ill Bell when, miraculously, the rain stopped and the sun came out again.

'We have the silliest weather in the world,' grumbled Abi, removing her waterproofs and stuffing them into her rucksack. 'I wish it would make its mind up.'

'What I can't understand,' said Philip, squeezing water out of his shirt collar, 'is that last night the sky was a deep red and in my fishing book it says "red sky at night, angler's delight". There's nothing delightful about being soaking wet.'

'Well you can't expect it to work, silly,' scoffed Abi, 'you're a walker not an angler. Anyway, you've got it wrong, it's "shepherd's delight".'

'No it isn't,' argued Philip. 'I'll get the book out if you like and you can see for yourself.'

'Don't bother,' I interrupted, 'we must be on our

way, we've got High Street to climb yet. Abi, will you lead Thor please.'

The flat summit of High Street looked very close, but the distance was deceptive. A path which seemed to lead in the right direction soon disappeared into a bog and we were left to find our own way up a long ridge covered in thick tussock-grass. At first it was heavy going for Thor. He tripped over the hard tufts of grass and slid into the hollows of soft peat, but as we climbed higher the ground became firmer and levelled out. With a loud cheer, Abi and Philip raced each other to be first to touch the concrete pillar marking the summit of High Street. Though the sun was still shining bravely the blue sky had turned grey and a chilly breeze pulled at the tufts of sparse heather dotted across the summit plateau. We agreed that soup would be more welcome than a cold drink and, in the shelter of a wall, the stove was assembled and the aroma of Scotch broth wafted into the thin air.

'Isn't it a strange name to call a mountain,' said Abi, as we sat against the wall and dipped oatcakes into our mugs of soup. She had the map spread over her knees and was studying our route. 'High Street. I wonder who gave it that name.'

'The Romans,' I said, reaching for the pan of soup and topping up the mugs, 'and what's really fascinating is that where we are sitting now is part of the same path we used when we left Ravenglass and walked through Eskdale. It was a great Roman highway which started at Ravenglass and connected forts they built in Eskdale and Ambleside. This fell, with its long, flat ridge, stretches for about twenty miles, so you can imagine how useful it must have been when they were advancing north towards Scotland. High Street was the perfect name for it.'

"Squeeze gently, don't pull" Philip learns to milk a cow

'Gosh,' breathed Philip, his wild imagination working overtime. 'I can just see the Romans charging along
here in chariots, waving their swords in the air and
chopping the natives' heads off.'

'Oh, you are a fiendish little horror,' squealed Abi.
'Stop it, you're putting me off my soup. The Romans
were nice people, they built baths and things and my
teacher said that they invented ice cream.'

'Invented ice cream,' jeered Philip. 'How could anyone have invented ice cream? There's always been ice

cream, even when grown-ups were at school!'

The sound of approaching voices put a stop to the argument and a party of cheerful hikers arrived and crowded around Thor to examine the pack-saddle and offer him pieces of chocolate.

'It must have been a great sight to watch the fell ponies racing up here in the old days,' shouted one of the hikers as they departed towards Kentmere. 'You ought to reintroduce it.'

I waved my acknowledgement as they disappeared over the ridge.

'Fell pony racing up here?' said Abi, looking puzzled, 'what is he talking about?'

'It was chariot racing,' said Philip gleefully, 'I knew I was right. The Romans used to race each other and the one that lost had to fight a lion.'

'What rubbish,' said Abi, shaking with laughter. 'Where does he get these wild ideas from? Didn't your teacher ever tell you it was the Christians that fought lions, not Romans.'

Philip looked crestfallen, but he soon bounced back. 'Oh well, I don't care. If it was Christians, I'll bet they weren't girl Christians.'

Abi had no answer to that and took a sudden interest in dismantling the stove.

'If you two would stop arguing for a minute,' I said, 'I'll tell you about fell pony racing. It had nothing to do with the Romans, in fact fell ponies were not bred until hundreds of years after the Romans had left Britain, but that's another story and there isn't time to talk about it now. It was local shepherds and farmers who started the pony racing. Nowadays, Lake District farmers take stray sheep back to each other's farms in vehicles, but in the old days farmers living in the valleys and dales round High Street used to meet once a year on the summit to hand back stray sheep they had collected during the year. It was a long walk just to exchange a few sheep so they made it a real day out. They organised sports, with competitions for wrestling, fell racing, hunting, singing and horn blowing. A lot of farmers rode up on fell ponies and one of the highlights of the day was a pony race from the summit cairn of High Street to Thornthwaite Crag. That's the peak you can see sticking up there at the southern end of the fell. They used to call it "Racecourse Hill".'

'But if they were galloping, how did they stop themselves falling over the edge?' asked Philip.

'It's a good point,' I said. 'Perhaps one or two did fall over when racing first started, because eventually they made a rule that if a pony went faster than a trot the rider would be disqualified. No doubt the farmers tried all sorts of ways to get their ponies to trot faster than their neighbours' and some people say it's one of the reasons why a good fell pony can trot faster than some horses can canter.'

'I'd love to see the ponies racing along here,' said Abi eagerly. 'Why don't they have races now?'

'Well I'm afraid that's life. Things go out of fashion and loose popularity as time goes by. Very few farms use fell ponies these days and since every farmer has a vehicle the annual meets are held in the valleys. The High Street pony races are part of history now.'

The sound of thunder in the distance warned that bad weather was not far away and, bundling the stove and pan into a bag, we beat a rapid retreat from High Street's exposed summit, down the north ridge to the Knott, an imposing little peak standing out from the main ridge like the battlements of a castle. It was an impressive view down a steep sided valley close to Hartsop, but there was little time to enjoy it. Thunder was rumbling ever closer and a few heavy spots of rain heralded worse to come. Sammy was frightened by the thunder and walked close behind me, whimpering each time it boomed round the fells. Thor took an excruciatingly long time to negotiate the path down the side of the Knott and though each clap of thunder sounded closer than the last, I dared not hurry him. The surface of the path was very badly eroded and each step had to be taken with the utmost care. At the foot of the Knott we were still a long way from Patterdale and we hurried along a boggy path towards Angle Tarn. The bog petered out at a long expanse of shattered rock which further delayed us while Thor was coaxed across awkward steps and round large boulders and all the time the storm drew nearer. Soon the glistening waters of Angle Tarn came into sight and, slithering down to it on a switchback of shiny peat, we reached the safety of a good path. Thor was panting with the exertion of being almost dragged along in an effort to keep ahead of the storm and when he spied the tarn he insisted on taking a long drink, pausing between mouthfuls to gaze imperturbably at the approaching clouds.

'Come on Thor, we'll be caught in the storm,' yelled Abi and Philip, but Thor simply licked his lips, sucked up another mouthful of water and gazed into space.

'You are a thickhead at times,' I bawled, grabbing his rope and leading him back on to the path. 'If we don't get off this fell soon, we'll be in trouble.'

We had only gone a short way when the storm burst over us. We were blasted and buffeted by the fierce squall, but to move faster than a snail's pace would have been exceedingly dangerous. Away from the safety of the broad plateau by the tarn, the path traversed airily across the side of the fell and we looked down an almost sheer drop into the valley. A short section of the path had been washed away by previous rainstorms and guiding Thor across it was a nightmare. The water-logged ground broke away under his weight and for a heart-stopping second he almost toppled over the edge. With a huge leap he bounded across the gap and as he did so the ground where he had been standing slid away and poured down the fellside in an avalanche of boulders and mud.

'Gosh!' exclaimed Philip. 'That was a near thing. I wouldn't like to cross there again.'

Half hidden under her anorak hood, Abi looked as though she had seen a ghost. 'I was really frightened when Thor started to slide,' she said. 'I hope we don't have to cross any more places like this.'

'No, we're safe now,' I assured her. 'A short distance ahead of us is Boredale Hause and it's all downhill from there.'

Wave after wave of driving rain sluiced down on us, making progress very difficult, but when we reached Boredale Hause and the start of the pack-horse track to Patterdale, the worst was over. The buildings of Side Farm which from high above had looked so tiny, grew larger as we approached and though the rain did its best to make us feel miserable, it failed. We were so happy about reaching Patterdale, we sang all the way down to the farmhouse.

'You can't camp in this weather,' said Mike Taylforth, the farmer, as we dripped water on to his porch carpet. 'Carry on down the lane for about half a mile and you'll come to a barn. You'll be much drier in there.'

We found the barn in the corner of a field and, having rewarded Thor with chocolate biscuits and mint cake, we turned him loose to gorge himself on the thick grass. Inside the barn it was dark and smelt of musty hay, but there was plenty of room to move around and it was a great joy to change into dry clothes. An old farm trailer made an ideal table to prepare dinner and when I assembled the stove Abi made a meal of dried potatoes mixed with chunks of corned beef, followed by pâté and biscuits and the last of the fruit cake. During the night a strong wind moaned round the barn and drove the rain against the roof slates, but snug in our sleeping-bags on the trailer, we slept undisturbed, with Sammy stretched across us.

The sound of a cow bellowing in the field jolted me awake the following morning. It was almost dark in the barn, but when I looked at my watch I was amazed to

A change from camping - Mike Taylforth's barn at Patterdale

discover it was nearly nine thirty.

'Come on, it's time to get up,' I shouted. 'Are you awake?'

'Yes,' came the muffled reply from inside the sleeping-bags, but there was no movement.

'Find them, Sammy,' I ordered. Sammy wriggled into a sleeping-bag and began to lick the occupant. It was Abi.

'Go away, you horrible dog,' she complained, pulling the sleeping-bag over her head, 'I'm trying to sleep.'

But Sammy thought it was a marvellous game and dived on top of her.

'Ouch, get him off,' she yelled, 'I'll get up.'

Philip did not wait for Sammy's attentions, he kicked off his sleeping-bag and was dressed in a flash.

'Open the door and see what the weather is like,' I said. Lifting the heavy iron catch, he pushed the door open and immediately the barn was filled with brilliant sunlight.

'Come and look,' shouted Philip from outside, 'it's a super day.'

One of the nice things about the Lake District is that although it rains a lot, when the weather does clear up and the sun shines down out of a blue sky, it is an experience never to be forgotten. The barn was perched high on the fellside and we had an absolutely breathtaking view across Patterdale to the sharp peak of Dollywaggon Pike and the long, spiky ridge of Striding Edge, which leads to perhaps the most popular of all the Lakeland summits, Helvellyn, looking down from its lofty height of nine hundred and fifty metres. Below the barn, the surface of Ullswater flashed and sparkled in the bright sunlight and a red funnelled steamer sailed across the calm water, leaving a wide, rippling wake behind it. Where the field reached the edge of the lake, a heron was standing on a rock, glaring at a group of calves playing 'chase me Charlie' round a tree and spoiling his fishing by rushing into the water. In the end he gave up and, with wings flapping and spindly legs trailing, he took off and headed for a quiet bay on the opposite side of the lake. Thor was fast asleep under the shade of a tree, totally unaware that he was surrounded by a herd of inquisitive cows, who sniffed and snorted at the strange creature which had mysteriously arrived in their field. As they sniffed they became bolder and one cow mooed loudly in Thor's ear. He shot to his feet as if he had been stung and the terrified cows took one look at the huge, black beast rearing in front of them, then careered madly away, tails in the air and bawling with fright. They crowded through a gate at the far end of the field and were gone. Thor watched them go with a puzzled expression on his face then, with a long sigh, sank on to the grass again and continued his sleep.

'How would you like to spend tonight on top of Helvellyn?' I asked as we sat in the sun outside the barn and ate our breakfast.

'What a smashing idea,' exclaimed Abi. 'Would we camp up there?'

'No, there's a walled shelter on the top. It hasn't got a roof, but we'll take plenty of clothes and food and sit there and watch the sun come up.'

'Oh great,' said Philip. 'I've always wanted to see the dawn from the top of a mountain. Won't it be very cold without a tent and sleeping-bag though?'

'Well that depends a lot on the weather. It seems fairly settled now and provided we've enough warm clothes we will be safe enough. We'll have a rest day today and dry our wet clothes, then in the early evening we'll have a meal and set off for the summit.'

'Will we go along Striding Edge?' asked Philip

eagerly. 'I've heard it's a knife edge ridge with a fantastic drop on either side.'

'Well, it's not quite as bad as that,' I said, 'but it's certainly a narrow ridge and needs to be crossed very carefully. We'll go along it to the summit of Helvellyn and tomorrow we'll climb down Swirral Edge to Red Tarn and rejoin the Patterdale path. If you look at the map you'll see we'll be walking in roughly the shape of a horseshoe. It's only about eight miles altogether but there's a lot of climbing involved.'

Tying a rope between two trees, we hung our wet clothes over it and spent the rest of the morning lazing in the sun, cleaning our boots and coating the pack-saddle with dubbin.

'It's to make it supple and waterproof,' said Philip, with the superior air of one who has spent hours rubbing it into his football boots. Abi pretended she did not hear him.

'By the way,' she said, vigorously polishing lengths of harness with a piece of cloth and handing them to me, 'when we were on High Street yesterday, you said you would tell us about fell ponies.'

'Oh yes,' said Philip. 'I'm going to write about fell ponies in my notebook. If the Romans didn't breed them, then where did they come from in the first place?' As he spoke, he dabbed his face with a cloth, forgetting he had just dipped it in the dubbin tin and instead of mopping up sweat he plastered his forehead with sticky brown dubbin. 'Bother,' he said irritably, trying hard not to say anything stronger, 'it's all over my face.'

Abi giggled uncontrollably. '"It makes it supple and waterproof,"' she mimicked. Philip glared at her and stalked off to the barn to find a dry cloth.

It was some time later, when we were sitting in the shade of a tree eating biscuits and cheese and drinking lemonade brought from the farm, that the subject of fell ponies came up again.

'The strange thing about the fell pony,' I said, 'is that although it is considered to be the native pony of the Lake District, it originally came from Galloway in southern Scotland and, in fact, there's many an old Lakeland farmer who still calls them "Fell Galloways". They used to roam in wild herds and very likely, as food became scarce, some strayed into the Lake District by crossing the Solway Firth when the tide was low. The farmers would catch them and use them for work around the farm. But the true fell pony breed that Thor belongs to all descend from a stallion found roaming about on a moor to the east of the Lake District, after Bonnie Prince Charlie's army retreated back to Scotland in 1745. When the stallion was found he was grazing on ling, that's a kind of heather, so they called him "Ling-cropper".'

'Was it fell ponies that the smugglers used?' asked Philip.

'Yes,' I said, 'smugglers used them a lot and if a smuggler happened to be a farmer, as they often were, he would use them for ploughing as well. The fields were too steep to use large horses, so they used to hitch four ponies to a wooden plough. We've passed quite a number of slate mines on our travels — when quarrying started in the Lake District, the only way slates could be brought down to the roads was by pack-pony and all the quarries had stables to keep their ponies in at night. They were used a lot in Northumberland, in coal mines, as well.'

'Oh no,' exclaimed Abi. 'Surely they didn't take them under the ground in mines. It's cruel.'

'Well it doesn't sound very nice, I admit, but the miners were very fond of their ponies and always made sure they were well fed. They even got a week's holiday each year, which is probably more than the miners got.'

'I still think it's cruel,' persisted Abi. 'Imagine lovely ponies like Thor being shut up in a dark mine and covered in dust, it's horrible.' The thought of it made her feel sorry for Thor and she ran over to where he was sleeping to give him a handful of biscuits. He was not quite sure what all the fuss was about, but he snatched the biscuits out of Abi's hand and ambled off down to the lake for a drink. Had he been able to talk, he might have explained that the closest he has ever been to the dark depths of a mine was the time he sneaked into a building, thinking it was my pony nut store, and it was only when the door slammed shut behind him, he found himself trapped all night in the coal-shed!

Chapter Seven

About five o'clock we had a light tea, packed our rucksacks with waterproofs, spare sweaters, socks, gloves and balaclava helmets, torches, first aid kit, map and compass, mint cake, chocolate and lemonade crystals. Leaving Thor in the field, we put Sammy on a lead and set off through Patterdale village to Grisedale and a rocky path climbing diagonally upwards towards the skyline and Striding Edge. There was a large party of lads and girls ahead of us, heavily laden with tents and rucksacks and they stopped so often for rests we soon caught up with them. They were a very cheery bunch from a Youth Club in Edinburgh and were on their way to camp for the night at the edge of Red Tarn. We promised to look out for them on the following morning and, with a wave and lots of shouts of 'enjoy yourselves', 'see you tomorrow', we left them having a friendly argument about whether the girls should help to carry the rucksacks.

When we left the barn the weather was very pleasant, the sun shone from an almost cloudless sky and every ridge and peak stood out in the clear air. But almost as soon as we set foot on the path to Striding Edge the weather began to change. Cloud began to drift in from the west, thin wisps of white at first, but as we climbed higher it increased to thick blobs of grey that settled on the summit of Helvellyn and poured down on

Resting after a hard day

to Striding Edge like a cauldron of porridge boiling over. A chilly wind sprang up among the rocks making the bracken dance and ruffling the wool of the sheep scattered over the fellside. The sun took one look at the changing scene and retreated behind a cloud.

We toiled up the rough path until a large, flat rock provided an opportunity to rest and get our breath back. Philip lay with his chin on Sammy and stared upwards at the clouds drifting over the ridge.

'It seems to be getting thicker,' he said miserably. 'I hope we don't have to go back.'

'Isn't it just typical,' stormed Abi. 'It's been hot and sunny all day and as soon as we decide to do something exciting the silly weather has to spoil it.'

'Don't worry, it's not as bad as it looks,' I said, trying to sound cheerful. 'It might ruin the view, but it won't stop us sleeping on the top. We'll carry on until we reach Striding Edge and see what conditions are like up there.'

I hoped I sounded convincing. Although I did not show it, I was worried about the change in the weather and at the back of my mind I knew there was a distinct possibility that we might have to abandon the plan to sleep on the summit and retreat to the barn. Up and up we climbed, staggering over mounds of loose rubble and peat, where winter storms had torn away the surface of the path. Conversation was out of the question, every ounce of strength was needed to force our legs to keep moving towards Striding Edge, looming tantalizingly close above our heads. The path steepened and became even rougher, but with a burst of energy we clambered up on to the ridge and sank down behind a large rock. Philip's face was almost as red as his hair.

'I'm absolutely worn out,' he gasped, 'can we have a drink?'

'Not just yet,' I said, 'we'll save it till later.'

'But why?' howled Abi, 'I'm so thirsty I could drink a whole lake.'

'You're only thirsty because it was a hard slog up the path. If you have a drink now you'll hardly taste it and there's only about a pint between us. Later on we'll find a sheltered place away from this wind and stop for a drink and something to eat.'

The ridge leading to Striding Edge ran from east to west and started with easy walking along the top of Blaeberry Crag. The cloud, although it swirled and spiralled around the crags, was not as thick as it seemed from below and the summit of Helvellyn was clearly visible ahead of us. It was a tremendous boost to morale

Striding Edge - the arrow marks the place where we bivouaced

and we surged forward through a huge heap of boulders to the top of High Spying How. Here the tearing action of the glaciers millions of years ago had piled the rocks up on edge and the easy walking was over. In front of us stretched a true mountain ridge, narrow jagged rock and a sheer drop on either side.

'It's fabulous,' exclaimed Philip, bracing himself against the wind. 'I've never seen anything like it.'

Abi was more down to earth. 'Is it safe?' she asked, looking dubiously at the thin path running along the crest and climbing a steep spur to the summit of Helvellyn.

'You've absolutely nothing to worry about,' I assured her. 'Striding Edge is one of the safest ridges in the Lake District in good weather. There's a little bit of rock scrambling at the end of it, but you'll manage all right.'

'What about Sammy?' said Philip.

'He'll probably manage better than us,' I said, 'but we must keep him in front of us all the time, in case he comes barging past and knocks us over the edge.'

The wind increased slightly and we slithered down to the shelter of a large rock to pull on our sweaters and waterproofs and eat a bar of chocolate. Wisps of cloud began to drift around the rocks and when I stood up and looked along the ridge I could hardly believe my eyes. In the few minutes we had spent sheltering the weather had completely changed again. Long banks of cloud had obscured the summit and were gradually creeping along Striding Edge.

'Let's get going,' I called. 'Keep close behind me and don't loose sight of each other.'

Helped along by the wind, the cloud soon enveloped us, but lifted again after a few minutes to reveal Red Tarn far below on our right. Again the cloud closed in, reducing visibility to a few metres and we were forced to stop. By now it was late in the evening and darkness was not far away. Soon I would have to make a decision to go on or go back. The cloud lifted once more and we made a little progress but when it returned it was so thick I could hardly see the two shadowy figures walking close behind me.

'It's no use,' I said. 'We can't go on in this, it's far too dangerous; we'll have to go back.'

'Oh no,' groaned Philip, 'we've come all this way and we're so close to the top. Can't we wait until the cloud lifts?'

'No,' I said firmly. 'I realize it's very disappointing for you, but it's better to be safe than sorry. We might have to wait a long time for the cloud to lift and it'll be dark soon.'

'Couldn't we sleep up here?' asked Abi. 'We could find a rock and shelter behind it.'

'Are you serious?' I said, half expecting her to admit she was only joking, but I was wrong.

'Yes, let's sleep here. I've always wanted to sleep on a mountain and I might not get the chance again.'

'Me too,' said Philip. 'I don't mind if it's cold.'

'Well all right,' I said, 'there's a wide ledge just in front of us. We'll be safe enough there and if the weather turned really nasty we could easily escape back along the ridge. Let's get settled before dark.'

The ledge was not far below the ridge and we clambered down to it and spread our rucksacks out to sit on. Wearing our sweaters, thick trousers and water-proofs, finished off with a scarf, gloves and woollen balaclava helmet, we were comfortably warm and Sammy lying across our legs made an excellent hot-water bottle. The ledge was about two and a half metres long by one metre wide and we shared it with a large iron monument bolted to a rock. It was in the shape of a gravestone and looked very creepy in the failing light, with long streamers of mist swirling round it like ghostly dancers. Abi leaned forward and shone her torch on the inscription.

'Waiting for the sun to rise' - Striding Edge

'"In memory of Robert Dixon, Rodings, Patterdale,"' she read out, '"who was killed on this place on the 27th day of November 1858 when following Patterdale Foxhounds."'

'Following Patterdale Foxhounds?' echoed Philip. 'Surely he didn't ride a horse along here.'

'No, he wasn't on a horse,' I said. 'This sort of ground is too rough for horses. He would be following hounds on foot and very likely he slipped on the rock and fell over the edge. If it wasn't for the mist, you would be able to look down from our ledge, a very long way, almost vertically to the ground below.'

Abi shrank back and wriggled between Philip and me. 'Ugh,' she shivered, 'I'm glad I can't see over the edge.'

We lay back against the hard rock and listened to the sounds of the mountain night. On the ridge above us the wind moaned through the deep fissures in the rock, rising and falling like the sound of a giant organ. Ravens called to each other with their strange 'kronk, kronk' and swished invisibly over our ledge in a flurry of wings. The cry of a lamb searching for its mother drifted up from far below and, as the wind changed direction, it brought the sound of water from a distant beck as it poured down the fellside. Now and then, Helvellyn stirred in its sleep and sent stones rattling and crashing down the screes into Nethermost Cove. We dozed for an hour or two and about midnight a break appeared in the mist and revealed a full moon suspended in an inky sky. It closed in again quickly but the moon shining through the mist cast an eerie light over our ledge and as if at a magic signal, the cold, sterile ground around us became alive with beetles scurrying hither and thither and delicate white moths flitted across our feet. At first I thought I was dreaming, but Abi saw them too.

'What on earth can they find to live on at this height?' she said, brushing off a column of beetles advancing up her boots.

'I don't know,' I said. 'Perhaps the beetles find food in the heather and grass, but I can't imagine what attracts moths up here.'

Philip stirred and woke up. 'Oh, my leg's gone numb,' he groaned. 'Can we swop places so I can lie on my side?'

We moved round, but there was not enough room to stretch out. There were so many spiky rocks sticking out of the ground, no matter how many times we tossed and turned, finding a comfortable position was impossible. To pass the time we ate chocolate and played spelling games, but by two o'clock we were so tired we could hardly keep our eyes open.

'Am I hearing things, or is that thunder?' asked Philip, as we squirmed about in an effort to get off to sleep. We strained our ears and listened. Sure enough the sound of thunder rumbled round the fells in the distance, but it was a long way off. Half an hour later the rumblings were much closer, though it was difficult to tell which direction the storm was approaching from. A sharp crack of thunder to our right, in the direction of Dollywaggon Pike, reverberated round the corries like a roll of drums.

'It sounds as if it's getting closer,' said Abi nervously. 'Will we be all right here?'

'Yes, we're quite safe at the moment,' I said, 'but if it gets any nearer we may have to leave.'

The thunder broke again, not as loud this time and it appeared to be moving away. Another crack confirmed that the storm had retreated and I felt a lot happier.

Suddenly, a tremendous flash of lightning pierced the mist, followed by an ear-splitting crack of thunder right above us. The air hummed and crackled with electricity and almost immediately another flash lit up the rocks with a fantastic blue light and the most awful crack of thunder shook our ledge like an earthquake. Poor Sammy howled with fright and dived underneath my coat.

'Follow me, quickly,' I said urgently. 'We must get away from this iron monument in case it's struck by lightning.'

For some strange reason the mist suddenly lifted and, as I climbed on to the rock above the ledge I witnessed a most awesome sight. A tremendous fork of lightning struck a pinnacle at the end of Striding Edge and bounced along the ridge, sparking like an electric cable. The entire area was lit by an incredibly powerful light, but within seconds it had gone and the ridge was plunged into darkness. Slowly the mist settled again, the crackle of electricity ceased and the rumbles of thunder receded into the distance. The storm had passed over. A few chunks of rock, broken off by the lightning, bounced down the fellside into the soft ground below and all was quiet.

'Are you all right?' I called down to Abi and Philip.

'Yes, we're fine, but it was scary while it lasted,' came the reply.

I rejoined them on the ledge and we managed to sleep for an hour or so before the dark mist slowly turned white with the approaching dawn. Visibility was still down to a few metres and it was bitterly cold.

'I'm absolutely frozen,' said Abi, thrashing her arms about. 'What time is it?'

'Nearly five o'clock,' I said, looking at my watch. 'Give Philip a shake and we'll do some exercises to warm you up.'

Philip grunted and tottered to his feet. 'Ggggosh,' he stuttered through chattering teeth, 'if it's so ccccold up here, I wonder what it's like on Everest.'

'You'll soon get warm,' I said. 'Climb up on the ridge.' To have met three hooded figures and a dog, jogging backwards and forwards along a part of Striding Edge would have given the strongest nerves a dreadful shock, but fortunately we had the ridge to ourselves and after twenty minutes we had warmed up and were ready for breakfast. It was only a bar of chocolate and a piece of mint cake each, washed down with cold water mixed with lemon crystals but it was very welcome.

'Wouldn't it be nice if we could see the view,' said Philip, licking sugary lemon crystals out of his mug. 'I wish this mist would go away.'

'There's no chance of that unless the sun comes out,' I said, 'and even then it could be late morning before it has any effect.'

'What are we going to do then?' asked Abi. 'Go back the way we came?'

'Not necessarily,' I said. 'Apart from the mist, the weather is quite good and if you are both feeling up to it, we'll go to the top of Helvellyn.

'Oh great,' they chorused, 'let's go on.'

'All right, it's the same rules as yesterday: keep close together and don't lose sight of each other.'

Sammy bounded on ahead into the mist and we followed, picking our way carefully along the narrow crest of Striding Edge. Even though the mist obscured the view beyond a few metres, we were very conscious of the drop on both sides and moved with the utmost care. For the most part, it was fairly easy, but right at the end of Striding Edge, barring our way to the summit, was a rock chimney about fifteen metres deep. In clear weather it would present little difficulty for anyone not afraid of a short rock climb, but when we peered over the edge the swirling mist made it hard to see the holds. I helped Sammy down first and left him guarding my rucksack while I went back to guide Abi and Philip, but they swarmed down without any hesitation. A short steep path led upwards and almost before we realized it we were standing on the summit of Helvellyn in front of a large cairn of stones.

'It's another monument,' cried Abi, using the sleeve of her anorak to wipe the moisture off a plaque fixed to the cairn. 'It's something about a dog guarding a skeleton. Come and look.'

The inscription was difficult to make out in the poor light and Philip shone the torch on it to read it aloud.

'"Beneath this spot were found in 1805 the remains of Charles Gough, killed by a fall from the rocks. His dog was still guarding the skeleton."'

'Isn't that sad,' said Abi softly. 'I wonder what happened.'

'It's a well known story, but no one is quite sure what happened,' I said. 'According to local people, Charles Gough was from Manchester and often spent his holidays in Patterdale, fishing and walking the fells with his little terrier called "Foxy". The year he died he stayed in Patterdale for a few days and then set off to walk over Striding Edge and Helvellyn to stay at an inn at Wythburn, on the edge of Thirlmere. He climbed the path to Striding Edge, carrying a pack and his fishing-rod, with little Foxy trotting beside him, and he was never seen again. There were no telephones in those days and the landlord of the inn where he had been staying naturally thought that since he hadn't returned he must have reached Thirlmere. No one gave him a thought until about three months later a shepherd gathering sheep at Red Tarn heard a dog barking among the rocks below Helvellyn. When he went to investigate he discovered a skeleton and Foxy standing guard over it. Apparently Gough had got lost in bad weather and fallen down the crags. The little dog couldn't understand that Gough was dead and, for three months, she had stayed by his side barking as loudly as she could in the hope that someone would bring help. When the shepherd found her she was so weak she could hardly walk, so he wrapped her in his coat and took her home with him and looked after her until she went to live with one of Charles Gough's relations.'

'What a lovely story,' said Philip. 'If I'm ever allowed to have a dog I'm going to call it "Foxy".'

Abi was staring at the inscription on the plaque as

though she was trying to read it through again, but as she turned, her face was caught in the light of Philip's torch and she hurriedly brushed aside a flood of tears.

'Come on, you great softy,' I said, squeezing her arm gently, 'let's go, it's getting cold.'

Visibility on the summit was down to a metre or so and I worked out a compass course to take us first to the Ordnance Survey's concrete pillar marking the highest point at nine hundred and fifty metres, then to Swirral Edge and the start of our descent to Red Tarn. At first Swirral Edge was rather like Striding Edge in reverse and in the mist it required great care. Stone shoots that looked like paths often ended on the edge of an abyss and a lot of time was spent making sure we were heading in the right direction. Unlike Striding Edge, which is part of a long ridge, Swirral Edge slants down and, having safely negotiated an awkward, rocky section we followed a good path to level ground. We could hear voices calling to each other through the mist and by the edge of Red Tarn we almost walked into the tents belonging to the Edinburgh party we had met on the way up the day before. The leader said the girls in the party had been terrified by the thunder and had spent most of the night weeping.

'This wee lassie must be very brave to have spent the night on Helvellyn in that sort of weather,' he said, smiling at Abi.

'There'll be no living with her now,' teased Philip as we left the campers and set off again, 'she'll be so big-headed because someone said she is brave, I'll have to ask permission to speak to her.'

'It proves that girls are just as good at things as boys,' said Abi, pretending to be haughty. 'You may carry my rucksack if you wish, my man.'

Philip replied by blowing a large raspberry.

I set a compass course from Red Tarn and after floundering through a wilderness of waterlogged peat, we reached a stile over a wall and rejoined the path leading to Patterdale. To our great joy we walked out of the mist and looked down on a sunlit valley and green fields.

'Are you tired?' I asked, as we stopped to pull off our waterproofs and spare sweaters.

'Yes, a little bit,' said Abi.

'My eyelids feel like lead,' said Philip. 'I could sleep for a week.'

'Well, I must say I am very proud of you both,' I said, 'and when we reach the village I'm going to buy you a slap up breakfast and then we'll go back to the barn and you can sleep for as long as you like.'

The only café in Patterdale spoilt my promise of breakfast by being closed and, very disappointed, we made our way back to the barn and lay in our sleeping bags with mugs of hot Oxo. Lulled by the warm drink and cosy sleeping-bags, we drifted off into a deep sleep. It was well into the afternoon before we surfaced and outside the barn the sun was beating down from a cloudless sky.

'Isn't it infuriating? Look at Helvellyn now!' exclaimed Abi, pointing at the ridge. 'There isn't a cloud to be seen.'

Every pinnacle stood out mockingly against the pale blue background of the sky and the air was so clear we could easily make out the concrete pillar on the summit.

'That's the way it is with the fells,' I said; 'the weather can be very unpredictable at times and you just have to learn to live with it. Mind you,' I added, jokingly, 'if you want to spend another night on Helvellyn and watch the sun rise, we can set off after tea!'

'No thank you,' said Abi quickly. 'I think I would

prefer to sleep in the barn if it's all right with you.'

'I wouldn't mind,' said Philip boldly, 'but I'm too tired to go tonight. I'll go tomorrow though.'

'Don't take me seriously,' I laughed. 'I'm only ribbing you. I'm sure it will be a long time before you forget the night on Striding Edge.'

We took a picnic down to the edge of the lake and spent the rest of the afternoon lazing in the sunshine and throwing sticks into the water for Sammy to retrieve.

'I think I'll fish for a while,' said Philip staring thoughtfully at the water. 'There's a tree hanging over the water up there and my fishing book says it's the sort of place where trout lie.'

He ran back to the barn and returned with his fishing-rod and a cardboard box full of worms he had dug out from under the stones in the field. Very solemnly he assembled his rod and went through the ritual of throwing pieces of bread into the water before he carefully placed a worm on the hook and, with a great flourish, cast it into the lake.

'I wish I was a good swimmer,' said Abi, grinning mischievously. 'I'd love to swim underwater and tie an old boot on the end of his line.'

'It would be great fun,' I laughed, 'but you know how lucky he is. Someone would probably come along and discover the boot was an interesting relic and swop him a bag of fish for it!'

Despite his enthusiasm, Philip never seemed to have much success with his fishing. The weather would be too cold, or too hot; the water too deep, or too shallow; the sun too bright, or not bright enough and, of course, there were always people. Though he often searched frantically through his fisherman's bible, there was no advice to be found on what to do about people and the shore of Ullswater was seething with them. No sooner had he cast his line than a large party, with yapping dogs and noisy children, arrived and proceeded to throw stones into the water and shriek with laughter when the dogs jumped in after them. While mums and dads lay on the grass, listening to a portable radio, the children paddled an inflatable dinghy round the bay, hotly pursued by their friends, trying to tip them out of it. They were having a marvellous time, but the noise frightened away every fish for miles. Philip abandoned his fishing spot to the revellers and, carrying his rod over his shoulder, walked dejectedly along the lake shore.

'It's a pity there aren't any sharks in Ullswater,' he muttered fiercely, as he trudged by on his way to the barn.

We had eaten very little in the previous twenty-four hours and for our evening meal we gorged ourselves on sausages, beefburgers and new potatoes from the farm, followed by biscuits, cheese and fresh fruit. It was a lovely evening and, after we had eaten, we sat outside against the barn wall and gazed at the wonderful panorama of fells and woods. The picnickers, bathers and noisy outboard motors were gone from the lake and placid cows stood knee deep in the cool water, lifting their heads now and then to stare at a fleet of dinghies with brightly coloured sails, as they glided by. The lake steamer curved in a wide arc round the bay, its green hull and bright red funnel glistening in the setting sun, as the captain steered it gently towards Glenridding. With a final puff of smoke from the funnel, it eased against the pier and stopped. Another day was over.

'Where are we going tomorrow?' asked Philip, when we were in our sleeping-bags on the trailer.

'Well, if you're not too worn out, I'd rather like to reach Borrowdale, if possible,' I replied. 'We'll walk up Grisedale, that's the valley where the Striding Edge path starts, climb up to Grisedale Tarn, then drop down to Grasmere. The village will be swarming with visitors at this time of the year and we could waste a lot of time looking for somewhere to camp. It's another six or seven miles to Borrowdale and there is a steep pass to climb over, but it will be worth it.'

'Let's go to Borrowdale,' said Abi drowsily.

'What about you Philip?' I said. There was no answer, he was fast asleep.

Chapter Eight

It took ages to find Thor the next morning. During our stay he had made friends with the cows and each day they took him on a tour of the fields and showed him their favourite hiding-places in the woods. We eventually found him snoozing contentedly under an old oak tree, surrounded by his tail-swishing, cud-chewing companions, who glared at us with watery red eyes and backed off, snorting angrily, when I slipped a halter over Thor's head and led him away to the barn. It was a perfect day for walking. Low cloud obscured the fell tops, keeping the hot sun at bay and it was pleasantly warm when we left Side Farm and followed a road round Patterdale Church to a broad track leading to Grisedale. On both sides of the narrow valley the fells towered into the clouds and when we reached the end of the level track and saw the old pack-horse route snaking upwards to a break in the clouds, it created an exciting feeling of venturing into the unknown. At first the uphill path was fairly easy, but crossing a wooden bridge over the raging waters of Grisedale Beck, it rose steeply to Ruthwaite Lodge, a climbers' hut perched on the side of the fell. It was a strenuous climb and by the time we reached the lodge our shirts were soaked in sweat and Abi's face was the colour of a beetroot.

'I'm aching all over,' she gasped, collapsing on the grass. 'I must have a rest.'

The pack-horse route in Grisedale with the Helvellyn range in the background

Philip lay on his stomach by the edge of a beck and sucked noisily at the water. 'That feels better,' he said, wiping his mouth with his shirt sleeve. 'I hope the rest of the path isn't as steep as this, I'm worn out already.'

The climb was nothing to Sammy and, as fresh as a daisy and lively as ever, he bounded up the hill with a stick in his mouth and dropped it on Abi.

'Oh go away, Sammy,' she groaned. 'I need my energy for walking, not for throwing sticks. Go and see Philip.'

But Philip pretended to be asleep. The trio of lazy humans stretched out on the ground was too much for Sammy and, with an impatient bark, he grabbed his stick and with his tail in the air, he trotted off up the path.

'Come on,' I called, 'if we don't catch up with the little pest he'll be in Grasmere hours before us.'

Beyond Ruthwaite Lodge the path became progressively rockier and, in places, was so rough and broken that Thor had to be led through it with great care. As we climbed higher the cloud began to break up and a hot sun beat down, lathering us in such a sweat that our already slow pace was reduced to a crawl.

'Not far now,' I shouted encouragingly. 'One more steep section and we'll reach Grisedale Tarn at the top of the Pass.'

We plodded relentlessly on up rock and scree until, to our immense relief, the path levelled out and there before us was Grisedale Tarn, nestling in a hollow between Dollywaggon Pike and Fairfield. Above the tarn, the path traversed across a wet, boggy hillside, then went to the opposite extreme, vanishing among a maze of broken rocks and scree. It was very difficult ground for Thor to negotiate carrying the heavy packs

Hurry up with dinner, we're ravenous

and it required a lot of coaxing, and sometimes actually lifting his legs carefully over a particularly nasty obstacle, before we reached the edge of Grisedale Hause and looked down a long, narrow valley towards Grasmere. But the worst was by no means over. To reach the valley we were faced with a very steep descent down a tumbled mass of boulders and loose scree, gouged and twisted by countless winter storms.

'Should we tighten Thor's breeching?' asked Philip, as we sat on a slab of rock and worked out the safest line to take down the fell.

'Yes,' I replied, 'take it in as far as it will go, otherwise the saddle might slip forward.'

The adjustments completed, we worked our way down through the boulders in a series of long zigzags. It took a very long time and there were a few anxious moments when Thor skidded on the loose scree and almost fell over, but eventually we reached the bottom and followed a good path down the valley to the main Grasmere to Keswick road. It was extremely hot and we rested for a few minutes in the shade of a row of cottages.

'We've got a choice now,' I said, consulting the map. 'We can either go across the road and follow a lane which will bring us out on the path to Borrowdale, or we can walk down the main road to Grasmere to buy ice cream and join the Borrowdale path later.' There was no hesitation.

'Ice cream, please,' cried two hoarse voices and Sammy wagged his tail.

Grasmere village was crowded with tourists and our strange procession attracted a lot of attention as we tramped along the road. Cars pulled on to the verge while the occupants stared curiously out of the windows or shrank back in their seats when Thor bared his teeth at them. Actually he was only pulling faces whilst chewing a lump of mint cake, but the display of teeth was quite spectacular. A small crowd watched our every move and when we stopped in the main square to sit on a bench and share our ice cream with Thor and Sammy, cameras clicked away by the dozen. Abi blushed a deep scarlet when an elderly American, festooned with cameras, stopped in front of us and said to his wife, 'Gee, ain't this little blond haired girl cute. Hold it right there honey, I wanna shot of you feeding your horse with ice cream.'

A shout from the opposite side of the square drew the attention of the crowd around us and they hurried away towards a procession advancing down the road.

'Thanks a million, honey,' called the American to Abi. 'We gotta go and take a few shots of the rush-bearing now.' Ramming a new magazine of film into his cine camera, he dashed away and was soon lost in the crowd.

'What's rush-bearing?' asked Philip, standing on the seat and craning his neck to get a better view of the procession.

'I'll tell you as we go along,' I said, untying Thor's lead rope. 'If we don't leave now we might be hemmed in the square for hours.'

Following the direction of a signpost pointing to Easedale we set off up a narrow road just as the head of the procession of little girls carrying bunches of flowers entered the square.

'I'm sorry we couldn't stop to watch,' I said, as we tramped along the road, 'but if Thor had taken fright, goodness knows what might have happened. I wondered why there were such a lot of people in the village, it's the annual rush-bearing ceremony in Grasmere Church. It goes back to the time when country churches had earth floors and the villagers used to gather rushes to spread over the soil. Every year, about now, they cleared the church out and filled it with new rushes then everyone got together and had a party.'

'Has Grasmere Church still got an earth floor?' asked Abi, unable to believe that anyone could be so primitive.

'No, they have nice stone slabs to walk on, nowadays, and it's become more of a flower festival; that's why the girls we saw in the procession were carrying flowers instead of rushes.'

'I don't think we have a rush-bearing ceremony in Ennerdale,' said Philip. 'At least I've never heard of one.'

'They probably had one years ago,' I said, 'but it's more or less died out now in Cumbria. The only other one I know of is held at Ambleside, but I believe there are two or three other churches around that keep the tradition going.'

The surfaced road wound upwards above the village to a cluster of large houses, half hidden among the trees, then ended abruptly at the start of a pack-horse track. In the days before proper roads were built to connect the Lake District communities, the track must have been a very important link between Grasmere and Borrowdale. For some distance beyond the road end it was well surfaced with cobbles and flanked on either side by dry stone walls. After the rough and tumble of the journey from Patterdale, it was a joy to walk on a good track and we strode along at a cracking pace, keeping time with the clinking sound of Thor's iron shoes striking the hard ground.

'I'm ravenous,' announced Abi after we had been walking for half an hour or so. 'Can we stop and have something to eat?'

'That's a good idea, my stomach keeps rumbling,' said Philip. 'I could just eat a bowl of soup.'

'Well all right then,' I said, 'we'll stop soon and light the stove.'

A walled paddock by the bubbling waters of Easedale Gill provided grazing for Thor and an ideal place to assemble the stove and prepare a pan of soup. I was about to pour it into the mugs when Philip discovered that the mound of springy grass he was sitting on was an ants' nest. With a yell, he leaped to his feet and performed a lively war dance in an effort to shake off a horde of angry ants swarming up his legs. Round and round he went, almost kicking the stove over, but I managed to grab the pan of soup and run with it to safer ground. Abi lay on the grass, helpless with laughter, while poor Philip raced round the paddock jumping boulders and crashing through bracken.

'I've never seen him move so fast,' she gasped, tears of laughter running down her face. 'We ought to enter him for the Grand National.'

Apart from a few red blotches round his ankles, he was none the worse for the ant attack and dangling his feet in the beck for a few minutes helped to relieve the soreness.

'Isn't it strange that there aren't many farms in this valley,' Abi remarked when we had finished our soup and were sitting against a wall gazing at the view. 'Look at all these little fields, they must have belonged to farms at some time.'

'They still do,' I said. 'Every bit of land is owned by somebody, even the tops of the fells. In the old days those fields would be owned by several small farms, but as time went by it became harder to make a living and gradually the people moved away and the houses crumbled. Imagine having potatoes and bread for almost every meal with, perhaps, a piece of mutton now and then. They had milk from their own cows and made butter and baked bread, but the farmers' families never knew what it was like to eat the sort of food we have. Quite a number of families almost starved to death in the winter; in fact there's a very sad story told about a farmer who lived in this valley.

One winter's day, the farmer and his wife left their six children at home and walked over to Langdale to a farm sale. While they were there it began to snow heavily and everyone made for home. The farmer's friends wanted him and his wife to stay the night in Langdale but he was worried about the children left in the care of the eldest girl, who was only nine. Anyway, they wouldn't stop and were last seen climbing up the fell in the teeth of a gale. In Easedale, huge snowdrifts were building up around the farm and, though the children waited and waited, darkness came and they were so tired they all fell asleep. During the night the blizzard increased and by morning the children were completely snowed in and couldn't go for help. Little Agnes, the one who was nine, managed to milk the cow and give her brothers and sisters a drink, then they all huddled round the peat fire to keep warm. They were there for four days, living on very little food, before the blizzard died down and Agnes was able to stagger through the snowdrifts to the next farm for help. A search party was formed and they hunted for almost a week without success, but then dogs were brought in and they found the bodies of the farmer and his wife buried in the snow.'

'Isn't that awful,' sniffed Abi, wiping her eyes. 'I think I'm going to cry.'

'What happened to the children?' asked Philip, almost in a whisper.

'Most of them were adopted by local families and

William Wordsworth, the poet, who lived in Grasmere at the time, organized a relief fund for them and raised about five hundred pounds, quite a lot of money in those days. Even the Royal Family heard about the disaster and sent the children some money.'

A jovial party of hikers helped to dispel the gloom of the story of the Easedale children with their laughing and singing, as they strode down the path towards us. They crowded round Thor and Sammy, taking photographs and questioning us about our journey. What did we carry on our pack-saddle? Where did we sleep at night? Did we carry food for Thor and Sammy? And so on until our heads were in a whirl.

'Come on lads, we'll miss the bus,' shouted the party leader. 'We've half an hour to get to Grasmere.'

Immediately there was a stampede of bodies, swaying rucksacks and tartan socks, as they raced each other down the track. With a loud cheer they disappeared from view and, loading the bags on to Thor, we continued on our way.

Towards the head of the valley the track crossed a ford over Easedale Gill and followed a meandering course towards the skyline.

'Look at that lovely yellow flower,' called Abi, pointing to a long stemmed plant as we picked our way through a patch of bog. 'Let's find out what it is.'

Philip produced the flower book from his rucksack and we leafed through it.

'I think it's bog asphodel,' he said, pointing at a page of yellow flowers.

'Well, it could be,' said Abi, peering over his shoulder, 'but I'm not sure. I'll have another look at it.' She turned to the flower and stopped, with a puzzled expression on her face. 'Hey, it's gone!' she called.

'Gone? How could it have gone?' snorted Philip.

'Well it has, look for yourself.' All that remained was a short piece of stem poking out of the grass. We stared in amazement, wondering where the flower could have vanished to.

'I know what's happened,' said Abi slowly, 'Thor's eaten it.'

I opened his mouth and there, all chewed up, was the flower.

'You are a greedy brute, Thor,' I scolded, 'now we'll never know what it was.'

We hunted round the bog, but there was not another flower to be seen. Higher up the fell we identified bilberry and sphagnum moss, but it seemed that Thor had devoured the only specimen of the yellow flower in the whole valley.

At the head of the valley the track wound up through a mixture of bog and peat to Greenup Edge, a long ridge marking the boundary between Easedale and Stonethwaite in Borrowdale. It was a strenuous climb and, with sighs of relief, we flopped in the short grass at the top and quenched our thirst with lemonade crystals stirred into mugs of cool water. In Easedale the weather had been warm and sunny, but as we descended into Stonethwaite it changed abruptly. A cool breeze swished through the grass on the fellside and to the west, long bands of dark cloud were drifting in rapidly from the Irish Sea

'I hope it doesn't rain and spoil this lovely day,' said Abi looking anxiously at the sky.

Philip spat on his finger and held it up to judge the direction of the wind.

'My fishing book says that if the wind blows from the west during the summer the weather will be cloudy, with rain or showers, and the wind is blowing from the west now.'

'Oh that fishing book again!' said Abi, with a disdainful sniff. 'It thinks it knows everything. If it's as good at forecasting weather as it is about telling you where to catch fish, we'll probably have a heat wave.'

Philip did not have a chance to reply. We were crossing an expanse of wet ground when Thor suddenly sank up to his belly in a bog.

'Grab his lead rope and hold him,' I shouted. 'I'll untie the packs.'

But before I could reach the ropes Thor floundered forward and got himself well and truly stuck. The more he struggled the deeper he sank, until I was worried that he would disappear completely. Abi and Philip hung on grimly to the lead rope, while I talked to Thor and fumbled with the ropes holding the packs. When I worked my way round him I discovered he had fallen into an isolated bog hole and in front of him was firm ground.

'Pull hard,' I yelled and at the same time pushed with all my strength on his hindquarters. His front legs found a hold and, with a gurgle like water running down a drain, he heaved himself forward, spraying us with lumps of wet moss as he jumped to safety. Fell ponies are particularly courageous in awkward situations and, although it had been a nasty experience for him, Thor spotted a patch of juicy grass and was soon chewing as if nothing had happened. Abi and Philip rubbed the wet moss off his body with handfuls of heather and, with a quick check to see that his shoes had not been pulled off in the bog, I led him down the steep path towards Stonethwaite.

A man repairing a gap in a dry-stone wall watched us intently as we approached and I was delighted to find it was a friend of mine called John Bulman, who works for the Lake District National Park. As an

Upland Management Officer, John's job takes him and his men all over the Lake District, making sure that paths and gates are in good order, looking after fences and woodland and perhaps most important of all, helping visitors to understand the life of the Lake District. Like so many men born and bred into hill farming, he is an expert at building dry-stone walls and we stopped to watch him work.

'If you don't use cement, how do you stop the wall falling down?' asked Philip.

John balanced a large stone on top of two smaller ones, then stood back to check his work. 'It would use up all the cement in the country if every wall in the Lake District was built with it,' he laughed. 'In the old days farmers had to make do with what they could find on the fell. Come over here and I'll show you how it's done.'

'Can girls build walls?' asked Abi, anxious not to be left out.

'Aye lass, of course they can,' smiled John. 'Though it's the wrong job if you want to keep your hands soft and clean. The rough stone will make your skin feel like sandpaper.'

I put the hobbles on Thor to prevent him straying and, dumping their rucksacks and anoraks on the heather, Abi and Philip joined John at the wall.

'Well, the first thing you've got to learn about a dry-stone wall,' he said, 'is that, unlike the wall of a house, which stands upright, the sides of these walls, lean in towards the middle. If you look along this wall now, you'll see that it's wide at the bottom and narrow at the top and that's one of the reasons why it doesn't fall down.'

Philip craned his neck and sighted along the wall. 'I can see what you mean now,' he said, 'but how do you lay the big stones on the bottom, in the first place?'

'Well that's where the art of walling starts,' answered John. 'Usually the base of a wall is about a metre wide and we dig a trench about fifteen centimetres deep and lay the biggest stones in first. These are called footing stones and we lay them in two lines on either side of the trench and fill the gap with small stones.' He pointed to the gap in the wall. 'Look at this wall where it's fallen down and you'll see how it was started. When the footing stones are nicely bedded in then we start to build the wall. A builder using bricks to build a house lays a row of bricks first, then the next layer staggered, so that each brick lies across the joint of the ones below. We do the same, except that our stones are all shapes and sizes and you need to be able to judge which ones will fit together. As each row of stones is laid, the gap in the centre is filled up with small stones, or "hearting" if

John Bulman shows Abbi and Philip how to build a dry-stone wall

you want its proper name, so that the finished wall is solid. When a few rows have been laid, making sure each side of the wall is leaning in at an angle, then we put a line of "through" stones on. These are long stones the width of the wall and they help to keep the two sides together.' John bent down and put a few stones into place.

'Right Abi, you fill the middle with small stones and Philip can help me to put this through stone on.'

Philip panted with the exertion of lifting a heavy, flat stone and almost dropped it as he and John heaved it into place. We spent a very enjoyable time helping to repair the wall and Abi and Philip were very proud of the finished job.

'Couldn't have done better myself,' said John, examining a neat row of flat stones leaning at the same angle along the top of the wall. 'These are called "cam" stones by the way, and they are not put on just to make it look attractive, they stop sheep from jumping over the wall.' Pausing to look at his watch, he wiped his hands on the grass and pulled on his coat. 'Thanks for your help, you've worked hard. I'm off home now.'

Before he left I scribbled a message on a piece of paper and handed it to him. He read it slowly, then a broad grin spread across his face.

'Righto, I'll see to it,' he said, thrusting the note into his pocket.

Collecting Thor and whistling Sammy, who was busy hunting rabbits, we waved good-bye to John and continued down the fell.

'I'm exhausted,' puffed Abi. 'I can't wait to crawl into my sleeping-bag. Now I understand why farmers are so angry when people climb over walls and knock them down.'

'I'm going to write about wall building in my book,'

said Philip. 'It must have taken ages to build some of them. Look at that one over there, the through stones are enormous.'

Working with John had sparked off a new interest and instead of being simply a heap of stones, the walls were now an exciting part of the scenery. All the way to our campsite the walls around the fields were closely inspected and different building techniques discussed with an air of authority.

'Your walls look as if they might be "bellying out",' said Philip helpfully when the farmer came to our tent for his camping fee, later that evening.

He glared at Philip for a moment then turned on his heel. 'Cheeky young pup,' he muttered.

Chapter Nine

The clouds sweeping in from the west when we crossed the fell from Easedale had completely filled the sky by morning and when I peeped through the tent door it was dull and overcast and a chilly wind whined through the branches of the trees and cracked the nylon flysheet like a whip. The air was too cold to sit outside and we ate breakfast lying in our sleeping-bags. Hardly a word was spoken and an unusual atmosphere of gloom hung over us. It had nothing to do with the change in the weather.

'It's our last day, today, isn't it?' said Abi miserably.

'Yes, I'm afraid so,' I replied. 'Ennerdale is only a few hours' walk from here and we should reach it by this evening. It's hard to believe we've been away for nearly two weeks.'

'I could carry on for ever,' said Philip wistfully. 'I like exploring the fells and there must be places we haven't visited that are teeming with fish. If we could stay for another week I'm sure I could catch a trout or a pike or something.'

'You've certainly not had much luck with your fishing-rod, but cheer up, I've got a surprise for you. That note I gave to John Bulman yesterday, asked him to arrange with Jim Loxham, a local mountain guide, to take you rock climbing this morning.'

'Rock climbing!' cried Abi, almost bursting with

excitement. 'Oh that's marvellous, I've always wanted to go rock climbing.'

'Me too,' said Philip eagerly. 'Which crag are we going to climb on?'

I unfolded the map and spread it across the sleeping-bags. 'We are here, in Borrowdale, and to reach Enner-dale we have to climb up Honister Pass. There are dozens of small crags up there and I've asked Jim to meet us at ten o'clock by the Youth Hostel at the top of the Pass. We've got about two hours so let's leave as soon as we can.'

The bags were packed and the tent rolled up in record time and in less than half an hour we were toiling up Honister Pass. Above the tiny hamlet of Seatoller the tarmac road was very steep and a sudden shower of rain made the smooth surface treacherously slippery. Several times Thor stumbled and almost went down, but after a mile or so the road lost its steepness and, following a line of tourist cars, we zigzagged slowly upwards to the Youth Hostel perched on the summit. Jim was waiting for us and led the way up the fell to the foot of a crag. Thor was turned loose with the hobbles on and Sammy and I sat on a boulder and watched Jim preparing his equipment. Abi and Philip were each given a safety helmet and a special type of body harness made of strong webbing and they were ready to start.

'Any fool can climb a rock face,' Jim explained, 'but to climb it safely there are a few rules you have to learn. To be safe, you have to be comfortable so never reach too high and don't lift your feet higher than knee level. Also, never move a hand and a foot at the same time, always keep both feet and one hand on the rock while you reach up with the other hand, or keep two hands and one foot on the rock while you step up with the other foot.'

Preparing for a rock climb with Mountain Guide Jim Loxham

They both doubled up with laughter when Jim demonstrated the wrong way to climb and fell off into the heather.

'Now look at the rock face we're going to climb,' said Jim. 'D'you see that ledge about ten metres up. Imagine we were roped together and I was standing on the ledge where Philip was climbing and he fell off, what would happen?'

'He would pull you off the ledge,' said Abi quickly.

'Exactly,' said Jim. 'So we have to have a way of safeguarding each other while we're climbing. It's called a belay and it's simply a means of tying yourself to the rock face when you are not actually climbing. The easiest way of belaying is with a sling like this.'

He produced a loop of rope and a large, steel clip. 'The sling is looped over a spike of rock and joined to your safety harness with this steel clip called a Karabiner and then if the person climbing slips, it should be possible to hold him on the rope without being pulled off yourself. Are you ready to have a go?'

They both nodded earnestly.

'Right then Philip, pay out the rope as I'm climbing.'

Jim moved steadily up the rock to the ledge and belayed. He hauled in the slack rope until it pulled taut.

'That's me,' Philip shouted.

'Climb when you're ready,' called Jim.

Philip stepped nervously on to the first foothold. 'Climbing,' he shouted.

'O.K.,' came the reply.

Philip's knees trembled as his hand searched feverishly for a hold.

'There's a hold just by your right shoulder,' called Abi. 'Yes, that's the one.'

He gasped with relief when his hand found it and, in a series of jerky movements, assisted by Jim pulling gently on the rope, he flopped on to the ledge like a fish being landed in a boat. He was tied on to a belay beside Jim and it was Abi's turn. She soon showed she was a natural climber by swarming up the rock almost as quickly as Jim could take the rope in. Jim tied her on to the ledge and set off up the next rock pitch. When it came to his turn again, Philip climbed with a lot more confidence and obviously enjoyed himself, even though he could look down a very long way to the cars moving slowly up Honister Pass. The three figures became tiny specks as they climbed higher up the crag and I finally lost sight of them among the jumble of buttresses and gullies. Over an hour passed before they scrambled down an easy gully and we collected Thor and returned to the Youth Hostel.

'Well, what was it like?' I asked, as we helped to carry Jim's ropes down to his van.

'Fabulous, really fabulous,' breathed Philip, his eyes glowing with pleasure. 'I was a bit scared when I started, but after the first pitch it was great.'

'Abi says she wants to be a mountain guide,' laughed Jim, 'but she won't believe me that the exams I had to pass are much more difficult than the ones she has at school.'

'But I can't understand why you have to pass silly exams to be a guide,' Abi grumbled.

'Think about it this way,' said Jim: 'if you flew in an aircraft you would expect the pilot to have passed exams to show that he was capable of taking the passengers safely from one place to another in all sorts of weather. Well, it's the same with a mountain guide. He takes people up rock faces or over mountains when they have probably never climbed before. The weather might be good or it might be a raging blizzard, but whatever it is, a guide has to make sure his party is safe. To be good at his job takes a lot of training and years of experience and, like any other job, to do it professionally you have to pass examinations.'

'Well, I still want to be a guide,' said Abi defiantly. 'And before I leave school I'll take guides' exams instead of "O" levels.'

'You'll make a good rock climber, I can tell you that,' smiled Jim, 'but one thing you must never do is to be tempted to climb on your own until you've had years and years of experience. 'Bye now, perhaps I'll meet you all again some day.'

Threatening clouds had been gathering all morning and, as Jim drove away a heavier shower poured out of the sky and sent us running for shelter behind a wooden hut. Sammy was nicely wedged in between us, but Thor stood out in the rain with water dripping off his nose like a leaking tap. He looked so miserable I gave him an extra large piece of mint cake and he chewed it slowly, pausing every few minutes to shake the rain off his back like a dog. Even in the shelter of the hut it was bitterly cold, and to warm us up I assembled the stove and heated a mixture of vegetable soup, spaghetti and corned beef. The shower increased to a heavy downpour and battered on the sides of the hut like a tidal wave. There was no question of moving on in such conditions and we huddled together and ate our soup.

'What's that building behind the Youth Hostel?' asked Philip, looking across to a long, stone shed.

'It belongs to the Honister Slate Company,' I said. 'They bring the blocks of slate down from the mine to be cut into lengths on special saws.'

'Someone must be working there now,' said Abi, 'there are lots of lights on. Do you think they would let us look round.'

'Well they have a show-room, we can take a look in there if you like.'

'Yes let's,' said Philip, 'it's freezing out here.'

We finished our soup and splashed through the rain to the show-room. The man in charge was very helpful and showed us how the stone was used for fireplaces, ornaments, paving stones and slates for house roofs. He told us that the mine had been in existence for hundreds of years and went deep into the ground under the very crag where Abi and Philip had been climbing.

'If you're really interested,' he said, 'I'll ask the

owner if he'll show you the machines cutting the blocks and how the roofing slates are made.'

The owner said he would be delighted to show us round, but Sammy would have to stay in his office. Sammy seemed quite content to lie in front of a warm stove and we left him and trooped into a workshop where a huge circular saw was slowly cutting through a block of slate.

'How does a saw cut slate?' bellowed Abi above the noise of the machine.

The owner switched it off and when it finally whirred to a halt he pointed to the edge of the blade. 'There's your answer — diamonds.'

Philip's eyes gleamed. 'Real diamonds. Gosh, it must be worth a lot of money.'

The owner smiled. 'Well they are diamonds, but not the type you would put in a diamond ring or crown. These are industrial diamonds, specially made for saw blades. They have to be well protected though and that's why a jet of water is sprayed on the blade as it cuts through the stone. I'll start this up then we'll move into the next shed.' He pressed a button and, with an ear-splitting whine, the saw continued its slow progress through the huge block.

We moved into a long shed where men were trimming different sizes of blocks for making fireplaces and ornamental fronts for buildings.

'What you have seen so far is all done by modern machinery,' said the owner, 'but follow me and I'll show you something that no machine will ever replace.'

He led the way to the far end of the shed where a man and a boy were sitting on stools with a block of slate between their knees. Each had a large hammer and a flat metal chisel and when they tapped the chisel on the block with the hammer a thin slate dropped off the

Abi tries her hand at cutting tiles

block and was stacked in a neat pile.

'These chaps are riving roofing slates,' explained the owner. 'It looks easy, but believe me, it takes a lot of skill to judge where to put the chisel and rive off the same thickness of slate every time.'

The boy grinned at Abi and offered her his hammer and chisel. 'D'you want to try?'

Placing the chisel on the block he offered, she hit it hard with the hammer. Nothing happened. She hit it again. There was a loud crack and the block disintegrated into several lumps. The boy roared with laughter and Abi's face went red with embarrassment.

'Don't worry about it, lass,' said the man, patting her on the shoulder. 'He did the same often enough when he was learning and, in any case, the wee devil gave you a piece of stone that's too hard for cutting roofing slates.'

He demonstrated how it was done and when Abi tried again she managed to cut a slate. It was rather a thick slate, but at least it was in one piece and she was so pleased she wanted to take it home. Fortunately, I was able to persuade her that it would not fit in her rucksack. When Philip tried he could hardly believe his eyes when a perfect slate peeled off the block.

'You're a natural for the job,' laughed the man. 'I'll ask the owner to sign you on.'

When we had finished our tour the owner took us back to his office and presented us with a small block of polished slate each as a souvenir.

Outside it was still raining and a thick, grey mist hung round the mine buildings, turning the heaps of waste slate and the cranes into ghostly shapes. The owner had given us permission to follow a very steep road built by the mining company up the side of Fleetwith Pike, and it was like walking up a waterfall. Floods of water cascaded off the crags and swept down the gravel surface of the road, gouging deep furrows as it went. Swathed in our waterproofs, we were hot and sticky by the time we reached the top and we stopped to rest Thor and eat an orange. Thick mist hung everywhere and I worked out a compass course for Dubs Quarry, near the summit of Fleetwith Pike. Soon the rain-soaked, abandoned workings of the quarry appeared through the mist and we paused again while I worked out another course to join a path climbing up to Blackbeck Tarn on Haystacks. The rain increased and visibility was almost zero as we threaded our way through a maze of hillocks and outcrops of rock. Skirting a large expanse of bog, the path dipped down into a hollow and climbed obliquely across the fellside. There was no proper surface and a confusion of rocks and scree made it very tricky for Thor as he picked his way over it very slowly. In the mist we had little impression of height, but when a breeze sprang up and cleared it away briefly, we looked down a sheer precipice to Gatesgarth and the grey waters of Buttermere. Keeping a firm grip on Thor's lead rope, I steered him away from the edge and scrambled up to the safety of level ground beside Blackbeck Tarn.

Setting a course for Ennerdale, we ploughed through knee deep heather and quivering bog until we reached the head of Loft Beck and a slippery descent to Black Sail Hostel. Abi jumped up and down with excitement.

'We've completed a full circle,' she shouted. 'How far do you think we've walked since we started?'

'I'm not exactly sure,' I said, 'but it will be well over a hundred miles. Wait until we reach Gillerthwaite and, when we've had a hot bath and tea, we'll work it out.'

Philip stood in the rain, with water dripping off his anorak hood, staring at Great Gable. 'I can't believe we've nearly finished our journey,' he said sadly. 'It's going to be awful sleeping in a real bed.'

Thor's normal pace is slow, but as we walked through Ennerdale Forest we could hardly keep up with him. He knew he was close to home and he pounded along like a racehorse, whinnying for his friends, Lucy, Flash and Crystal. An answering whinny echoed across the valley and they charged over the fields to greet him, jumping ditches and kicking up clouds of spray from the wet grass. Thor longed to stop and tell them about his journey, but there was still some way to go to reach the house and I tugged on his lead rope to keep him moving.

We were soaked to the skin, tired and hungry, but

there was a smell of wood-smoke in the air and we knew we were almost at Gillerthwaite. When the house came into sight and Sammy heard Fang, my other dog, barking in the yard, he could not restrain himself a minute longer. With one bound he cleared the gate and ran for the kitchen and his dinner bowl. By the gate we paused to look back at the fells. The great crags glistened with water and masses of black clouds swirled and twisted round the peaks. A storm was approaching, but this time we could ignore it. The problems of gales and rain, rocky paths and treacherous bogs were over. We were home.

Journey's end - Gillerthwaite wet and weary but triumphant

FINDING FAMILY AT THE CORNISH COVE

THE CORNISH COVE SERIES - BOOK TWO

KIM NASH

Boldwood

First published in Great Britain in 2023 by Boldwood Books Ltd.

Copyright © Kim Nash, 2023

Cover Design by Alexandra Allden

Cover illustration: Getty and Shutterstock

Every effort has been made to obtain the necessary permissions with reference to copyright material, both illustrative and quoted. We apologise for any omissions in this respect and will be pleased to make the appropriate acknowledgements in any future edition.

A CIP catalogue record for this book is available from the British Library.

Paperback ISBN 978-1-80549-473-7

Large Print ISBN 978-1-80549-472-0

Harback ISBN 978-1-80549-470-6

Ebook ISBN 978-1-80549-471-3

Kindle ISBN 978-1-80549-474-4

Audio CD ISBN 978-1-80549-465-2

MP3 CD ISBN 978-1-80549-466-9

Digital audio download ISBN 978-1-80549-467-6

Boldwood Books Ltd
23 Bowerdean Street
London SW6 3TN
www.boldwoodbooks.com

To Emily Yau
For loving my stories and for your editing flair and guidance in shaping them to be better. I'll always be grateful to you for giving me an opportunity to be a Boldwood author. Thank you from the bottom of my heart x

1

'No going back now. It's a deal! Congratulations, Gemma, you are now the proud owner of not one but two buildings.'

My heart thumped in my chest as I placed the pen next to the document I had just signed and reached out to shake Martin's hand. I tried to portray confidence; after all, I was a strong, independent woman who was expanding her business, but inside I was having the proper collywobbles.

One of the hardest things about being single is that you must make all the decisions alone. Yes, there are people that you can talk things through with, and that really helps. I'm eternally grateful that I'm so close with my sister Lucy and her husband James, probably more so since we lost our mother. I appreciate that they do their best to help and guide me but ultimately, it's all down to me. However, as my darling mum always said, you don't always have to be sure that it's the right decision, you just have to make one.

Mum was always coming out with words of wisdom. One of the many things I adored about her was her ability to calm people down when they were feeling anxious about something.

How, when they came into her café, she made them feel welcome and supported and she'd sit them down with a nice cup of tea and let them unburden themselves to her. They always seemed to leave the café with their heads higher and their shoulders straighter. In time, I hoped it was something I was remembered for too and when I took over her business I tried to keep this ethos in my mind.

When I jokingly mentioned to Martin, who owned the bric-a-brac shop next door, that I could do with him moving out and me expanding by knocking through, I had no clue that the thought would percolate in his mind and he would take me up on my offer.

Decisions had swiftly been made, and documents quickly drawn up and signed. No going back. Project Café Renovation was under way.

As I searched the cloudless blue above me, I yearned for my mum's wise words. *Show me a sign, Mum. Have I done the right thing?*

From the chipped wooden table outside my café where I'd plonked myself, it was easy to be distracted by the glittering turquoise sea and the golden sands of the sweeping bay before me. In the harbour, the slamming of a car door dragged me back to the pages of my new notebook, which were fluttering in the breeze. The first blank page stared back at me.

The sea normally inspired me when I was journaling, but today there was nothing forthcoming. Even the noisy clinking of the halyards in the harbour weren't helping. Greedy seagulls squawked and swooped, scavenging for any morsel of food that may have been dropped by an unaware tourist. Us locals knew better and held on to any food we had for dear life.

'Morning, lovely! You look like you've got the weight of the world on your shoulders.' Squinting, I held my hand to my brow to shade from the sun, to see Meredith before me, being yanked about by her puppy Alice who clearly didn't want to be standing still.

Meredith was my friend who had recently upped sticks from the Midlands and very bravely bought the local lighthouse, without even seeing it. However, with help from Clem, the local handyman and someone we grew up with, it had been transformed into one of the most stunning homes in the whole of Driftwood Bay. They had also had the bonus of falling in love while they were working together and were now a couple.

'Hey, you two. Which one of you is taking the other on a walk?' I leaned across to give Alice a rub of the head which she pushed into my hand, loving every moment.

Meredith smiled but then her brow furrowed. 'Gemma? Is everything OK?'

A huge sigh escaped from my body.

'Oh, I suppose so. I've just signed the contracts to move Martin's shop over to me.'

'Wow. Congratulations. But shouldn't you look a bit happier?'

'I am happy honestly. It's just so huge for me. Can't stop wondering whether I've done the right thing or not, and what Mum would think.'

'I didn't know your mum at all but I think she'd be super proud of you. However, I think most people would say that it's OK to be a tiny bit afraid too. I'm sure even the dragons on *Dragons' Den* are a little apprehensive when they make a new business decision. You can't get it right all the time but maybe think about what's the worst that can happen?'

'Now that's a great question, Mere.'

'So, if it doesn't work out, you just rent the space out. You're a great businesswoman, Gemma. You wouldn't have won Cornish

Entrepreneur of the Year last year if you weren't. As long as you have a plan B, surely that's OK.'

'I just don't want to fail.' I huffed. I'd been doing this a lot lately when I felt stressed. 'I already have a failed marriage behind me. The last thing I want is a failed business too.'

'Failing is part of life, mate. Nothing to be afraid or embarrassed of. What's that saying? "The one who falls and gets up is stronger than the one who never tried." It's very true. Failure is not the opposite of success, you know. It's where you learn from your mistakes and try something else instead. It's all part of the grand plan of life.'

I smiled at her.

'Thank you, oh wise one.'

'I do have my moments.'

She made it sound so simple. However, her past wasn't tied to Driftwood Bay like mine was.

'This café as I know it is where I grew up. It's the place where Lucy and I sat and did our homework after school. Where we spent our Saturdays and school holidays waiting on the few tables that we had. I've already changed it from a bakery to a café. Maybe that's enough. What if it's meant to stay as it is? This is where all my memories are.'

'Wrong. Listen, lady.' She took my hand and pressed it against my chest. 'This is where your memories are. In your heart and in your mind.'

We both watched in wonder as a white feather fluttered from out of nowhere and landed on my lap. I smiled. Was this my sign from Mum?

'What's your *why*, Gem?'

'Sorry, I'm not sure what you mean.'

'What is the reason that you took over the café originally and why do you want to expand it? Once you know that, then you can move forward and create the results you want to achieve. Just think about your *why*. Once you've worked that out, you're laughing. And then you can be excited about the future.'

Alice tugged on her lead and gave a little woof. She was clearly bored of our conversation already. We both laughed.

'Yes, Alice. We know that your why is that you love the beach. If you fancy a drink and a chat in the pub later, to continue this conversation, Gem, let me know.'

'That would be lovely. I've got some stuff to do here later but shouldn't be too long. I'll work out what time and text you.'

Why *was* I doing the expansion? To keep Mum's memory alive? It couldn't be that, or I wouldn't want it to change. Was it because I felt like I had something to prove? My heart started to beat a little faster. Maybe I was getting closer to the truth. But who was I trying to prove it to? Now I had another thing to ponder instead of worrying about whether it was the right thing. Now I was worrying about finding out *why* it was the right thing.

* * *

'Hey, Gem. Is the deed done?'

I nodded.

Lucy is my big sister. She's also my very best friend. We were close before we lost Mum, but since then, we've become even closer still. She'd been married to James for over ten years and when people used to say that they'd found their soul mate, I thought it was all a load of old crap. But they made me see that it was true. They were perfect for each other in every way and I envied their lives. James worked on the fishing trawlers and Lucy ran their boutique bed and breakfast which overlooked the beach. It used to belong to our aunty and Lucy had loved it since she was a little girl. She always said that when she grew up, she was going to buy it. And she did.

Lucy threw her arms around me and danced up and down. I laughed at her enthusiasm.

'Oh, I'm so proud of you. How blooming exciting. We must celebrate. Tonight. Let's go to the pub. This deserves champagne.'

'Calm down. I've already arranged to go to the pub with Meredith tonight so do come along. The more the merrier. I'm still freaking out about it all a bit to be honest.'

'Oh, love, why?'

'What if it isn't what Mum wanted me to do? If she wanted to expand, wouldn't she have done it years ago?'

'Oh, Gemma. Come on now. Mum was a single mother with two young daughters. And one of them was really needy.' She winked at me.

'Don't put yourself down, sis.'

'Ha, you're so funny! I'm surprised she had time to go to work at all, let alone run a successful business. I think her circumstances were a little different to yours.'

'Thanks for reminding me.'

'Sorry, love. You know I don't mean it like that. What I'm saying is that you have been given a huge opportunity here. One that you said you'd love to explore and one that you've been brave enough to go ahead with. Don't spoil it by worrying about it so much that it consumes you. This is the best thing that could have happened to you after... well... you know, everything that's gone on recently.'

'It just feels huge, Luce.'

My sister rubbed my back. 'I know it does, but we're here for you. James and I will help you as much as we can. In the times that the B & B isn't busy, I can come over and help you. It'll be like old times.'

I smiled at her. 'It will. But is there ever a time that you're *not* busy?'

The B & B had been going from strength to strength. Someone who was very high up in the Cornish Tourist Board had a relative who had been to stay, who just happened to be a travel writer and it had been featured in a local magazine as highly recommended – one of the 'most relaxing, warm and inviting B & Bs in Cornwall'. They also achieved the highest rating from the board possible. The number of visitors to our little seaside village had increased and local businesses were thriving, although now, after a busy summer, it was starting to slow down. The B & B's Instagram page had a huge following, and thanks to James and his early morning photography skills, they had a waiting list for cancellations. Lucy is *never* not busy.

'Well, we'll get you some more help. Advertise for staff. There must be some teenagers keen to find a job after school. They can get involved with the social media side of things as well. You always say you don't have time and maybe you could get someone who knows what they're doing.' I raised my eyebrows and she grinned. 'I pretend I'm crap at it, so I don't have to do it and James thinks he's an expert so I'm happy to let him crack on. Just maybe don't tell him.'

She always makes me smile and in that moment I felt like I could take on the world. Made me think that anything was possible. She'd been my rock over the last few years and I don't know how I'd have coped without her.

When Lucy left, I headed to the kitchen. My safe haven. Cooking allowed me to temporarily forget that my life had changed so much, so quickly and that I'd made the biggest busi-ness decision I'd ever made. When I baked, I could forget everything else that was going on in the world. It soothed my soul and made me feel I didn't have to worry about a thing.

I glanced at my watch. I had a few hours before I needed to meet everyone at the pub. That should give me plenty of time to get a huge batch of cooking done, load the car and deliver it to Truro, getting back without anyone noticing that I had disappeared. I wasn't ready to explain this situation yet, and maybe I never would be. Best crack on.

2

It had been a late night. Plenty of champagne had been drunk in the Harbourside Hotel, though Lucy remained remarkably sober as she was on antibiotics for a water infection, which she'd told me before we got to the pub. She didn't want to broadcast it to everyone so ended up nursing a glass that sat in front of her for most of the night. James, in his tipsy state, insisted on saying a few words about how proud he was of me, with my exciting new venture ahead. That was lovely of him and so typical of what a truly decent bloke he was. Along with Meredith and Clem's enthusiasm, I felt like I could finally be swept up in their excitement – something I hadn't allowed myself to feel up to that point. Maybe it would be OK after all.

The following morning, as I lay in bed, looking out of the window of my flat above the café, there was definitely a little flutter of something deep inside me that made me want to get out of bed and make plans. Clem had mentioned that he'd met someone who worked at the fire service who had recently moved into the area. This person's role was to do risk assessments of buildings etc. and Clem thought he might be able to guide me in the right direction for fire regulations. He'd given me his number so that seemed like an easy first job to tick off my list.

While I was waiting for him to return my call, I thought back to Mum and why she set up the business in the first place. It was originally a bakery and then she expanded so that people could sit in. A memory came flooding back of when she'd sat me and Lucy down and said she was making it into a café, not just for her but for the community. A place for people to come together, to chat, to heal, to make friends, to bond. This was why I loved baking and cooking too. For others. I wondered if that was what Meredith meant about finding my why. Maybe I did know what it was after all.

My mobile rang.

'Hi. This is Fire Safety Officer Adams from the Cornwall Fire Service. I believe you wanted some advice about building regulations. I'm in your neighbourhood tomorrow and wondered if you might be around?'

Very efficient and even a little abrupt. No messing around with niceties for this man. But great that he was able to pop in so quickly.

'I'm around all day from seven in the morning until the café closes at five, although I'll still be around in the back if it's after then.'

'It might be around then to be honest. Is that too late for you?'

'It'll be perfect, thank you.'

'Great.'

As the call disconnected, without even a goodbye from the other side, I wondered what this man was like. He didn't mention his first name. I hadn't a clue how to address someone from the fire service. Officer Adams or something like that maybe? Not something I'd ever thought about before. When he called by I'd have to remember to ask him.

* * *

I always started my days sitting on the window seat of my lounge, taking some time to drink my morning coffee while thanking my blessings for the view before me. The flat overlooked the harbour one way and the beach the other and it literally filled my heart with joy every single day. Fridays were busy days in the café and after another early start, the day had flown by. When I expanded and installed more seating space, it would get even busier and I would definitely need to get more help. Last year, I had a young girl helping out during the school holidays while her parents spent the summer here in their lodge. She'd gone home after summer had ended and I'd managed mainly on my own since, with my only other member of staff, Pat, even though we were both run ragged. And even though she was great for her sixty-five years, she wasn't getting any younger and she'd recently started to look a little tired. Not surprising though because when she wasn't working in the café, she was on granny duty. Lucy was right. I really did need to get some more permanent help. I honestly didn't know how Mum had managed, although I suppose she had me and Lucy to call on when she needed extra hands.

Whoever thought having your own business was easy needed a reality check. When that closed sign goes up on the door, it doesn't mean it's the end of the day. It just means that you stop being front of house. You are then every other department: finance, marketing, PR, social media, and because you don't get time in the day, that's when all that side of the business work happens. That's why I would fall into bed most nights after only reading a page of a book. Reading was something I used to love doing, and it was the one thing that had really gone by the wayside over the last couple of years. I'd like to have remedied that but was normally just so tired at night that I struggled to stay awake.

As I was pondering the idea of maybe putting the feelers out to see whether anyone might be interested in us having a book club in the café when there was more room, there was a knock on the door. Fumbling with the lock, I could see that the person stood outside was on the phone. He did a kind of acknowledgement wave and hovered with his back to me, and I couldn't help but overhear a very heated conversation where he sounded very much like he was being a total control freak. Still on the phone, he walked in and stood inside the entrance looking around. I didn't know whether I should stay or go but decided that I should probably go and wait behind the counter, leaving him to his heated call. The timer sounded on the oven and I removed the batch of scones I'd not long made.

'You can't just go off when you feel like it without telling me. Honestly, you need to think about other people sometimes. You can be a right selfish madam. We'll discuss this later. I have to go. I'll be home after this last call. Make sure you are there please.'

Crikey, he sounds like a bundle of fun. I wouldn't want to be his partner. He sounded like a controlling narcissist. No thank you! Sometimes I was grateful that I was single, even though the circumstances around why I was weren't of my own choice. There had been times in the last couple of years when I'd felt lonelier than I'd ever felt before in my life, even though I had friends and family nearby.

Frowning as he ended the call, he strode across the room and stuck his hand out, introducing himself with his full title as

Fire Safety Officer Adams, a bit of a mouthful in his own words. He apologised for being on the phone when he arrived and asked if he could have a walk round, which I of course agreed to.

While I was making a drink it gave me time to study him surreptitiously. Still frowning, he made some notes in a little book and stuck the pen behind his ear. When he'd finished, he broke into a smile and came back to the counter. Talk about a face changing when it smiled. When his eyebrows weren't furrowed together, he was incredibly handsome and as I looked up into big beautiful brown eyes my tummy gave a little flip. I clearly needed to get out more and meet more people. This was the first new male I'm come across in months, and he was having this effect on me just because he was tall, dark, handsome and beardy (I do love a beardy man!).

I invited him over to one of the tables and he pulled out a chair, sighing loudly. He sat down and took a sip from the mug I had placed before him along with a plate on which there was a warm scone with clotted cream and jam.

'You sound like you need that. Sorry it's nothing stronger.'

'You have no idea. And I think if you gave me something stronger right now, I might not stop. Also, I've not eaten a thing all day. I could eat a scabby horse.'

'Well, I don't have one of those, but hopefully the scone will help a little.'

'Thank you. I'm bloody starving. Such a busy day. And that's before I've got home and sorted out lots there too. We've just moved into the area and we're still unpacking. I thought moving to Driftwood Bay would be the end of our troubles, not give a whole new lot to wade through.' He let out another huge sigh and looked quite deflated. 'Sorry, I'm not sure what made me blurt all of that out. I haven't given you a very good impression so far, have I? Can we start again? God, this is delicious by the way.'

There was that smile again. Wowsers.

'Now tell me about your plans for the business and do you have the keys for the building next door? I'd love to take a look around if that's possible.'

He was incredibly knowledgeable and very helpful, giving me lots of things to add to my project list to make sure that everything would meet the required regulations. As he stood up to leave, he thanked me for the food and drink and asked if he owed me for them. I waved a hand and said it was my pleasure. When he reached the door, I remembered a question I had for him.

'Oh, what do I call you? Fire Safety Officer Adams?'

'Well, they call me Adams at the station, but you can just call me Jude if you like.'

Jude. Nice name. I thanked him for his help but he left without saying goodbye once again. I stood at the door, twiddling the business card he'd given me in my fingers, and wondered about the mystery lady he had been talking to when he arrived. If his good looks were anything to go by, I'd imagine she was his gorgeous wife.

As I watched him walk up Driftwood Bay high street, I couldn't help but think that if his body looked that fit with his clothes on, imagine what he looked like without. I honestly did not know where that thought came from. I'd sworn off men, since Lucas and I had split up. Well, since he left me for another woman, which was a different thing, and this was the first time that I'd felt anything resembling attraction to someone else.

A little woof alerted me to the fact that I had company – Meredith and Alice, who were out on a walk around the harbour.

'Who's that hottie you've just let out of the café, Gem? Have you been having hot rampant afternoon sex with a man without telling me? Your new BFF?'

Flustered at the thought of what Meredith was implying, and more about the fact that me getting 'back on the horse' didn't sound quite as awful as I originally may have envisaged when my darling brother-in-law had suggested it at the pub the other night, I grinned.

'That's Fire Safety Officer Adams.'

'Gosh, he sounds like a bit of a mouthful.' Meredith grinned. 'No pun intended.'

Blushing, I felt an overwhelming desire to explain.

'He's just helping me with some of the plans for the café.'

'I bet he is. Good work, Gemma! Very impressive.'

I bent down to tickle Alice behind the ear, if only to hide my blushes.

'Nothing more. Just because you and Clem are all loved up doesn't mean you have to go round matchmaking for everyone, you know.'

'Oh you spoilsport. There's not much else to do round here. It's so quiet now the summer holidays are over and the few tourists have gone home. Let me have some fun.'

'Talking of fun,' I said. 'I have an idea. You got time for a cuppa and a scone while I throw an idea at you? They're still warm…'

'I've always got time for a cuppa and a scone with you, my friend.'

'You only want me for my baking, Meredith Robinson.'

'Too right!'

'The cheek of it.' I laughed. 'Go and grab a seat out the back and I'll bring everything out. May as well make the most of the end of a lovely sunny day even if it's starting to get a little cooler in the evenings now.'

Through French doors, off the corridor to the bathroom, there was a quaint little courtyard garden in which I had carefully chosen hardy rattan furniture. Tall palm plants in colourful pots sat in the corners and on the back wall there was a long ceramic trough with fragrant lavender, mint, chives, basil and coriander. I always made sure that the string lights were lit from dusk onwards. It was a gorgeous space, and when needed in the colder months, the heat from two large patio heaters made it look and feel cosy. Now that time of year was getting closer, people could still enjoy the crisp sunny fresh days if they didn't want to sit in the less sheltered patio area at the front of the building.

We whiled away a very pleasant hour coming up with a plan for how we could start our very own Driftwood Bay Book Club. I was pretty pleased that I had managed to avoid any further questions about Fire Safety Officer Adams who was still, for some reason, on my mind.

In my head, the renovation project seemed massive. Clem was an absolute superstar and not only did he offer to do a lot of the physical work, but he'd also offered to manage the whole project for me. I was so pleased because I couldn't work out how I was going to get everything done, while keeping the café open and running for as long as we physically could before shutting totally for the final couple of weeks.

A lot of the work would be happening next door to start with. Martin's shop was huge when empty and as I stood at the door with Clem, I was wondering where the hell we were going to start and what the hell I'd ever made this decision for. I let out a huge sigh and my shoulders dropped.

'Don't look so worried, Gemma! Just keep thinking of how it will be in the end. Just keep visualising how you want it to be. I always tell my customers to think about what it will look like when all the work is finished. Have you done a mood board or anything to keep you going?'

I raised my eyebrows. I didn't think Clem was the sort of person who went for mood boards and I was quietly impressed.

I hadn't shared mine with anyone, thinking that everyone might think I was quite mad.

'You have, haven't you?' He grinned at me. 'You've got to share it with me. I am your project manager after all. I need to know your innermost thoughts and desires, you know.'

At that precise moment, Jude walked past the entrance.

Clem clicked his fingers.

'And back in the room. For the café, I meant.'

'Ha, you're funny, that's exactly what I was thinking.'

'Actually, I could do with grabbing Adams. Won't be a sec. Fancy putting the kettle on? You know what us worker types are like for drinking tea.'

When he returned two minutes later, Jude was in tow and they were discussing the regulations. Jude smiled at me and I blushed a little as I offered to make him a drink.

I went off to make Jude's tea and when I came back into the building, I could hear them chatting.

'Honestly, Clem, she's a bloody nightmare. Thinks she can just sit around on her arse all day with a face on her. I told her that she couldn't keep this sulking up. I know we moved here despite her not wanting to but I didn't really have a choice in the matter. She just needs to suck it up and get on with life.'

'I don't envy you, mate. Not sure how you are going to turn things round to be honest. Maybe just giving her a bit of time will work wonders. When she meets some of the locals and makes friends, it might all feel different for her. We're all very nice, you know.'

Hearing Jude talk about his wife or girlfriend in this way was awful. He didn't seem to be very nice about her at all. He'd spoken to her dreadfully that first time I'd met him, and now he wasn't being pleasant about her again. I felt sorry for the poor woman having to put up with him behaving in that way. No wonder she was a sulker. He might be a good-looking bloke but listening to the way he talked about their relationship, living with him couldn't be easy.

'You'll have to come out to the pub with us next time we have a night out. It would do you good and I'd love you to meet Meredith.'

'That would be nice and it'd be good to get out. Get me away from the miserable mare for an hour or two.'

Mum had always taught me that there were two sides to every story, and while I was trying not to judge too much, I was really finding it hard in this instance.

I walked towards Jude and handed him his mug, not saying a word. He smiled and said thanks and then I just headed off back to the café and up to the flat. I would go and get the mood board and let him and Clem chat. This wasn't a conversation I wanted to be part of.

When we were kids we lived in Bay View Cottage, situated at the top of the hill, away from the café as Mum didn't want to be on site. Our home was lovely and we were lucky to have views of the whole bay so I've always had the sea as a view. I couldn't imagine life without it.

When I returned from my time away from Driftwood Bay, after Lucas and I had parted ways, the flat above the café was vacant as the previous tenant had gone to live with her daughter to be nearer to her grandchildren. I decided that I would move in temporarily while looking around for something suitable. I had forgotten what a lovely place it was. I couldn't bear to be in Mum's house after she'd gone. Some time later, when Meredith's mother had decided that she wanted to live in Driftwood Bay permanently, she had fallen in love with it and rented it from us. Lucy and I were delighted that the house was lived in again by someone who loved it as much as we had but more importantly as much as Mum had.

The flat had needed modernising to bring it up to spec, but with Clem's handywork, Meredith's interior design eye and me making it loved and lived in, it was now amazing. The light was glorious, flooding into the lounge, and as it was on a corner, it was perfectly situated for both sunrises and sunsets. I often sat with an early morning coffee or a late evening glass of Pinot Grigio thinking how lucky I was to be in a place like this. The view from my window made my heart happy.

My mood board was on the dining room table propped against the wall. I hoped Clem liked my concepts and Meredith had said that he was a whizz at coming up with ideas as he worked. That was what he'd done with the lighthouse, which is how they'd met. And Meredith was going to help too. Her interior design and upholstery business was thriving. She'd done an amazing job of turning what was a hobby into a business, and I was really looking forward to us working together, creating a place full of ambiance that I knew that Mum would be proud of and for the benefit of the local community too.

As I walked down the stairs into the café, I heard Clem shout, 'See you next Saturday night then, Adams. Right, Gemma, let's see that board.'

His brow furrowed and, as he took in the pictures that I'd pinned to the board, along with the swatches of material and paint colour chart, he scratched his stubble. He started to gently nod as his eyes moved around the board. I didn't realise I'd been holding my breath while waiting for his verdict. His opinion was incredibly important to me.

'Nice. *Very* nice. I think this will work well. So, let's get planning, shall we? And I hate to tell you but you'll need your payment card as we need to order some stuff from the builders' yard. This is the worst part, I promise. Or, when we knock through from one building to the next might be the worst part. Certainly, the dustiest. But let's not worry about that at this point.'

That little bit of anxiety over whether I had done the right thing flashed into my brain again but it was a little late to do anything about it now. A few inconspicuous deep breaths made me feel slightly less uneasy as we made calls, ordered building materials and planned. Thank God that Clem was helping me because I honestly would not have known where to start. We set a provisional date for the grand reopening, with a few days either side for snagging and some wiggle room just in case we needed it.

Lucy had already said that she'd love to help me plan and organise the grand reopening evening and I really wanted her to be involved. We'd arranged to get together over at the B & B later in the week and I was really looking forward to it. My sister is my best friend. We are incredibly lucky to be so close; I know not all families are. And she'd been so good to me with her constant love and support since I'd come back to the area.

James and she had never once made me feel like a spare part and for that I was truly grateful. He was a lovely man and I couldn't wish for a better brother-in-law. He'd been so understanding when I came back to Driftwood Bay and Lucy and I had sat up till late at night, mainly with me crying and Lucy helping me to make sense of the world. It had been a terrible time in my life. To come home one day and find that Lucas had left me was awful, but the reason behind it was even worse. Before then, he'd always said my inability to give him a child would never be a deal breaker. That it would never affect our love and it wouldn't matter to him as long as we were together. He lied and he broke my heart.

James was wonderful, making me feel truly welcome while I was staying at his and frequently making himself scarce, so that my sister and I could talk. He was also great at hugs, particularly those he gave before I left to go to the café each day. I'm sure he was pleased to get his wife back properly once I'd moved into the flat, although he never made me feel that way.

The café meant such a lot to Lucy and me. Our memories were there. It was Mum's world, so our hearts were enormously invested. I wanted the new business to be something that she would have been proud of and it was so important to me that she approved of everything that I'd done. Lucy and I had talked briefly about the launch but it all needed ironing out and confirming.

One of the first things I needed to do was to advertise for a permanent member of staff. There was no way, with the new extended opening hours, that I could cope with doing all day and all evening. I knew I needed to put a notice up in the local mini-market and generally put the word out. But it was hard to trust your business to someone else. You wanted someone to love it as much as you did. Yet some people just wanted to come to work, get paid and then go home. They weren't wrong. They were just different to me.

This was my own business, and because of everything that went with it, it was incredibly precious. I needed to pick my staff wisely.

Writing a job advertisement was harder than I thought it would be. Esther, the previous tenant of the upstairs flat, had always helped Mum out in the café in the past when we needed help. The money always came in handy for her and as she was only ever upstairs, we could call on her when in need of that extra pair of hands when we weren't expecting it.

Finding Pat had been a gift. She'd worked in one of the

hotels out of town, but it had closed down and she decided that she didn't want anything full time to replace it, so she helped out when she could. But now, it was definitely time to have another someone. Maybe a teenager, as Lucy had suggested, who was looking for some extra hours after school. The local comprehensive closed at three o'clock each day and there were always kids in the café or milling around on the beach. A bit different to my day, when I was pretty sure we were at school until at least three thirty. Kids these days don't realise how lucky they are. Although, in fairness, I'm glad I didn't grow up in a time where everyone lives their lives on social media.

Talking of which, resurrecting my social media profiles was a priority too. It was something that Lucy was always on at me to do, I just didn't have the time or the energy when I finished work for the night, but I also knew how important and useful it would be for the business. The renovations might be of interest too. People seemed to like before and after images. I might even manage to find a new staff member that way. If people could share that I was looking, maybe that could help.

As my dear mum used to say, I just had to hold a little hope in my heart. Hope that the universe would give me a little helping hand and that the right person would come along at just the right time.

4

Nearly a whole week had flown by and we were at the Harbourside Hotel for dinner. Luckily, all the guests at the B & B were out for the evening at a wedding, so Lucy and James were able to take a well-deserved Saturday night off which they'd not been able to do for a while. And Meredith and Clem had also joined us.

The thing I loved most when I went out with these two couples was that the women sat in one group and the men sat separately, which made it less obvious that I wasn't part of a couple. I was never made to feel the odd one out, it was always just a pleasant night.

These days, our nights out often took place at the B & B so that Lucy and James could pop in and out as needed and rarely were they able to do it together. I didn't think I'd ever seen Lucy so happy as when James dropped a kiss onto her head as he walked by her on his way to the bar. Her eyes followed his every move and he turned to her and winked. They were a very touchy-feely couple, in a good way. He couldn't walk past her without running a hand over her shoulder or squeezing her hand. It was lovely that they were still very much in love. I was quite envious.

Lucy still wasn't drinking, so must still have the infection she'd mentioned last week. With all the excitement of the renovations starting I hadn't had chance to ask her about it and didn't like to mention it in front of the others. I must remember tomorrow. She clearly wasn't too ill though. She was looking fabulous.

I was just shoving the last bite of a dirty great burger into my mouth, when the lads returned from the bar with another round of drinks. I looked up into those familiar dark brown eyes again. Jude Adams. I'd completely forgotten that Clem had invited him. I had so much on my to-do list these days I was becoming a right scatterbrain. If it wasn't on a list, I didn't have much chance of remembering it.

Looking very casual out of uniform, he was dressed in dark blue jeans and a short-sleeved white shirt – which looked like it could have done with an iron before he came out – and a pair of sporty trainers. I didn't realise that I was staring at him for longer than was necessary, so when he caught my eye, I quickly glanced away.

'Hi, Gemma, mind if I sit here?'

The only available seat had to be next to me, didn't it? Great! I couldn't speak because my mouth was full and I could feel something dribbling down my chin as I nodded my agreement. He grinned as he sat down and passed me a napkin from the table.

'You've got a bit of...'

I wiped my chin and looked at the napkin. Great, mayonnaise *and* tomato sauce mixed. I'm sure that must have looked most unattractive. Good job I wasn't trying to impress him.

Meredith, who was sat to my left, gave a sideways glance at me, over to Jude and back to me again and winked.

'Watch out there, Gem, you're dribbling!'

'Ha, so funny!' I brushed off her comment, knowing that she was referring to Jude rather than the burger, but could feel my face getting warmer. She turned her body towards Lucy – intentionally, I'm sure – leaving me no alternative than to talk to Jude.

'Good week? Put out any fires?' I didn't think I'd be winning any awards at all soon for my scintillating small talk.

'If I had a pound for every time I was asked that I'd be a very rich man. I'm not a frontline firefighter these days. Had a bit of an injury and that's why I'm more involved with fire safety now.'

'Oh, sorry to hear that.' I racked my brain, trying to think of something else to say. Everyone else seemed to be deep in conversation, so I couldn't really drag them into anything. An uncomfortable silence fell over us. Luckily, Clem seemed to notice.

'Left Occy at home, have you, mate? Was she OK about you coming out?'

'Well, "OK" wouldn't really be what I'd say from her face, but I'm sure the minute I was out the door she was on the phone to her old mates, slagging me off. She just seems to hate me all the time.'

To be honest, he didn't sound like he liked her much either. I always wondered why some couples stayed together. But who was I to offer relationship advice? I was the only one sat round the table who was single so perhaps I should keep my thoughts to myself. Maybe I could ask him about his wife. Yes, that would give us something to talk about.

'So, you've recently moved to Driftwood Bay, have you? You and Occy?'

'Yes, that's right. I was stationed in Exeter before that so lived that way. But the accident meant I couldn't do the job there, so I've been moved to this part of the world. I grew up not too far away and it's always been somewhere I fancied being nearer to.' He looked out of the huge picture window at the harbour beyond. 'It's so beautiful here. Peaceful and calm. Definitely a bit different on a Saturday night here. Much more pleasant.'

'Shame Occy doesn't think so,' Clem chipped in. He laughed.

Jude didn't look that amused.

'Does Occy not like it here?'

'Oh God no, she hates it. None of her friends are nearby and she's had to relocate schools too. And I won't allow her to have the dog that she desperately wants. I'm very popular in our house. Not!'

So, a fireman and a teacher. An interesting combination.

He sighed. 'I hope she'll come round in time. Anyway, enough about me, how's work developing on the café? Can you see anything taking shape at all yet? I know how quick Clem works when he's got his mind set on something.'

We chatted about the renovation work, the plans we'd made that week for the relaunch and what my dreams for the café were and he ummed and ahhed in all the right places. Maybe he wasn't so bad after all. When I mentioned me getting more involved in social media, and promoting the business that way he said he thought it was a great idea. He even suggested that maybe Occy could give me some pointers. He said she was on it all the time and it would be great to see her putting her skills to use; would it be OK if he passed my number on to her? I didn't feel like I'd got anything to lose so agreed.

Maybe someone with experience would be just what I needed to point me in the right direction and get me started with some ideas. It did cross my mind as to why she'd have the time to help when she'd be busy marking books and doing lesson plans. Maybe she wasn't full time. I had a friend who was a teacher and even though she only worked three days a week, she spent tons of time in her holidays, evenings and weekends marking. It could have been because she loved her job and put in more than was required but I didn't know many teachers that didn't love their jobs and would put in over and above what was necessary to make sure their students had the best possible chance in life.

Jude turned out to be quite pleasant when not talking about his wife and he joined in the chat around the table, mixing well with everyone. He had a fantastic sense of humour, often cracking jokes at his own expense. I noticed a glance between Lucy and Meredith and hoped that they didn't think that just because I was single, I was eyeing up all the local talent. I'd be putting them straight the minute I got them on their own.

When I tucked myself up in bed that night, I realised that I had had a lovely evening. Chatting to Jude had been easy. I hoped that if Occy did join us another time, it wouldn't spoil the dynamic. It's funny how sometimes just one person can do that. But, in fairness, if I had a husband, I might not like him being in the pub with other women. Not that it was like that or anything. Also, who's to say that even if he wasn't married, I'd be his type anyway. He wasn't particularly mine. I preferred a less rugged look and I wasn't keen on the way he spoke about his wife either. No thank you.

However, I did feel that it was good to have friends of the opposite sex. And I know that when Meredith arrived in the bay, she said that it was nice to get to know new people whoever they were. It does appear to get harder later in life to meet new friends. Maybe Jude or Occy were readers and might fancy coming to book club once it was up and running. That was on the agenda now I'd discussed it with Meredith, and Lucy thought it was a brilliant idea too. We were really looking forward to getting it off the ground.

There it was again. That little frisson for the future and all that it held.

I might have been single, and lonely from time to time, but I reckoned that was OK. I had no intention of getting involved with anyone for a long time to come, if at all ever again. What had happened with Lucas had put me off being part of a relationship completely. You invest so much of your heart and soul and your life into someone and suddenly, in the blink of an eye, it can all come crashing down around you. Life is funny, isn't it? You think you are heading in one direction and then *bang*; it can change beyond recognition, totally out of your control. I never thought for one minute that my life would end up that way.

Lucas had always been a bit of a player. I'd been in love with him for years and he'd really strung me along for a while, much to Lucy's disgust. But after a few years he seemed to grow up and wanted to settle down and even she had to admit that maybe leopards did change their spots after all.

After those initial blips early on in our relationship, I thought that Lucas and I would be together forever. That's what we had promised each other when we said our wedding vows. Through sickness and health. For richer or poorer. But clearly not if one of the wedded couple changed their mind.

And now I was a divorcee. Something I never thought for one minute I would be. I was always so sure of our love and felt that he was my destiny.

Oh well, no point dwelling on the past and raking all that up again. I knew now, after a lot of work on myself, that I didn't need anyone to complete me. I'd spent the last couple of years working through lots of things in my head with the help of Emma – a great therapist – Lucy and James, and since I'd known her, Meredith too. With their help, after a while of wallowing, which they allowed me before giving me the kick up the backside I needed, I picked myself up, dusted myself off and started again. There are always choices and I chose the option that meant that I would never allow anyone to be so close to me that way again. I ensured that it would never happen to me again.

It was only in the last few months that I realised something very important.

That I was enough.

As I sipped my morning coffee the following day, watching the glory of the sun rising over the harbour, feeling at peace with the world, the silence was interrupted by a text tone from my phone.

Hey. Bin told 2 message u because you want 2 talk about socials. LMK when gud 4U. Occy Adams.

Jude must have already spoken to his wife then. It was kind of her to get in touch so quickly, even if she was clearly in a rush, evident by her use of quick text talk. I returned the message straight away.

Hi Occy, thanks so much for getting in touch. Jude told me how fabulous you are at social media and said you might be able to help me with some advice. It would be lovely to meet you. If you fancy popping by the café on the corner of the harbour any day after you've finished up at work, I'd love to chat with you. If you can let me

know in advance that would be great and I'll arrange some cover.
Look forward to seeing you soon. x

Sundays never used to be as busy as Saturdays and sometimes I wouldn't even open at all, but with the uptake in visitors
to the area throughout the summer, I realised that there was a
lot of trade about and it had quickly become one of the busiest
days of the week. Lots of the locals had said that they loved a
cooked breakfast on a Sunday morning, especially one that they
didn't have to cook themselves. Oh, the luxury. There weren't
many meals these days that I didn't cook myself, which was why
I was devouring that delicious burger last night when Jude came
into the pub.

I did go to Lucy and James's occasionally for tea and, once a
month, Clem and Meredith, Lucy and James and I took it in
turns to host a dinner party, which was always good, but it was a
bit of a busman's holiday for me. I loved the times when I went
to them more, although it was also nice to cook for others. I'd
got out of the habit and it never seemed worth just cooking for
me when I was home alone. I normally just grabbed something
from the café and chucked it in the microwave. I know I cooked
for people in the café all day long, but it wasn't the same as
sitting down to dinner with someone else, chatting about your
day, passing the time, and even sitting watching the TV with
someone. Even if you weren't talking it was nice to be in
someone else's company and I did miss that companionable
silence I must admit.

I wondered what Lucas was doing now. Whether he thought
of me. If he ever wished he'd made a different decision. We
hadn't stayed in touch even though he'd suggested it. It hurt my
heart too much. Lucy had said that it was typical of him to want
to stay connected. Keep me dangling just in case he changed his

mind. I didn't see it that way but I still decided I needed to make a clean break.

Come on, Gem, get moving. No good can come from sitting around dwelling on the past. Keep on moving forward.

I could hear my lovely mum's voice in my head. That's exactly what she would be saying if she were right beside me.

* * *

By the time I got out of the shower, I still hadn't had a response to my text to Occy. I hoped I hadn't offended her by anything I said. I reread it just in case. I had dithered a little over sending a kiss at the end, but wanted to come across as friendly and approachable, which I am, but it's sometimes difficult to portray that in a message. The last thing I wanted was her popping in unannounced and the café heaving and me not being able to give her my full attention. Since splitting up with Lucas, I've realised that I never really had his full attention in the latter part of our relationship. He was either on his phone or watching the TV and not really taking in what I was saying. He even used to check his phone while we were eating dinner which used to drive me insane.

I know everyone is busy these days and trying to do two or even three things at once but it's about being present for me. And showing people that they are important enough for you to spend time focusing on them.

We live in a world where phones do seem to be taking over our lives. While they are great in one respect, they are a menace in others. The ability to check everything at the touch of a button, check Google, read the news, do your shopping, check your social media profiles means that we are rarely away. It's no wonder a lot of the world finds it hard to concentrate on things for long spells of time. The constant pressure of life is exhausting. I remember when I first started working in business, you wouldn't dream of sending anyone an email after five o'clock or before 9 a.m. These days, people send you emails and social media direct messages at all times of the day and night and expect you to be on hand permanently.

As the café got bigger and hopefully busier, it was going to be hard to set my own boundaries, but I'd resolved to try to do so after the relaunch. I think the whole world needs to learn that people have to have boundaries and there's no other way to lead than by example. I know I have only one voice, but if we all did our bit then maybe we could make the world a better place. I decided to ask Occy if that's something she could help with. Maybe she was used to running the school social media sites. That must take some doing with the mentality of some of the parents these days.

I once went out for the day with a friend and when we got back, she said that she hoped I didn't mind her saying that she felt she wasn't important to me because I hadn't been giving her my full focus. I was really offended at the time, feeling she clearly didn't understand that I just had a busy life, but when I thought about it, I realised she was right and I was mortified. Since then, I've wanted to be better in this area of my life. That was the plan anyway.

So, let's hope Occy will be the answer to all my prayers. Those ones anyway.

Talking of prayers, I grabbed the notebook from the coffee table in front of the window to look at what jobs I had on my list for today. Plenty to keep me going.

* * *

Four hours later, after that first ring of the bell above the door and a constant stream of customers in the café, I finally got a breather and made myself a coffee. It had been a busy morning; one of those crisp, sunny days that brought people out, and the special autumn service at the local church had people from the village showing what a great turn-out Driftwood Bay put on when we tried. Thankfully, lots of those then came to the café when the service had finished.

Though despite the larger than normal audience, the vicar didn't look that happy when he walked through the café doors.

'Morning, Gemma, how are you?'

'Better than you by the look of it. Everything OK, Reverend Rogers?'

'I do wish you'd call me Tom.' He looked around to make sure no one was listening and lowered his voice. 'The bishop was coming over this morning and I was desperate to show him how many people were there but he had to cancel last minute. He's talking about closing the church, if truth be told.' He mimed a zip movement with his fingers across his lips. 'Our secret, Gemma. I'm going to sit in the window table if that's OK. Ponder life and what message this is teaching me. Make the most of Driftwood Bay just in case I get moved on.'

The trouble with people sharing secrets with you is that while they've offloaded, and yes, a problem shared is a problem halved as they say, you then have the weight of their secret on your shoulders and it becomes your load. I should know. I had a couple of whoppers of my own. Keeping secrets was hard.

People would be devastated if they knew about the church though and I think he was doing the wrong thing by not telling anyone. He'd been our community vicar for as long as I could remember. It would be such a shame to see the beautiful old church be closed down. Can 'the Church' even do that? Surely, they couldn't just leave the building empty. I had so many questions, but judging by the sadness on his face, now was not the right time to ask.

When he left after devouring a full English, he seemed to leave his sadness behind and it took all I had that afternoon to shake it off. When I headed over to Lucy's for the evening, walking round the bay to get to theirs, I was still worrying about the church.

Autumn was settling in. The nights were getting darker and colder but the twinkly festoon lights hung all around the harbour always gave me goosebumps. I was so happy to be living back in Driftwood Bay again. Driving here to work every day from Truro wasn't the same. When I was living with Lucas, it always felt like I left a little bit of my heart behind as I locked up the café and got in my car. I felt safe here. I could walk around the streets at night without having to look over my shoulder. The people were warm and friendly, and you were always bumping into someone who would stop and chat, passing the time of day. It was this community feeling that I loved and my mind drifted back to Jude and his wife, who had moved from a big town. I hoped they'd settle and enjoy being part of what we had.

Hopefully, we'd find a solution as a community to keep the church open, although if the community didn't know it was a problem, then they'd be unlikely to be able to help. I'd visit the lovely old church in a day or two and try to persuade Reverend Rogers to share the news with the villagers who I knew would want to help.

6

Monday was my day off. Well, when I say day off, I mean that the café wasn't open. I'd not had many actual days off since I had the café. It was more of a way of life, but I didn't mind. I loved my café and while most of the time I was run off my feet, I couldn't think of anything else that I would rather be doing.

One thing I was looking forward to though was a nice early walk on the beach. When I moved back here, I vowed that I wouldn't take my surroundings for granted. I wanted to appreciate how fortunate and grateful I was and most of my days started with a soul-satisfying walk.

When I arrived at the beach, there wasn't another person to be seen and I became lost in my thoughts as I wandered along at the water's edge, filling my lungs with the fresh salty air. I'd taken off my trainers and they were dangling from my hand. Occasionally the cold swish of the gentle lapping waves on my feet took my breath away but it felt invigorating at the same time. In the distance I spotted someone in the sea, swimming back into the shoreline. How blooming cold they must be – or mad. I didn't get the whole cold water swimming thing myself.

Not for me. Despite always being a bit of a mermaid as a child, it took a lot for me to get in the sea these days, even in the summer, let alone this time of year.

Another hobby of mine from when I was younger was looking for pieces of driftwood on the beach. I bent down to lift quite a large piece from under a pile of wet, slimy, stinky seaweed and wondered whether I could clean it up and put it to use in my home or the café. Lost in my little world, I didn't notice that the person in the sea was now close. As I turned and saw the man starting to stride from the water, I couldn't help but appreciate the half-naked body that stood before me. It was only when I looked up from the perfectly sculpted chest, and that little trail of hair that crept towards the top of his board shorts, that I realised it was Jude Adams.

My face flushed as his eyes locked onto mine. One of us had to break the silence.

'And there was me thinking I was brave dipping my feet in.' I smiled nervously, and kept eye contact, hoping he wasn't thinking what a perve I was, ogling his body.

'It was a little colder than I thought. It surprised even me this morning. But I'll soon recover. It's supposed to be good for the soul, so I'm told.'

'Rather you than me.'

'If only I knew someone with a coffee shop who could make me a hot chocolate to get my temperature back to normal.' He grinned. He really was very handsome when he wasn't scowling.

'If only you knew someone with a coffee shop who opened on a Monday more like.'

'Just my blooming luck. Story of my life.'

'Well, I was just heading back and I suppose I could maybe help you out if you fancy a little something to warm you up.'

One of his eyebrows lifted slightly then he bent down and

grabbed a towel from a nearby rock and started to rub it over his body.

Oh, my word. I stumbled a little over my explanation. This man seemed to get me in a proper tizzy.

'Er, fire up the coffee machine, I mean. Make you a hot drink.'

Jude tilted his head to one side and his eyes bore into mine.

'As if I thought you meant anything else.' The pause that came next seemed to last for minutes. 'That would be lovely, Gemma, if you don't mind.'

'I'll head up and leave the door on the latch; come straight in when you arrive.'

He nodded and I walked away thinking what a complete idiot he must think I am. I was not a person to flirt and certainly not with someone who was married. I was just being friendly and hoped that he was taking it in the spirit that it was intended.

Not long after, despite my thoughts, my heart skipped a little when the bell over the door tinkled to signify his arrival. I'd been daydreaming again and it startled me a tad. I couldn't help but notice how his tousled damp hair framed his face as he smiled at me and reminded me of how he looked doing his best Daniel Craig impression when he left the water.

'It's lovely and toasty in here.'

I rubbed at my neck. Yes, it was definitely warm in the café this morning. It must be the contrast with the cooler morning outside.

He looked around. 'This is such a lovely place, you know. It's no wonder people want to come and spend time here. It has such a nice feel about it. It's not just the decor either. If it doesn't sound daft, it's like it has a nice soul. Have you had the café for long?'

We spent a very pleasant hour chatting over our hot chocolates – two cups each, in fact. He was good company and was great at asking questions. That was a nice quality in a person. So many people these days are self-obsessed and just talk about themselves. It was nice to share some of my memories of Mum and the café with him. Made me feel very nostalgic.

As he was leaving, I remembered the text.

'Occy messaged me yesterday by the way.'

'Oh good. Finally, she has done something I asked her to do. That's a result.' His frown seemed to return. 'Let me know how it goes. I'd be interested to see how long it takes her to slag me off when she meets you.'

With that, his whole demeanour changed and his shoulders slumped as he gave a little wave and closed the door behind him. I watched him walk up the high street and wondered what on earth was going on with him and his wife. I hoped that they managed to sort things out. It was a shame when relationships broke down.

After he'd gone, I felt a bit desolate. It was so quiet. Maybe it was just the fact that I'd gone from company to none again. I still struggled to get used to that so put the radio on as I rattled around preparing trays of food to go into the oven, shimmying around the kitchen, singing along to Ed Sheeran. It really lifted my spirits, especially after the sadness of yesterday's news from Reverend Rogers. I thought about the wording for the advertisement I was planning to put up in the mini-market for a new member of staff and decided that I'd pop up there at lunchtime. I had a busy afternoon ahead, but, as always, I lost myself in the art of cooking.

* * *

After what was hours later, but seemed like five minutes, I had piles of plastic tubs full of food which needed loading into larger trays to transport. I'd managed to persuade the nice super-market delivery man to leave the trays behind when I told him what they were for. He was the only person who knew anything at all about my special project and after swallowing a huge lump in his throat, swore that he wouldn't tell a soul. He was very happy to help and said no one would even notice that a few had gone missing.

As I nipped into the mini-market before I headed off to Truro, I noticed Dilys chatting to her daughter Sophie, who looked like she was fit to burst and give birth at any moment. She was rubbing her hands over her belly in that protective, natural way that pregnant women did and I felt a little pang in my heart that I would never get to experience that feeling.

I still struggled with how I felt when I was around pregnant women. Now I knew that it would never happen for me, I tried so hard not to let it affect me. There were times when I could cope, but there were other times when I felt raging jealousy and anger. The counsellor I'd seen told me that all the feelings I had were totally natural and that I had to go through a grieving process. And that wasn't just grieving for the now, but for a future that I always assumed I would have but now knew that I never would.

However, the logical, practical side of me knew that feeling sorry for myself wouldn't help or change anything and that I just needed to put on my big girl pants and get on with making a different life for myself.

It made me think of Lucas again. I wondered what he would be doing right now. Was he thinking of me at all? Was he going about his life preparing for his future and that of his now girlfriend?

'Hi, Gemma, how are you, m'lovely?' Dilys greeted me with a smile. 'Gorgeous day, isn't it? Are you after anything special today?'

I'm glad she broke into my thoughts and I snapped back to the reality of the here and now.

'Can I put a notice up in your window please?'

''Course.'

I handed the card over to her and she skimmed her eyes over it and raised an eyebrow.

'About bloody time you got some help, young lady. You can't do everything on your own, you know.'

I smiled. 'It's taken me a while to realise that but it's finally sunk in. I just hope I can find someone now.'

'When I first opened this shop, I didn't think I'd need anyone's help. But a wise woman, she used to own the café, you might know her—' she winked '—told me that you don't have to prove anything to anyone. Not even to yourself.'

I smiled at the thought of Mum dishing out her wonderful advice again.

'She said help is there when you need it the most and it's not a weakness to ask for it if needs be. If it's meant to be, the right person will come along just at the right time. Don't you fret.'

'I do hope so. Keep your fingers crossed for me.'

'Will do, m'love. I'll pop this up now. Sooner the better.'

She gave me a little wave as I left, my walk on the beach a distant memory now.

A little chime from my phone signified a text had been delivered.

Fancy dinner on Friday night, hun? James is out so I thought we could have a girly night. He's promised to get us a takeaway curry before he leaves.

It had been ages since I'd had a takeaway. In this small village, there weren't any food places and you had to drive to a couple of towns away as they didn't deliver here because it was too far out in the sticks. Just thinking about a curry was making my mouth water.

Sounds fab. Try and stop me. Is Meredith coming too?

Those little three dots appeared to show she was messaging back and then they disappeared. Then they appeared again. And went. Then a few minutes passed by. She must have been called away. I started tapping out a text to Meredith when my phone flashed up with a message from Lucy.

I thought it might be nice if it was just you and me. Some sister time. It's been ages since we've done something on our own. Don't mention it to Meredith. I don't want to leave her out but I'd like you to myself.

Mmm, that seemed a little unlike her.

Is everything OK, Luce?

Those dots again. It felt like I was waiting for ages before a message came through.

Yep, just thought we could have a proper chat on our own. All fine though. Nothing to worry about. Just can't catch up till then because we have a busy week and I know you do too. See you Friday. Love you xx

Something didn't feel quite right. My instincts were

normally right and my spidey senses were working overtime. But Friday would be here before we knew it so I'd have to wait till then. Hopefully it would be nothing and I was overthinking things. I did have a tendency to do that, especially since all the business with Lucas. I'd try to distract myself till then. I had plenty to be getting on with.

I wasn't quite sure my head was going to hold up with all the banging going on next door. Maybe I could buy myself some noise-cancelling headphones for when the café is closed.

After popping a couple of brownies on a plate, I grabbed the two coffees that I'd made and headed out of my front door and in through Martin's.

'Morning, Clem. Time for a cuppa?'

'Perfect timing.' He stood up and stretched, rubbing the base of his back. 'I'm sure I'll be getting too old for this building lark soon. Good job I love it, isn't it? Hope all this noise isn't too much for you?'

'No, not at all.'

Why do we do that? Why don't we tell the truth? Isn't honesty the best policy? I decided to try it for a change.

'Well, it is a bit distracting, I suppose.'

'Ah sorry, hopefully there won't be much more after today for a while. It's just getting rid of all the fixed furniture in here and dismantling the counter.

I silently thanked whoever was watching over me.

'Crikey, there's hardly anything left in here,' I said, as I glanced around.

'I know. I'm pleased with the progress so far. I was just thinking about when the best time would be to knock the garden wall down so we can extend your outdoor area. I was also thinking that maybe we could raise some of it and have a higher seating area to make even more of the view. I know it wasn't in the original plan but what do you think?'

'God, Clem, that would be fab. I never even thought of that. You're good, you know.'

'Ha. Maybe I can do the majority of the knocking down bit next Monday while you are closed to give the least disruption. I've got a mate who said he'd be up for helping. Unless you fancy taking some aggression out on a brick wall? You'd be very welcome, but, if not, you might want to go out for the day to avoid the noise.'

'That's not a bad idea. Maybe I can persuade Meredith to come out for a day and we could go and look at furnishings.'

'You know she'd be up for that anytime. It's her favourite pastime ever. Apart from spending time with me of course. Scrap that, I think it's even more a favourite than that.'

I knew that he was making light of it, but Meredith did think the absolute world of Clem. After a divorce from a somewhat controlling husband, she was finding her own feet in an unfamiliar part of the world as well as starting an unexpected relationship. I thought she was brave to start all over again by choice. She was a real inspiration. At fifty, she wasn't old by any stretch of the imagination and these days most women of her age were kick-starting their lives. She was living proof that it was possible to have a new adventure and do all the things that you've always wanted to do. She'd moved to Driftwood Bay for a new start and not planned to do anything but live in a different place and make some friends. What she hadn't banked on was finding love and while their journey so far hadn't always been an easy one, with him being a good few years younger than her and her not believing she was worthy of someone his age and so lovely, it had worked out well in the end.

Meredith and Clem had a lovely relationship but were still taking things slowly. Clearly, they loved spending time with each other and were the best of friends as well as lovers. While there was evidently a passion for each other, those fiery sparks that some younger relationships hold tend to be the downfall, and in many cases, jealousy and drama can take over. But not with them. It was lovely to see them share a healthy sensible approach and they had gone into the relationship with their eyes open and their hearts too.

I envied Meredith's easy way of negotiating and slipping reasonably seamlessly into making a new life for herself and balancing her relationship. Clem lived on a yacht in the harbour, while Meredith lived in the lighthouse and loved living alone. They adored being with each other and spent time staying over at the other's homes but they didn't live in each other's pockets.

I suppose this was how a successful relationship should be, but in some, the balance does seem to be off kilter where one half of the partnership seems to be lesser than the other. It wasn't something I was aware of until I had my counselling, but I realised that in mine and Lucas's relationship, we were definitely more like 75 per cent him and 25 per cent me. We always had been right from the start. When we first got together, I considered myself so lucky that he had chosen to be with me that I suppose I would have done anything to keep him happy.

Therefore, I suppressed my needs and wants to satisfy his, without even noticing really, which shifted the balance very much from when we first met. Back then, he was happy to do things that he knew I liked, made more of an effort, but when we slipped into a more familiar life, all of that seemed to go by the wayside. He was a much stronger personality than me, and more selfish and demanding too. While I was happy to go along with what he suggested and wanted, most of the time I found myself agreeing just to keep him happy.

Maybe it's the whole men are from Mars and women are from Venus comparison and men are naturally more selfish. Although I probably shouldn't generalise; maybe it was just the men I knew. Bizarre really, and I know that decisions that are made in relationships are about compromise in a lot of cases but since I've been aware of it, I look at relationships in an entirely different way.

Lucy and James, for instance, have a definite even split, just like Clem and Meredith. If I ever did get into another relationship, which really wasn't on my radar, it would certainly be different to how I lived through the last one. It didn't feel wrong at the time, but when it ends up with one partner leaving the other and their life being totally upturned, you do wonder what all that compromise was for. I would never leave myself that vulnerable again. To put your trust in another person for so long, to have it whipped away so devastatingly, just tears you apart and it takes a long time to recover from so much loss and pain. It wouldn't be fair on another person to take on the pain of my past.

I gathered the cups and plate and took them back, telling Clem to pop round when he was ready for some lunch. It was the least I could do when he was charging me mate's rates for all the work he was doing *and* the consulting and design ideas too. I was very lucky to have him as a friend.

Lunchtime flew by and around 3 p.m., the door flung open, crashing into the wall, nearly coming off its hinges.

'Shit sorry. I didn't realise it would fly back that far.'

When I looked up to see what the commotion was, I saw a dishevelled teenage girl stood there. Her hair looked like it needed a good brush and she had a full face of make-up – all contours and stripes and her skin looked a bit orangey. The patchy fake tan on her arms was quite a contrast to the greyish-white school shirt she wore and her short tartan skirt showed lily-white legs that didn't seem to match the rest of her body. Bless her. She looked like she needed someone to take her in hand. It wasn't often that we got that many strangers in the café.

I smiled at her. 'Hello. What can I get you?'

She mumbled something which I really couldn't decipher at all.

'Sorry, I can't hear you with the coffee machine gurgling away, can you shout up please.'

'I'm here about the job.'

'Oh OK. Have you done anything like this before?'

'Depends if it'll go against me or not.' I could only just make out what she'd said.

'Do you want to take a seat and I'll bring you a drink and we can have a chat?'

She put her hand in her pocket, counted some change out and shook her head as she pocketed the money.

'No s'all right thanks, I'm OK.'

She looked gutted.

'It's on the house?'

She smiled and her whole face lit up. What a pretty girl she was under all that make-up.

'Really?'

'Yep absolutely. Tea, coffee, Coke, hot chocolate. Anything you like really.'

'Could I have a hot chocolate please?'

'Sure, I'll be back in a mo.'

She sat with her back to me, and I watched her as I made the drinks. She seemed a little bit nervy and when the door went, she flinched, though it was only the postman dropping in some letters.

'Here you go. So, tell me why you think you'd be good at working in a café. I presume you haven't done it before. In fact, how old are you?'

'I'm fifteen, nearly sixteen though. I know I'm still at school, Year 11, and I saw that you're looking for someone in the day times and at weekends too. I could definitely do after school and weekends. I want to earn some serious money so will do all the hours I can.'

'OK, well, I'd have to check into that because there are laws to say how many hours you are allowed to work.'

Her face dropped. 'Oh!'

'Are you saving up for something in particular?'

'Yeah.' She seemed reluctant to share, and I didn't want to push her.

'Do you live in the village? I've not seen you around before.'

'Yeah, we've not long moved here.'

Great that she was local. That was always helpful.

'So maybe on weekdays you could do a couple of hours after school a couple of nights a week and then hours on a weekend too? Does that sound about right?'

'Yeah, and I could do school holidays too, but don't you want to know more about me?'

'Well, if you live around here, it's not like I won't be checking you out. I'll be asking around before you start.'

'Great.' She grinned again. So pretty.

'There are a few things you'll need to know and that I will ask you for, but if you agree, then maybe we could do a trial later in the week. You may have seen that I'm having some work done next door and my plans are to expand so I definitely need more help.'

'OK.' She looked at me and chewed her lip.

'For starters, you'd have to tie your hair up. I can't have your hair dangling in drinks and food.'

She nodded.

I pointed at her hands.

'I think those false nails might have to go too. People won't want to be finding them in their full English breakfasts.'

She laughed. 'They pop off all the time anyway so not a problem.'

'And the lashes too.'

'But...'

'Sorry, but I can't have someone thinking that they've got a spider in their soup if one falls off.'

'They are quite hard to keep on to be honest. OK. I won't use them when I'm at work.'

'Great. Also, I don't allow phones at all when people are working here. You can have it in your pocket for emergencies, but I mean proper emergencies. OK?'

She nodded, her eyes wide, waiting to see if there was anything else.

'I don't want to find out that your schoolwork is suffering. If you're in Year 11, I'm sure that you have your GCSEs ahead of you next summer and you must ensure that you study. If it goes quiet here, you can sit in the corner and do some revising or your homework. This is a really important time of your life and you must do as much as you can to do well in these exams.'

She nodded and just about managed to stop herself from rolling her eyes. 'You sound like my dad.'

'Well, he sounds like a very sensible man.'

'Yeah, right. You don't know him.'

I ignored her barbed comment.

'And all of this is dependent on whether this is OK with your parents.'

'Er, anything else?'

'Just one final thing. I'd want to see that lovely smile more often instead of the scowl you had on your face when you arrived.' She beamed at me. 'Yep that's the one. Can't have you putting off the customers with a frown now, can we? So, how does that all sound?'

She jumped up. 'Can I start now?'

I laughed.

'Not today. I'm not at all prepared for that. But how about Thursday if you are that eager. It's only a trial, mind, but I will pay you for it. And this is all dependent upon your parents, don't forget.'

'Yes. Yes. Yes please. That's brilliant. I'm made up. Thank you for giving me a chance. I won't let you down.'

'I shall look forward to it. Now I'm Gemma and the one thing you haven't told me is your name.'

'Oh it's—'

The door flung open for the second time in half an hour and Jude Adams strode into the room, his face like thunder.

'Why the hell didn't you come straight home? I've been worrying to death about you.'

'Chill, Dad. I've got myself a job. Meet my new boss, Gemma.'

'Hey, Gemma, I take it you've met my daughter Occy then.'

I glanced from one to the other. I could feel my mouth twitch and a smile start to form. So, Occy wasn't Jude's wife; she was his daughter. Everything started to slot into place in my mind, but, more than that, there was such similarity between the two of them, now I knew, it was kind of funny.

Jude's brow was furrowed as he glared across the table and Occy's face had returned to the sullen expression she had had when she first burst through the door. There was no mistaking that these two were related. I tried to hide my smile.

'Coffee, Jude?'

'Please. Then maybe you can both tell me what's going on here.'

I returned to the table where both were scrolling through something on their phones. I placed another hot chocolate, this time with whippy cream, mini marshmallows and chocolate sprinkles, in front of Occy. Ironically, on the top of Jude's coffee, I'd used a happy smiley face template. He raised an eyebrow at me when I put it in front of him.

I smiled as I sat and blew on my own chai latte.

'So, what's occurring?' he asked.

We all took it in turns to look at each other. I winked at Occy and she gave me a crooked grin; from her father I received another raised eyebrow.

'Occy would like to come and work with me at the café. To earn some cash. We hadn't got much further than discussing that before you arrived.'

'You didn't think to speak to me about this at all, Occy? You've got exams coming up. You'll need to be revising.'

She glowered at him from under her long false eyelashes.

I cut in. I didn't know why but I felt she needed someone to help her out a bit.

'We've discussed this. We've talked about the possibility of just a couple of nights in the week and then one day at a weekend maybe, or a few hours split across Saturday and Sunday so there's lots of time to study. I've also said that if it's quiet, I expect her to use that time to revise. And I also told her this had to be OK with her parents.'

'Oh. Right.' He paused. I could see his mind working over-time. 'I know you don't eat lunch at school and wait to eat it as soon as you get home.'

'You know I hate eating at school, Dad. It's such a rush to the dining room, you have no time to eat before you go to your next lesson.'

'I do and I've said that I'll talk to school about that.'

'No, Dad. Absolutely not.'

'But you can't go till teatime without eating. It's not good for you. How will you manage that?'

Occy nudged my knee under the table.

'Yes, we've discussed that too.' Occy's head jerked towards me. 'On the days Occy is here, she can have something to eat and drink as soon as she arrives. The last thing I want is a teenager passing out on me in the middle of a busy café.'

'Oh. OK. Seems like you've both thought this through pretty well.'

'Please, Dad, let me do this. You keep telling me not to sit around at home being miserable. This is a good way of me meeting new people and learning some life skills. I might even learn how to cook so we don't have to live on cheesy beans on toast for the rest of our lives.'

His face twitched at this. 'I thought you liked cheesy beans on toast.'

'I do, but not every night.'

'Spoilsport!' He looked across at me. 'And it's just a trial to start with?'

'Absolutely! She might hate working for a tyrant like me.'

His face relaxed. 'I doubt that very much.'

'Thank you, but you don't know me at all. I expect hard work and I have high standards.'

'Please, Dad. I can do this. I know I can. Please give me a chance?' She fluttered those long lashes and when her father's face broke into a smile, I knew that she – well, we – had won him over.

'OK, only a trial, mind.'

She jumped up and practically ran to his side of the table, flinging her arms around him. Then she did the same to me.

'I won't let you down. Either of you. I promise. Thank you so much.'

We both laughed at her enthusiasm.

'I'm going to go home now and do my homework. See you in a bit, Dad.' She surprised me by kissing my cheek. 'Thanks, Gemma. I'm going to be the best worker you've ever had.'

She burst out as quickly as she had burst in.

Jude turned to me.

'Well.'

'Well indeed.' I smiled. 'That explains a lot.'

He grinned back and the relief I felt was quite overwhelming.

'Maybe you'd like to explain what you mean by that?' He drained his cup.

'I completely got the wrong end of the stick.' I gestured to his cup. 'Want another?'

When I returned, Jude was gazing out to sea, lost in a world of his own. He turned to me and sighed.

'That's the most animated I've seen my daughter since we moved to Driftwood Bay. I don't know what magical spell you've cast over her, but, honestly, she's like a different child.'

'So that's good, isn't it?'

'It is yes, but I can't believe that it has happened through someone else. I'm so grateful to you, Gemma. We've really had a breakthrough here but I feel like it's nothing to do with me. I am such a bloody failure as a dad.' He ran his hands through his hair and looked back out the window.

Jude went on to explain that Occy's mother had left them when she was two. He'd discovered that she'd left Occy on her own a couple of times because she needed some time to herself. One of her neighbours had reported them to social services and a custody battle took place. After fighting tooth and nail, he'd won full custody of her. Occy's mother had stuck around for a few months and was allowed to have supervised visits with her daughter but a lot of the time didn't turn up when she should have. Said she had decided that she wasn't cut out to be a mother.

Jude had had to have strong words with her, telling her to

pull herself together and put her daughter first – or get out of her life completely. He never thought for one moment that she would take him literally and apart from the odd birthday card, which sometimes turned up late, they never heard from her.

'This last year has been the worst. Occy told me that she was being bullied at school and when I had it out with her school, they did some digging around and found that *she* was the one doing the bullying. When we finally got to the bottom of it, it was because the other girls were being horrible to her saying that she was such a bad person that even her mother didn't want her.'

'Oh my God. That's awful. Kids can be so hurtful at times.'

'She lashed out at them and punched one of them in the nose. Of course, after that, she was excluded. The school said that, even though there were extenuating circumstances, they couldn't tolerate such behaviour. So here we are in Driftwood Bay, making a new life for ourselves. Her trying to make new friends in a new place and new school and me trying to work out how to be a good dad and hold down a full-time job and failing miserably at both.'

He put his head in his hands.

'Maybe Occy working here will be the making of her,' I offered. 'She can learn some life skills and earn some cash while studying. I can help a bit. I might know a little about being a fifteen-year-old girl. I was one once, you know, even if it was a while back.'

I nudged his arm playfully. He smiled but it didn't quite reach his eyes.

'Thank you, Gemma, for giving her this chance. For giving *us* this chance. I just hope it works out. I don't know what either of us will do if we have another failure in our lives.'

'Ah well, you're talking to someone who knows quite a bit about failure. But that's a story for another day. We'd better make sure between us that it's not then, shouldn't we?' I stopped, a question forming itself in my mind. 'How did you know where she was by the way?'

'Oh, I was chatting to Clem on the phone and told him she wasn't at home. He said he'd seen a young girl walk past. When I described her, he said it sounded like her so I thought I'd pop by and check. Just lucky I guess.'

'Or meant to be maybe. So, what's on the menu tonight in Chez Adams, then? Cheesy beans on toast?'

'Ha. I don't think we've got any beans or bread or even cheese for that matter. I meant to go to the supermarket while I was up in Exeter earlier, after my meeting, but totally forgot. I'll pop to the mini-market on my way home and try to dredge up some enthusiasm for cooking. After a full day's work that's not easy.'

'I'm sure we can do better than that.'

I wandered off to the kitchen and came back with a bag full of food containers. Helping others was something that made me feel good and if you couldn't help your friends, then who could you help?

'There must be something in that lot that you'll both eat. There's pasta sauce, stew, stroganoff, mashed potato and other stuff. There's a label on each saying what it is and what to do with it.'

Jude stared at me, seemingly taking a moment or two to gather his thoughts. He frowned.

'Who are you? Some kind of angel or something? I can't take this.'

'You can and you will. I insist. I can't have one of my workers not eating properly now, can I?' I tilted my head and grinned. 'Or one of my friends.'

'How can I thank you? This is so lovely.' His voice wavered and his eyes filled with tears. 'I don't think anyone has ever done anything this nice for me ever before.'

'Hey, it must be really tough doing what you do for a job. Doing that *and* having to be a solo parent when you finish work must really take it out of you. You must be shattered. Let me help. It's helping me as much as it is you anyway. I was going to put these in the freezer anyway. There's no way I could eat that lot on my own.'

He reached across and, most unexpectedly, kissed my cheek.

'You, lady, are a very lovely human being. Thank you again. I promise, I'll repay you in some way.'

He picked up the bag of food and left, waving as he walked past the window. His shoulders seemed to have lifted. He was clearly a nice man trying to do the best for his family and it warmed my heart to know that I'd been able to help in some small way.

I touched my face where he had kissed me. If, and it was a huge *if*, I was looking for someone to share my life with again at some point, I had always thought that someone who already had children would be a big no for me. That I would be jealous of the fact that their child would always come first and that I'd always feel like I was second best. But maybe it wouldn't be such a bad option after all.

Irrelevant anyway as I wasn't looking to fill a man-shaped space in my life. But when I thought about Occy, and how she looked like she needed some love in her life, maybe her working with me here at the café could be a step towards filling a child-shaped hole instead. I felt like I needed her as much as she needed me and hoped that our trial would work out. I would do everything in my power to make it work for both our sakes.

As I reached to turn the open sign to closed, I realised once again what my darling mum often said, that not only did she do what she did for the community and for her friends but also because it filled her own heart with joy too. That sometimes *filling* a hole made you *feel* whole. Bless her.

'God I'm stuffed!' I rubbed my belly with pure satisfaction. 'That chicken tikka masala was the best I've ever had. And that keema naan.' I smacked my lips together. 'Bloody delicious. Thanks, love. Fancy a glass of wine now?'

A bottle of Merlot sat on the coffee table.

'Oh, I'll have mine in a bit,' Lucy said. 'Honestly. There isn't room in my belly for anything else at all right now. I can't move. I don't think I can ever eat anything ever again.'

She burped loudly.

'God sorry!'

She reached over and broke off a little bit of the leftover poppadom, shoved it in her mouth and grinned at me. 'Well, apart from that. I think that burp created a tiny bit more room.'

We laughed. As kids, we were only ever allowed to have pudding if we'd eaten our dinner and Mum always said that if we couldn't eat all our dinner, we couldn't possibly have room for anything else, but Lucy always argued the fact that there was always room for a little something else, especially once she'd had a burp.

Lucy swung her feet round and perched them on my lap. I knew that was her way of asking me to rub her feet. She'd done this since she was a little girl and I always pandered to her wishes, which I did now. She closed her eyes and sighed, clearly loving her foot massage.

'Tonight has been lovely, Gem. I've loved having you to myself. It's so rare that we do it these days. I love Mere but I needed this. Just you and me.' I noticed her glance my way shiftily. 'In fact, there's something important that I need to talk to you about.'

'Ah, so that's what getting me alone is all about is it, you crafty old mare?'

She peered at me and suddenly I felt a shift in the atmosphere. I shivered.

'What's going on, Luce?'

She sat up straight and drew in a big breath.

'Gemma, I—'

'Oh my God, you're ill, aren't you? I knew you were lying when you weren't drinking last weekend. Oh, Luce, what is it?' Random thoughts were swirling through my head and I could only pick up on certain words she was saying.

'Doctors... Tests... Hospital... Scans... Results...'

I was trying to make sense of what she was saying but they were just like random words being thrown at me.

She reached for both of my hands and held them in hers. Somehow, I managed to hear the next two words perfectly clearly – I thought I'd never be able to unhear them.

'I'm pregnant.'

She bit the side of her cheek and stared at me.

It felt as if someone had just punched me in the stomach. Shit! Pregnant. Of all the things she was about to tell me, I didn't expect that. Pregnant.

I realised she was studying me closely, waiting for me to say something.

Shit! Shit! Shit! My hesitation must have spoken a thousand words.

Pulling myself back to the present, I reached across and took her in my arms. Totally sideswiped.

Speak Gemma. Say something. You need to react here and you need to react well.

'Oh, Luce. Congratulations. God, I'm so sorry. You took me totally by surprise. I was expecting you to tell me you were dying or something. Oh my God, Lucy. What amazing news. How wonderful.'

While I knew that the right words were all coming tumbling out of my mouth, I knew that they were sounding flatter than they probably should have. I held her at arm's length and looked into her eyes, summoning up every little bit of enthusiasm I could.

'Lucy, I'm delighted for you. I really am.' I painted on a smile that I really wasn't feeling from the inside but I knew that this would have been just as hard for her as it was for me. 'Honestly. Wow. I'm going to be an aunty. How exciting is that?'

She laughed and snorted at the same time, probably in relief that she'd finally broken the news to me.

'And you're going to be a mum. A mum. God, Lucy, you nearly gave me a heart attack. I honestly thought you were going to give me some bad news.' I pulled her to my chest again. 'I'm so glad you are not dying.'

'Me too! Are you sure you are OK with this? There was a little bit of me that was dreading having to tell you.'

She looked so worried and I felt so incredibly guilty for the fact that telling me probably the most important news she would ever have had made her feel this way. I knew how much my next words would mean to her.

'Lucy. You are my sister and I adore you. You are going to be the most wonderful mother to my nephew or niece. And James will be a wonderful father. I am honestly over the moon.'

I pulled her to my chest once more and felt a tear roll down my cheek. She held me away from her and put her hand to my face and wiped it away with her thumb.

'You are going to be the best aunty that anyone has ever had.'

'Damn right I will.'

'Mum would be so proud of us both right now Gem. God, I wish she were here to share this with us.'

We fell towards each other again and clung on for dear life as we both cried with joy, mixed with a little bit of sadness on my part. My sister was going to become a mother and I was going to become an aunty, and it truly was wonderful. A gift.

But we also sobbed for the grandmother that our mother would never be. All that babysitting and hand holding that she'd never get to do. We also sobbed for the mother that I would never become and the future that I would never have with my own child.

My happiness was tinged with sorrow for all those things but the news that she had just given me had broken my poor already fractured heart just a tiny little bit more.

10

After a restless night's sleep where Jude invaded my dreams and told me he and his wife were having a baby, I woke to a soggy pillow wet with tears.

I left the B & B not long after Lucy had broken the news. I'd said that I was fine and just tired, but she's my sister and she knows me better than anyone else has ever done; my painted-on smile betraying the secrets of my soul.

My darling Lucy must have been in such a quandary knowing that she had to share her news with me, being so ecstatically happy about something that would make me so sad. The last thing she would ever want to do is to make me unhappy.

After checking that it wasn't too early, I fired off a text to tell her that I was still revelling in their fantastic news. I really was but it was bloody hard knowing that she was going to have all the things that I had always dreamed of. The last person I ever thought I'd be jealous of was my own sister.

Facebook friends' posts around new school term time were something I avoided like the plague. All those proud mothers posting photos of their darlings in their uniforms. I tried my hardest not to be jealous and to just accept what was my lot in life. I wasn't the only person in the world not to be able to have children and I wouldn't be the last. The only person who would miss out was me and avoiding people wasn't really the way to be. However, it was the only way I could accept things right now.

My counsellor said that it was still early days. It had only been two years since we'd had the news that Mum had weeks left to live. Obviously devastated, it was a double blow when Lucas left a month later. And it was only another month after that that I'd bumped into an old friend of his and he'd told me that Lucas's new girlfriend was pregnant. A further massive blow at a time when I was already fragile. For three days, bed was the only place I found solace and Lucy had been the one who'd made me face reality again, telling me kindly that I had to deal with this. I felt awful because she also needed me as we were both grieving for Mum, but she'd seen her way through it and had booked me an appointment with Emma, my counsellor, and it was with her help that I started to accept the enormity of what had happened.

She told me that I had to somehow find a way to forgive Lucas for his actions. If I didn't, the only person who would suffer was me. And I needed to be free from that pain so that I could concentrate on grieving. Losing a parent is colossal. For thirty-seven years Mum was in my life and then she was gone. Literally life changing. Mum taught me everything I knew, apart from the one thing I needed: how to live without her.

So, I wrote Lucas a letter, telling him how I felt and didn't hold back on anything. Told him exactly how I felt about not being able to have children.

In my next session with Emma, she asked if I was ready to show her the letter. I shook my head. I really wasn't. She smiled and told me that it was time to let go. Time to move forward. She held my hand as we threw the letter into the fire. I watched the flames lick the corners of the paper and take a stronger hold, turning my words into ash.

Now, I could concentrate on the loss of my darling mother, be there for my sister and together learn to be kind to ourselves, accepting something that we couldn't change.

That night, my sleep was sounder than it had been in weeks and it really felt like a turning point. And since then, I'd become more accepting of the situation, even though there were certain things I avoided like driving past the primary school when the children would be coming out. Mother's Day was particularly hard. Not only was I sad because my own mum wasn't around to spend the day with, but my regrets about never being a mum myself seemed stronger than ever.

But as I sat in bed the morning after hearing of Lucy's news, I was reminded of my strength back then. I realised I could sit here pondering how crap it all felt, while gazing into the horizon, or I could get my arse into gear and get up. There were so many things and people that I was lucky to have in my life and I could be and was thankful for. So, in that moment, I made a pact with myself to start each day with a grateful heart. That day, I was grateful for a warm, cosy home in a stunning location with a view most people would envy. For a sister who was my best friend, who loved me and cared deeply for me. And finally, because I was going to be an aunty, and that was a wonderful thing to be. I really was going to be a bloody fabulous aunty; I'd make damn sure of it.

Admiring the spectacular view from my bed, while good for my soul, wouldn't get the café set up for the day so I jumped in the shower and washed away all the sadness and the negativity I'd been feeling. When I wrapped myself in the fluffy bath sheet, I felt a real shift in mindset. I had missed my inspirational walk on the beach this morning and thought I must make the effort to get down there at some point during the day.

In the distance, I could see Jude strolling across the beach and watched him walk towards the café. I stepped back into the shadows as he turned to look up at my window. I didn't want him to think I was looking out for him. Which obviously I wasn't. I just happened to be looking out at the time that he was there. The last thing I needed was the complication of having a crush on someone. Oh God. Did I have a crush on him? Where did that thought come from?

Maybe it was because he was the nicest looking single man I'd seen for ages. Everyone knew everyone around here, so someone new was interesting. And yes, we were both single, and I'd dreamed about him, but it didn't mean a thing. Did it?

I quickly got dressed, tied my pinny round my waist and went down to the café. I walked towards the entrance and put the door on the latch. I turned the closed sign round to show that I was open for business and headed back to the counter. I'd literally just reached it when the bell over the door tinkled and, lo and behold, there he was. My heart skipped a tiny beat.

I tried to act normal but my words tumbled out.

'Morning Jude. Can't stay away, eh?'

Oh lord. Why did I say that?

'Er hi. I just thought I'd grab a cuppa while I saw you opening up. Not too early, am I?'

'No 'course not. Takeaway or sitting in?'

'Depends if you can join me. Wondered if you had a minute for a chat about Occy.'

'Oh. Well, I can't really join you right now. I'm getting prepped, but if you want to sit at the counter, I can chat to you while there's no one here if that's of use.'

He perched easily on one of the stools. So much easier when

you're six foot tall, unlike little old short-arsed me who really made a meal of getting up on one. They weren't made for people who were only five foot tall.

'How did the trial go then? Occy hasn't said a lot to be honest.'

'OK. More than OK actually. She was good. I've asked her to come back and do a couple of hours this afternoon. God, I hope that's OK. Maybe I should have asked you first.'

'It's fine. I have a couple of work calls to do later. Maybe I could swing round and pick her up when she's finished. At least she won't be sat at home on her own while I'm out. On her phone.'

'Ha, she absolutely won't be doing that, I can assure you. It'll be much busier later, so she'll see what real work is and whether she really likes it. The other time was dead quiet and not a true picture of what working here is really like. Although it was nice to see her get her schoolbooks out at the end of the shift and do some revising.'

His eyes widened.

'Did she? She never mentioned it.'

'Maybe she doesn't have to share everything with you. She's probably at that age where she just wants to get on with stuff in her own way, you know? I went through a stage of being quite rebellious. If I decided to do something then I would, but if my mum asked me to do the exact same thing, I'd throw a proper hissy fit and totally refuse. I think it's about making decisions for ourselves. It wasn't until years later that Mum admitted she found it hard to accept a child, who she had to make all the decisions for, becoming a young adult who wanted to make – and was perfectly capable of making – their own choices.'

'I never thought of it like that. She says I'm on at her all the time telling her what to do.'

'Well, I don't want to tell you what you should and shouldn't be doing with her. I'm not a parent.' I swallowed and felt a lump forming in my throat and coughed to clear it.

'You're not, but I do appreciate a second opinion. I just feel like I'm a really crap dad. Whatever I do, all I seem to do is upset her. I can't win.'

'Maybe just back off a bit and see if it makes a difference. Try it for a few days. You've got nothing to lose and everything to gain. And if it doesn't work out, you'll be in exactly the same place as you are right now.'

'Thanks, Gemma. You are wise, you know.'

'Ah, well, I had an excellent teacher.' I looked across at a photo of me and Mum on the wall.

'Your mum?'

'Yep. Bless her.'

'You must miss her.'

'More than you'll ever know. And right now especially.'

That slipped out without me meaning it to.

'Gemma, is everything OK? You don't seem like yourself today. You look, I don't know. Kind of sad maybe? Something on your mind? Can I help? A problem shared is a problem halved.'

He reached across the counter and grabbed my hand. I looked up into his big brown eyes and seconds turned into what felt like at least a minute, or even two. The doorbell tinkled again and a party of four women came in, laughing and chatting loudly. I was literally saved by the bell.

I pulled my hand away, and touched my neck, which I could feel getting warmer.

'Maybe another time. I must get to work now.' I turned to the women, hopefully hiding my blushing cheeks. 'Morning, folks. If you'd like to grab a table, there are menus out and I'll be over to take your order in a jiffy.'

'I'll leave you to it then. Thanks, Gemma. I hope this afternoon goes well.'

'See you later, Jude.'

He saluted, grinned and walked towards the door.

As I headed over to the table of four, who were sitting in the window overlooking the bay, I was watching Jude's every move. I sighed before turning to the women. 'Now what can I get you?'

'Him for starters. What a dish.'

11

'Blimey! Is that what a Saturday afternoon is normally like?'

'I'm afraid so. Too much like hard work for you?'

'Absolutely not.' Occy puffed her chest out. 'I'm not afraid of anything, me.'

'Glad to hear it because if you can continue to work like that, under that sort of pressure, and if it's OK with your dad...' a big grin broke out across Occy's pretty face '... then I would love to have you work with me. Oomph!'

I felt like I'd been tackled by a rugby player as Occy flung herself at me. As she clung on, I breathed in a heady mix of cheap make-up, fake tan and flowery deodorant. As I held her, it occurred to me that she might not have embraced another woman for a long time. I came from a really huggy family and Mum always hugged me and Lucy and told us she loved us, even when she said we were being right royal pains in the bum.

We were mid-hug when the doorbell went and Jude walked in.

'I take it you got the job then?'

'Not yet,' I said, breaking away from Occy. 'There's one condition.'

They both looked at me, waiting for my next words.

'It's down to you, Jude. If you allow Occy to work here, then I'd love to have her on the team. She's done a cracking job today and worked hard. She's even made friends with Betty.'

He tilted his head to one side. 'Betty?'

'Yes, Betty the Beast. Our coffee machine.'

'Well, maybe she needs to make her favourite dad a drink then I'll give my verdict.'

She laughed. 'If my favourite dad was here, then I would.'

He held his hand to his heart.

'You wound me, child. Good job I love you. You making me that drink or not?'

'Great idea,' I said, untying my pinny. 'Occy, me and your dad are going to sit at that corner table. Pretend we're just two normal customers and come and take our order.'

'Gemma, you are not serious?'

'I am. Come on. Show your dad what you've been doing all afternoon.'

Jude and I took a seat in the far window. Occy followed us over.

'Good afternoon, what can I get you?' She smiled and a little giggle escaped from her lips.

'May I?' His eyes searched mine, questioning whether it was OK for him to take the lead.

I nodded back at Jude.

'Two of your finest hot chocolates please, young lady.'

'Certainly, sir. Would you like whippy cream with that?'

'Yes please.'

'Marshmallows?'

'Please.'

'Chocolate sprinkles, sir?' That giggle again. She was enjoying this role-playing. Still a child at heart even though in a teenager's body.

'Gosh all the questions. Yes please. The full works.'

'I'll be right back.' Her wide eyes questioned me and I nodded my approval.

Five minutes later, she returned slowly, very carefully balancing the drinks on a tray, concentrating hard and not spilling a drop. After placing the tray on the table, she breathed out a sigh of relief and handed us each a mug. She looked over at her father who was keeping a very serious face as he thanked her.

She took the empty tray and headed back to the counter, where she placed the tray down the side, and leaned on the counter with her elbows, looking towards us.

Her dad picked up the mug and took a sip.

Too impatient, Occy was suddenly back at his side.

'Dad? Just tell me, right.'

'You're a bloody marvel, Octavia Adams. This is the lushest hot chocolate I've ever had.' This time it was my eyes that widened. He coughed. 'Equally as good as the one Gemma made me after I'd been for a swim the other day.'

We all laughed.

'Can I work here, Dad? Please? Please? I won't ever ask you for anything again. Ever. I'll even stop bugging you to get a dog.'

'That'll be the day. Can I have that in writing?'

'If you say yes, then I'll go and get a piece of paper and a pen.'

They locked eyes and finally he nodded. She punched the air, gave me a high five and flung her arms around him.

'I'm made up. Thanks, Dad. You're the best. And thank you,

Gemma, too. I'm going to be the best waitress you ever had. Watch me. I'm going to go and tell Lizzie that I got the job.'

'Lizzie?'

'Yep, my friend from school. I told her I'd meet her on the beach after my shift.'

Jude raised his eyebrows.

'OK, don't be long, as I'm going to drink this and then head home. I'll be doing tea as soon as I get back. Well, warming up what Gemma gave us the other day...'

'OK, I won't.' As Occy reached the door, she swung back round. 'Oh, and Dad, if you ever call me Octavia again, I *seriously* will leave home.'

Jude spat his hot chocolate all over the table at that.

Occy slammed the door behind her and we both winced at the noise. I really would have to teach her how to open and close a door without it nearly coming off its hinges.

'Thanks, Gemma,' Jude said, his eyes full of warmth. 'Honestly, I don't think I've seen her that happy for years. She certainly hasn't hugged me like that in years. I honestly thought I'd seen the last of her hugs. Funny when you have kids, you never know when the last time will be. The last time they hold your hand, the last time they kiss you goodnight. It just kind of stops with no warning. If only you knew...'

He drifted off and then looked up at me, noticing that I couldn't actually speak.

I knew that my smile didn't quite reach my eyes. How I'd love to have had that hand holding and the kisses goodnight in the first place.

'Gemma, are you OK? You haven't seemed yourself today.'

'I'll be fine. Not something I want to talk about right now if you don't mind but maybe at some time I will. Thank you for noticing though.' I stirred my spoon in my drink and smiled for real this time. 'See? You're not all bad, Jude Adams.'

'I'll take that. Right now, my daughter thinks I'm great and that's a big win. Your food, by the way... It's lush! I might have to put in a regular order with you. It's made life so much easier this week. No one ever told me that being an adult meant that you've got to think about what you're going to have for tea every night for the rest of your life. It's so repetitive. Most of being an adult is repetitive when I think about it. I'm sure life should be more exciting than this. I felt envy at work today because someone said they were taking their wife to the cinema next weekend. How sad is that?'

'Not sad at all! The hard part about being on your own is not having someone to go and do things like that with. I can't remember the last time I went and saw a film.'

'Oh, I can. We argued about it for days, because I wanted to go and see an action film and Occy wanted to watch some girly romance thing – my worst nightmare. We rowed so much at the cinema that we got back in the car and came home instead. She was really upset that she didn't get to see the film she'd been wanting to see for ages.'

'That's funny. I blooming love a girly romance film but then again I don't mind an action movie either. You can't really go on your own though, can you? I'd feel like a proper saddo if I did. I'm sure no one would really care but I would feel a bit daft.'

'Yeah, I don't think I'd go on my own either.'

'Actually, I might have just had an idea. I wonder if Occy might like to go and see something with me. She could come with me and Mere and maybe Lucy too. In fact, she could ask her friend Lizzie and we could make a girls' night out of it.'

'She'd probably love it.'

The more I thought about it, the more of a great night this could turn out to be.

'She might be fed up with me by then though, now she'll be working for me.'

'I doubt it very much. She hasn't stopped talking about you for days. Gemma this, Gemma that. You've made a real impression on her, I have to say.'

'That's nice to hear but I'm sure it will soon wear off. She probably won't be so complimentary after she's worked with me for a few more weeks and I've been bossing her around.'

'Well, she hates me bossing her around so it'll be interesting to see.'

'But you're her dad. You're the closest person she has. The person who she can truly be herself with. There's always going to be that sense of being a little bit on her best behaviour that comes out with other people.'

'It's so hard to get it right, Gemma.' He sighed and looked out to the sea.

'I can only imagine. My mum said I was a right horror to her at times. She just kept on telling me how much she loved me even if I was being vile to her. Teenage girl hormones can be monsters, you know. It's like there's an alien in your body that you can't control. And there's even more pressure on them than ever these days to look good too. Even at her age. Especially at her age.'

'I reckon I'd have liked your mum.'

'She was amazing. But so are you. You've brought up a fifteen-year-old. How cool is that? God, I wish I could say that about myself.'

'Did you never want children, Gemma?'

I knew I couldn't go there, not now. Jude and I didn't know each other well enough for me to share too much of my personal history with him and especially not when a lot of the feelings I had were at the forefront of my mind, Lucy's news still making me feel quite raw.

'You know she's been great today,' I said, changing the subject. 'The customers love her. She's like a breath of fresh air and hasn't stopped smiling.'

'My daughter? Are you sure we're talking about the same person here? The same moody madam I live with?'

I laughed. 'Maybe we've just found something that she really wants to do. This could be a turning point.'

'I really do hope so. It would be amazing. I've been so worried about uprooting her and moving her to a new place. But she's been like a different kid this last week. Even seems happy to be getting up and going to school. Working with you has been something to look forward to and it's done her the world of good.' He reached out across the table and covered my hand with his. 'Thank you for everything you've done for her.'

Those big brown beautiful eyes bore into mine but, a little embarrassed, I pulled my hand away. 'It's great, I think I need her as much as she needs me.' Then, my voice lowered, I said, 'Maybe we found each other when we needed to.' I stood and abruptly collected the mugs before I could say any more. 'I should... you know, get on.'

'Yes, I'll make a move. Thanks again, Gemma.'

He smiled and held my gaze again, and I felt a fluttery feeling in my belly.

'Bye, Jude.'

He turned to the door but when halfway through, turned back.

'And if you ever fancy seeing one of those action films one night, maybe we could... you know... go together.'

Jeez, I wasn't expecting that. He was asking me out. Shit!

'Oh! I... Er... Thanks but no thanks. I'm really not looking for anything like that right now. I'm just happy on my own.'

The words, 'even if you do make my tummy tingle a lot', remained unspoken.

'Oh God! I don't mean like that. As mates. I can't be doing with all that dating malarkey either, thanks very much. Not that you're not...' He stumbled over his words. 'I mean, you're...' He waved his hands at me. 'You're perfectly lovely... In fact, better than lovely. You're... I mean... it's just not what I'm looking for. However, if you fancy a night out with someone else who never gets much chance to go out, then maybe we could go together. Not a date. Definitely not. Like a *not-date*. No pressure though.' He tapped his hand on the door handle, evidently feeling as embarrassed as I did. 'I'm going to go now before I make even more of a tit of myself. Night, Gemma.'

And then he was gone and I was left staring at the door.

Better than lovely, he said. I'll take that. And if it was not a real date, then maybe a *not-date* would be a nice way to spend an evening. And those tummy tingles, that could just be wind, you know.

12

The beauty of a sunrise never ceased to amaze me and bring joy to my heart and today, as the rising sun cast a rosy hue over Driftwood Bay, was no exception. Mother nature at her best. Another brand-new day bringing with it hopes, dreams and in my case a to-do list as long as a fireman's pole.

Note to self: stop thinking about firemen.

The flurry of early morning activity from dog walkers and those out for a run made me smile, grateful that I'd been able to afford to have the café's bifold doors put in place last summer to make the most of the stunning view.

Meredith waved as she passed by with Alice. Returning the gesture, I wondered when Lucy would be sharing her news with others. Bottling up secrets and emotions wasn't good for me. Maybe my session with my counsellor later would help. At least with her, I could tell her exactly how I felt with no judgement and no bias.

Yesterday had been a busy day again so Monday mornings were always nice as time was more on my side and allowed me to sit and drink my morning coffee in peace and quiet, pondering the world, gathering my thoughts.

Making a massive batch of food was my morning priority, and then onto Truro with the car loaded full of food. Not even Lucy knew what my Monday afternoons held. It was my little secret for now, the only thing in my life just for me. Something that left me feeling like I'd done my little bit of kindness for the world.

Lucy was always curious as to where I go but I passed it off as meeting up with friends from where I used to live, shopping out of the village or an extra therapy session, and luckily, she didn't press any further. I didn't know if I'd ever be able to share it with her – some secrets were better left unsaid. It was also good to be away from the noise of the work going on, especially today as I knew Clem was going to be knocking down walls. Being out of the way would be good and as long as he could contact me by phone, which he could for most of the day, maybe some time away from the bay would do me good as well.

I checked my emails and found one from someone called Rachel asking about the job. She'd seen the ad I'd placed in a local Facebook group. I gave her a quick call and she said that she was going to be moving quite close to Driftwood Bay soon and wondered if the job might still be available in a couple of months' time. When she talked about her past roles and her experience, she sounded perfect and, for the right person, I could definitely hang on. Sometimes more damage could be done by having the wrong person so I explained that I was having some work done and was looking for some permanent help nearer the launch date. We agreed that she'd give me a call back, when she knew she'd be able to get over to book some time in with me. She seemed nice. Quiet but polite and personable. Hopefully she'd be back in touch. I'd learned not to put too much of my hopes in other people and had to trust that it would work out if it was meant to be.

I wouldn't stop looking for other suitable people just in case. I already had some part-time help from Pat and with Occy helping too I reckoned that I could manage for the time being, even if it was going to keep me busy. It wasn't like I had much else to do either.

Maybe being busy was just what I needed while I got my head around the news. I'd put off speaking to Lucy for the last couple of days, sticking to texts which felt safer. I could send emojis and effusive wording that I wasn't really feeling in person. I did feel bad because this was the first time for literally years we'd been a little distant, and this was such a huge thing for Lucy. It must have been such a traumatic few weeks for her, finding out her amazing news and being happier than she'd probably been in her life, contrasted so much with the knowledge that it could upset me beyond words. It must have been so hard for her to cope with. For them both in fact. I loved James like a brother, and I knew he'd never want to hurt me. I was sure she and James had spent ages discussing it and working out when and how to tell me.

She had said to me that while, in a way, I was the first person she wanted to tell, at the same time she didn't want to tell me until they knew it was a safer time for them. God forbid anything should have happened early in the pregnancy and it would have all been for nothing – although I was her sister and would have wanted to help her through it, had anything gone wrong.

After a day or two of lying low, and nursing my bruised pride, ego and any other part of me that was feeling particularly battered, I decided to make the effort to pull up my big girl pants and be the support that she needed me to be. It was sad really that she felt the need to treat me differently, although maybe my behaviour now was exactly the reason why she did.

As my big sister, she would only ever want to protect me, I knew, and she'd always been the one who would save me from hurt, especially after Mum died, when she'd almost taken on the maternal role in the family. She saw it as her job to make sure that I was OK and that's why she in particular was my rock when my life fell apart. It was just a shame that the reason my life fell apart was the very thing that was being brought into our relationship right now.

I hoped that time was all I needed, and that when the news had sunk in, and I wasn't feeling quite so tender about everything, I could, should and would be properly enthusiastic. It needed nipping in the bud really and dealing with quickly before it escalated and became something that destroyed our relationship.

After all, I was going to be an aunty. And that was exciting. We were having a new family member and there was a tiny little bit of that realisation now seeping through to my brain. I needed to get over myself and be Lucy's sister and her baby's aunty, to the best of my abilities. I couldn't let this be the thing that came between us.

I hoped that in the next day or so, we could sit and talk, maybe both tell each other how we felt. Put her mind at rest that she shouldn't have to hide away her pregnancy for my sake, and risk upsetting me. It was raking up demons from my past, but what I needed to do was slay those dragons once and for all. Or if not quite that dramatically, at least lock them away in a cage for a while.

Crikey! I hoped Emma was prepared for my session today. She might be thankful when it was over. I was sure by the time I was walking out of her room at the end of the session, she'd be pouring herself a bloody great big glass of wine. I was damn sure that's what I would be doing when I got home.

13

The cinema trip came about much quicker than I thought it might. The following evening Occy burst through the door in her normal whirlwind style and told me that her dad had told her about our conversation. She asked if I'd go and see the latest romcom with her while her dad went to watch an action movie that was on at the same time. She'd asked her friends at school and none of them could make it and she didn't want to go on her own.

I wasn't entirely sure that she particularly wanted to see it with me to be honest. I think she just hadn't got anyone else to go with. But the film she wanted to see was only on for one week and, when I looked it up, it did look like something I'd enjoy. So, after much pleading from her, I agreed. It would be a jaunt because the cinema was in Truro, but the journey turned out to be quite enjoyable with Jude driving and Occy hardly taking a breath and chatting all the way there.

When we arrived, while Occy nipped to the ladies, Jude said that he hadn't seen her as fired up as this for years and he was delighted that she appeared to have turned a corner. He believed that getting the job in the café had really helped her, even though she'd only just started.

He'd offered to buy the tickets for us all as a treat but when he tried to book the action film, we discovered there was a problem with the screening, so it wasn't showing. Occy and I found it hilarious that her dad was going to have to sit through the romcom after all.

When it was over, Occy and I were saying how much we enjoyed it, and we both fell about laughing at Jude giving his critical analysis of the film, saying how predictable the plot had been, how much of a doormat the main male character was and that he could have written something better himself. He went on to describe his idea of a plot which had way more action in it and much more blood and gore. Occy and I tried to explain to him that it was all those things he was complaining about that make people love romcoms. It's the fact that you know it's going to be a happy-ever-after ending and that it's all about the journey.

'It just confirms that I don't know the opposite sex at all. I thought women wanted big strong men and not weak "wetters".'

I proper laughed out loud at that, especially when Occy snorted in hysteria, which only made me laugh all the more.

Once the initial flurry of people had gone, we headed to the door and the usherette smiled at us broadly.

'Oh, it is lovely to see that people still have a family night out. And that teenagers want to go out with their parents. My son wouldn't be seen dead on a night out with me and his father. You're so lucky. We don't get many happy families in here these days.'

We didn't have the heart to correct her, however her comments made us laugh even more. I supposed we must have looked that way. Funny what the eye sees without knowing the story behind it.

I offered to treat us all to a McDonald's on the way home. It had been a while since I'd had one but as we were on a retail park and we were all starving it seemed like a good option.

'Hey, Gemma.' I swung round towards the person who was coming in the door as we were heading out.

Shit! I hadn't even considered that we might bump into someone I knew. Let alone Mike of all people. Mike was someone from my Truro world, which was so disconnected from Driftwood Bay and my life there that I couldn't get away quickly enough. And that's the way I wanted it to stay for as long as I could keep it under wraps. I'm sure he must have thought me incredibly rude when I turned quickly and scooted under his arm and out of the door.

'Oh, er, Mike. Hi. I'm so sorry but we can't stop. Lovely to see you.'

I scurried back to the car, making furtive glances over my shoulder to make sure Mike wasn't following me. I couldn't bear it if he referred to our Truro project and was clearly fretting about it so much that it made Jude ask if all was OK.

A split-second decision made me cover up with a whopping lie.

'Yes of course. Just an old school friend who's a bit weird. Shall we go?' I replied.

* * *

Driving back into Driftwood Bay always lifted my heart, and as we approached the road down into the bay, I had to stifle my normal groan of pleasure when I saw the twinkling street lights and the glimmering sea. Coming home always felt perfect, that feeling that everything in my world was going to be OK. Jude had offered to drive me to my door but as it would have meant him going round the one-way system, I told him that I'd walk from their place.

Jude was renting a property at the top of the village and he invited me in for a cuppa. As I always loved a nosy round people's houses, and I'd had such a lovely evening in their company, I took him up on his offer. Occy said she was heading off to bed and gave me a peck on the cheek.

While Jude was in the kitchen, I cast my eyes around the lounge. The walls were white and bare, the harsh lighting showed up the dark grey furniture and the room felt cold and unloved. Masculine even, with a distinct lack of cushions, rugs, or colour. There was no sign of any personality; no pictures hanging on the walls or trinkets around except for a framed photo of a woman holding a young child. I took a step towards it.

'That's Occy's mother if you hadn't guessed.'

I hadn't heard him come into the room.

I wrinkled my nose, thankful that I hadn't quite been caught peering too closely at something so very personal.

'Sorry, you must think me terribly nosy.' I moved away from the mantelpiece where it clearly took pride of place.

'Don't worry. It's hard not to see when it's centre stage. Not where I would have put it. In fact, I wouldn't have it up here at all.' He lowered his voice as he moved towards the door and pushed it to. 'Occy doesn't know the half of it where her mother is concerned. Sometimes not knowing the truth is easier than knowing.' Those words cut deep within me.

'You must find that hard.'

'She doesn't need to know; no good could come of it. It's hard sometimes to bite my tongue when she talks about her; she's always put her on a bit of a pedestal. She thinks she must have gone on to bigger and better things – if it meant leaving her family behind. Although now she's a little older I think it's more a case of her realising things for herself, working out that her mother isn't Beyoncé or Lady Gaga. I've also learned the hard way that it's OK for her to say things about her mother but no one else can. Not even me. But to be honest, Gemma, she doesn't need me to keep telling her that her mother is a grown-up and can make her own decisions. She could have changed things around for the sake of her daughter but she chose not to. But it's not my place to say. It's really not helpful.'

'I know you don't think it, but you are a good dad you know, Jude.'

'Ah thank you. But you are seeing a different Occy to the one I've seen for the last year or so. So very different and long may it continue. You're clearly having an excellent influence on her. Thanks for all you're doing for her. I think she's missed having a female influence in her life, so I'm really thankful.'

'It's no problem. She's a good kid at heart. I enjoy having her around.' I hesitated before opening up about the fact that I couldn't have children. For some reason it felt natural to tell him.

'I'm sorry to hear that, Gemma.'

His response was perfect and genuine.

I stayed for another drink and we chatted amiably. It was nice to sit and talk to someone new. Jude was interesting as well as entertaining and stories of his antics in the fire brigade made me laugh. He asked lots of questions and showed interest in me as a person too. The conversation flowed freely, which I knew was something I shouldn't take for granted, especially after hearing so many stories from Meredith, who made me howl with tales of her dating escapades. She'd told me how most of the first dates were with people who just wanted to talk about themselves. The thought of having to go through all that meeting new people absolutely horrified me. An old school friend of mine said she went on the dating apps because she'd got nothing better to do, but to be honest, my problem in life was that I didn't have *enough* hours in the day, so I didn't have any time to waste. In fact, I struggled to understand why some people did. That was why this 'not-date' had been a huge success for me. Getting to know a male friend with absolutely no pressure for it to be anything else was just what I needed.

'Thanks for the cuppa and the chat,' I said. 'And the night out. I've really enjoyed it. I'll make a move though now. I'm not a great sleeper so will be up with the birds.'

'It's been lovely,' Jude replied with a smile. 'Thank you for coming with us. Let me grab my coat and I'll walk you back.'

'No, you're fine.'

'I insist. I'm not going to let you walk home in the dark.'

'I'm a big girl, Jude, I'll be fine. This is Driftwood Bay after all.'

I always enjoyed walking around the harbour at night. Sometimes when I couldn't sleep, I'd pop my coat on over my pyjamas and wander around in the dark, just lapping up its beauty. I'd never felt as safe anywhere else in the world as I did in Driftwood Bay.

'I don't care. I'm a big burly fireman and I will ensure that you are delivered safely to your door. It's against my principles for a woman to walk home alone. I know you women are all about women's rights but I'm old-fashioned and insist.'

'Thank you. I'm all up for equality.' I grabbed my coat. 'But only when it suits.'

He laughed and held the door open for me.

It was a crisp, cool, dry autumn evening with a full moon illuminating the bay. We could have strolled back down the hill to the café, which would have only taken a few minutes, but we walked via the harbour instead, our footsteps and the hypnotic jingling of metal on metal on the boats the only sounds to be heard.

We stopped at the side door to the café and Jude looked around.

'Bloody love it here. I reckon you've got one of the best spots in the harbour.'

'Hard not to agree. It's lush, isn't it?' I looked around, taking in the beauty of the spot. My safe haven. 'Thanks again for tonight, Jude.'

'My pleasure. It's lovely to go out with someone when you both know you're just friends. Much to the disappointment of my mates at the station, I'm not looking for someone in my life at the moment. Having Occy is taking up all my time and energy and it's important to me to focus on her. Maybe when she's got through these last couple of years at school and we know what her next few years hold, it'll be a different matter.'

'Same here. It's been nice knowing that this is just a night out as mates. Not going through all that wondering about whether someone likes you in that way, or whether you've impressed them.'

'Well, you always impress me, but not in that way – if you don't mind me saying.'

We both laughed and shuffled round a little awkwardly.

'So, what do we do now then?' he asked. 'Shake hands? Hug? Fist bump? High five? What would happen now in one of your smushy romcoms, Gem?'

He raised an eyebrow before reaching across and gave me a gentle peck on the cheek.

I nodded my approval.

'OK, that'll do it. And at least you know I wasn't going in for a full-on end-of-the-date snog.'

'Oh God, can you imagine?' We both fell silent for a second longer than was perhaps necessary, holding each other's gaze before we broke eye contact.

'Right then. See you soon, Gemma.'

'Night, Jude.'

I watched him walk away and grinned to myself as a thought popped into my head: if this *was* a smushy romcom, I bet Jude would be an amazingly good snogger.

14

Occy arrived at the café ten minutes after school finished for the day, again whooshing in through the door with boundless energy and a great big smile.

'Hey, Gemma, how's it going?'

She flung her school bag behind the counter and I stopped in my tracks. Her actions took my breath away. It was almost identical to how I would greet Mum, grabbing an apron from the hook in the kitchen and tying it around her waist, while automatically tying her hair back and wittering on about her day. Exactly like I used to.

Once this thought properly sunk in, it just made me smile. She was literally like a mini-me.

'What?' She raised her hands in the air and pulled a face, totally oblivious of the memories she had just raked up, which tugged on my heart.

The bell announced that we had company and I promised to tell her what was making me smile once the rush had died down. This was always a busy time of the day. School mums congregated in the café both after the morning school run and after picking up on an afternoon.

I had always wanted it to be the sort of place that parents could bring their children to and give them something to do, while taking some time out to relax for themselves. There were a couple of highchairs in the corner for those who brought babies and toddlers, with a big wicker box full of colouring pencils and pads and drawing books along with a bookshelf with a selection of popular books.

Someone just last week came to thank me, saying, 'As a young mother, I didn't realise how rewarding motherhood was but also how exhausting too. I always wished I could just go somewhere to chill out if only for a few minutes' respite. And then I stumbled across your fabulous café and I'm so pleased I did. It's my favourite time of the week where I can just be. I tell all my friends about you. But then also hope that they don't come at the same time as me.'

We'd laughed together and I'd said that she was allowed to be selfish with her precious time. Just to hear her say this had made my day.

This was exactly my intention when I created these areas. Mum always used to say that when we were young, she couldn't even go to the loo in peace and used to laugh with us saying that our downstairs loo wasn't the family meeting room. In those days, there wasn't the stuff available that there is now, so hopefully I'd managed to get the balance just right.

For the older kids, there was an internet corner where they could play some of their favourite games and have some chill-out time watching videos. I was told that the local kids loved my café, just as much as their parents did and I hoped to make each of these areas bigger when the extension work was complete.

There was nothing in many towns for teenagers to do or

places for them to go. Mum always used to say that there should be more youth clubs around. I didn't have the room for ping pong tables or trampolines like she had in her youth, but I hoped she might be watching down on me, proud of what I had achieved, and what I was hoping to do in the future for the community.

I hoped that Occy might make use of these areas too if she needed to do some homework and as I was in the café until quite late most days. I was very happy for her to stay. The company would be welcomed.

With my head constantly down and hardly noticing who I was serving, I looked up in total surprise when a familiar voice said my name.

'Gem...'

I gulped.

'Luce. Hi. How are you? Is everything OK?'

She smiled, but it didn't quite reach her eyes. She moved from one foot to the other.

'I thought I'd pop in just before closing. You got time for a cuppa and a chat?'

I supposed that I couldn't put things off for much longer and smiled back at her.

'Yeah sure. Grab that table in the window and I'll bring us some drinks over.'

When Occy found me in the kitchen a few minutes later, I was hiding behind the door, doing breathing exercises.

'What the f—'

'Don't even think about finishing that sentence, young lady.'

She'd never know though how much she made me snap out of my state of panic.

'OK. So... What's up with you?'

'Sshh! For goodness' sake. She'll hear you.'

'*Who* will? What are you on about? There's no one here apart from that lady over there.'

It took a while for the penny to drop.

'Ah, it's *her* you are hiding from. Want me to tell her to do one?'

I gave a brief derisory laugh.

'No, but thank you. I must go and face the music sometime. May as well get it over and done with. Can you bring two lattes over please?'

Poor Occy looked so confused. I would have to fill her in at some point soon.

I pulled myself straight, took a deep breath through my nose and breathed out through my mouth and flung open the kitchen door, pasting a smile on my face. It was time to put on those big girl pants.

'Luce.'

'Gem.'

She stood and hugged me. It was what we always did but for some reason that day it took me by surprise. I sat opposite her.

'How are you doing? You're looking...' I looked into her eyes. Really looked. I could see that she wasn't herself and that her eyes were a little red. 'You're looking well. How's things?' Despite how I was feeling, I hoped with all of my heart that she wasn't here with bad news.

'Oh, I'm OK, but I needed to see you. I needed to know that you were OK. Are you?'

''Course I am.' I smiled at her.

'Are you though? Really?'

I didn't realise that I'd sighed out loud until she mentioned it. I looked at her face. She normally had a twinkle in her bright-blue eyes and a smile as big as an ocean, but both seemed absent today. I don't know why it suddenly hit me this way, but in that very moment I realised that I was the one responsible for dulling her sparkle.

'I'm sorry that you can't have children, Gemma. Sorrier than you'll ever know but I don't know how to be around you right now. I love you more than anyone in the whole world. Maybe you could not mention that to James by the way.' I smirked at this. 'I want to be happy that I'm having a baby and I want to include you, but I only want that if it's what you want too.'

'Oh, Lucy! I'm sorry. I've been too busy feeling sorry for myself that I didn't think it would be affecting you too. What a selfish cow I've been.' I took her hand in mine. 'Can you forgive me? I do want to be part of this... this amazing thing that you...' I waved my finger around in a circular motion aimed at her belly '... have got going on.'

'I've never in my life not known what to do around you, Gemma, even after everything happened with Mum and then again with Lucas. But right now, I think you need to tell me what you do and don't want me to do.'

She looked so sad, I couldn't bear the thought that I'd been the one to make her feel this way. I looked over at Occy where she was hovering by the counter with our drinks, not wanting to intrude on what she could see was a very intimate conversation. Talk about reading the room. Her perception skills were first class. She was an expert at it already, even at her young age. I waved her over.

'Sorry, didn't know whether to come over or not.'

'This, Occy, is my sister Lucy. Lucy, this is my newest and most favourite member of staff. What do you think? Should we tell her?'

Lucy nodded. 'If you promise not to let it go further, I might let you into a very big family secret.'

Occy's eyes opened wide and a grin broke out.

'I swear.'

'You nearly already did that earlier.'

'Oops, sorry.' She giggled.

'I promise then.'

'I, owner of this establishment, am going to be... drum roll please...'

Occy drummed her hands on the edge of the table and waited patiently.

'... am going to be...'

'Oh, get on with it.' She laughed.

'... am going to be an aunty.'

The high-pitched squeal that escaped her lips made us both wince; probably made the dogs in the neighbouring village prick up their ears too.

'Oh-mi-God! Oh-mi-God! That's fantastic news. Congratulations.' She flung her arms around me and then ran round to Lucy, hugging her too. 'Oh, I love babies. Can I babysit? I can't wait to have a baby of my own.'

'Don't let your father hear you say that. He'll have a heart attack.' I laughed. 'And at the age of fifteen, I hope you'll be waiting for a good while yet.'

'Ha.' She scoffed. 'I don't mean now. Not for ages yet. Not till I'm ancient, like at least twenty-five or something.' Lucy and I caught each other's eye and laughed. 'I've got years ahead of me, but it's something I've always wanted. I know exactly the type of mother I want to be. Someone just like you, Gemma. A friend to chat to, someone to have a laugh with and someone to guide you. You are going to be such a sick aunty.' She flicked her wrist at me and couldn't stop grinning. 'You must both be so excited.'

I glanced across at Lucy, who had tilted her head to one side, listening intently.

'We absolutely are,' I said. 'It's the best news in the world. I am going to try to be the best aunty possible, but, more than that, I'm going to look after my sister all the way through this pregnancy and make sure she enjoys every minute from now on.'

I reached across for Lucy's hand again and looked into those eyes. It was just like looking into my mother's eyes and a little lump formed in my throat. Sometimes grief struck me completely out of nowhere; I sometimes missed Mum with such intensity it took my breath away.

'Mum would have loved this. I wish with the whole of my heart that she could be here right now. And while we can be sad that she's not here, we can also be happy that she was the best mum that we could have ever wished for. She taught us to be the best versions of ourselves and I know she's smiling down on us right now. You've got this, Luce. We've got this. Together.'

Occy chewed the inside of her cheek as she stood and quickly announced that she was going to get off. There must be at least a little bit of her that wondered about her own mother at times like this. I hoped we hadn't upset her with this talk of ours. I'd find an excuse to message her later to make sure she was OK. Or message her dad. Maybe that might be a better way to deal with the situation.

Once Occy had gone, I explained to Lucy what I knew.

'You and Jude seem to be getting friendly. How do you know all of this?'

'Yes, it's nice to have friends. Nothing more than that, so you can take that smirk off your face. Neither of us are looking for anything else right now. Jude has Occy to focus on and I have the café. No room for anything else.'

Lucy raised her eyebrows at me again.

'If you say so, Gemma. If you say so...'

15

A few enquiries had come in via the phone and a couple more people had popped in about the job though all of them were not at all suitable in my opinion. One had seemed pleasant enough, a local man, but he talked more to my boobs than my face. I knew I'd always been blessed in that department, but seriously, it felt like he was a bit of a lech and I couldn't have someone like that around Occy. She might not know how to handle them and, anyway, she shouldn't have to. Not that I was an expert, but as a fully fledged grown-up, I could certainly look after myself.

Another person was another schoolgirl, pleasant enough but she had the grubbiest nails and looked like she needed a good scrub in general. The thought of her going anywhere near food scared me to death. I'd have the environmental health people up in arms.

Maybe Meredith was right and the most appropriate person would come along at the right time, so it was exciting to get a call from the lady who had contacted me previously. Crossing my fingers, I arranged a time and day for her to come in and I was looking forward to meeting her as she sounded like she could potentially be a good fit, having way more café and restaurant experience than anyone else who had applied.

When she arrived, I explained that I might have to keep popping away as there was only me in that day. Pat had received a call not long after she'd arrived earlier in the day, from her granddaughter's school, to say that she was poorly and needed picking up. Her daughter couldn't do it as she was away at a conference so she'd had to go. I knew that she hated to leave me in the lurch but sometimes these situations couldn't be helped.

Rachel was tall and slim of build, casually – but smartly – dressed in black from head to toe, with tied-back hair, and minimal make-up. Her broad, radiant smile was one that I knew my regular customers would take to straight away. As she sat, I glanced at her hands. My mum had always said that you can learn about someone from their hands. Her nails were neat and relatively short and French manicured. And clean!

Her easy-going nature was a breath of fresh air; in fact we chatted so easily it was as if I'd always known her.

'So, what brings you to Driftwood Bay?'

'I've been staying in the Bristol area and am planning to move down here in the next couple of months. I've had lots of experience of working in bars, cafés and restaurants as I've moved around various towns throughout the years and have always been lucky enough to pick up hospitality work.'

Fully prepared and armed with references and numbers of people that I could call who would vouch for her, she seemed to be well organised, a quality that is much needed in a business such as mine. Even though she was quietly confident, she showed a little vulnerability too, and when she shared that she had led a troubled life for a while, I could understand that was maybe why she came across as being really likeable. Impressed with her brief explanation of how she'd left behind her past and made a new life for herself, she said maybe she'd tell me more if she got the job and we came to know each other well. I loved nothing more than helping someone if I could and felt there were times in all our lives when we all needed a little helping hand. Everyone deserved a second chance.

The sound of chatter from outside drew our attention to a small crowd of people in a range of colourful coats and walking gear that had gathered outside the door. One of the group came in alone and introduced himself.

'Hi there, I'm Julian, and I'm the leader of a rambling group. We've been out hiking round the coast for hours and we're all ravenous. I know it's a big ask but I don't suppose you might be able to fit us all in for lunch, would you? I am a numpty and should have phoned ahead. We were going to head further on but thought that your place looked so delightful, it was unanimous that we'd like to stop off here.'

I did a quick head count and there was around twenty of them. I dithered but Julian's pleading face and the fact that I certainly couldn't afford to turn away business like that made me realise I had to get over myself and get on with it. Any new customer could be a potential customer for life and they might introduce others to the place too. I apologised to Rachel, explaining that I would have to cut our chat short, and told Julian to invite his group in and grab a seat; I'd work as quickly as I could under the circumstances.

'Why don't you let me help you now, Gemma?' Rachel said. 'No time like the present.'

It seemed like the perfect solution but I didn't want her to think I was taking advantage of her good nature. She'd grabbed an apron and started tying it before I'd even agreed.

'Look. I insist. You need some help. It'll take you hours to get through this lot and that's without anyone else coming in. I have time on my hands and I can prove myself to you at the same time. What have you got to lose?'

And prove herself she did. That and then some. Swift and efficient, she sure knew her way around a kitchen and was great at cleaning up as she went along. We worked so well in perfect harmony. Her lovely sunny disposition was a real hit with the customers and she clearly had the ability to stay calm under pressure. A definite prerequisite in a place like this.

Two hours flew by and when she'd finished cleaning the last table, she went over to the counter and hovered for a minute or two before approaching me in the kitchen.

'So, what do you think? Could I be the sort of person you might be looking for?'

'You really are, Rachel,' I said. 'Thanks so much for all that you've done. I honestly don't know what I would have done without you. Do you want to let me know when you know more about your moving dates? If we keep in touch, it should all come together. I reckon you'll fit in well and you'll love Pat. I have a young girl called Occy working here too who is a little superstar, and I reckon between us we'll make a cracking team. I'll keep you posted about the launch date too when I know a bit more about how Clem's getting on next door. I haven't even had chance to go round yet to see how it's shaping up. It's been a bit mad.'

'Look, I'm OK for another half an hour or so. I'm happy to hold the fort here if you want to pop on over. It's gone quiet anyway. No pressure obviously. I know you don't really know me. But you will only be literally next door and I can shout you if I need to.'

Did I trust someone that I had known for just a couple of hours? I looked up and bit the inside of my cheek while I pondered. But then I also thought, what's the worst that can happen? If she ran off with the till money, then it was just a couple of hours' takings, which I know no one can really afford but in the grand scale of things, it's only money. Even if it is mine. I glanced at the clock.

'I really want this job, Gemma. More than anything. That's about all I can say to make you put your trust in me. It's entirely up to you and no offence taken at all either way.' She held her palms up.

'I'll be no more than fifteen minutes. I promise. My number is next to the till if you need me.' I untied my apron. She took it from me and folded it up, smiling.

'I won't let you down. I promise.'

I believed her.

I grinned as I picked up a pair of tongs and plucked a brownie from the domed cake stand and popped it in a bag. Most people found it difficult to resist my raspberry and white chocolate brownies and I knew Clem would be no exception. Keeping him happy would mean that I had a happy builder on site.

* * *

'Hellooo! Clem?'

'Hey, Gemma, wasson?'

'All good thanks. Here you go. Little snack for you.'

He peered inside the bag and licked his lips.

'Working for you isn't doing my waistline any good, you know.'

'Ah, a little of what you fancy does you good once in a while. I'm sure you're burning off lots of calories working in here.'

'It's certainly keeping me active. Have you got time for me to go through where I'm up to?'

'Go for it.'

Having Clem describe and show me what he'd done so far, and what his plans were next, made me beam from ear to ear. He really was fabulous at his craft and I could already see huge differences. He was working so hard and I was delighted with his progress. We went through dates in the calendar again for when the major knocking through work was going to take place – when I'd need to totally close the café – and I made a note of what I needed to prepare to ensure the closure was for the minimal amount of time. The launch night was discussed again and a tentative date put aside; fingers crossed, if all went to plan, we'd be up and running again the first week of December.

Seeing it all taking shape was exciting and for the first time in a while I think I was finally losing the fear and starting to look forward to the future. When everything happened with Lucas, I know I fell apart for a bit, but with help from my family and the best of friends, I managed to piece my life back together, building a new future. That was one of the hardest things I've ever had to do and all at a time when I needed my mum more than ever. Though part of me was glad that she'd passed away before everything kicked off because I don't know how she would have coped with that as well as her illness. At least when she left us, she saw her two daughters contented and safe. And that's what we all thought as well.

There'd been a shift within me. I'd stopped thinking about the last couple of years in terms of how sad it had made me. The toughness of those times had made me the person I was today and Meredith was right. Maybe I was brave and courageous; it takes more guts to try something than not.

The worst that could happen was that things could go wrong, but again, as Mum used to say, it's better to have tried and failed, than never to have tried in the first place.

Finally, I was looking forward to this new stage of my life. A new adventure. So what if it wasn't what I thought the future held for me at one time? It was what it was now and I was going to grab it with both hands and make the most of it. Life is too short not to live it. Mum had made us promise her that we would always live our best lives.

Singing happily away to myself, I wandered back over to the café, peering through the window before entering to see Rachel laughing with one of the regulars. At the same time, she was using the coffee machine with ease. Typical. It had had taken me weeks to fathom Betty the Beast, and she'd managed it within just a couple of hours.

I re-entered, thinking about how all was well in my world and feeling grateful for all that I had. Lovely friends, a cosy home, an expanding successful business that I loved, with a team that I felt would work well together. To top all of that, I lived in Driftwood Bay; in my opinion, the most beautiful place in the world.

I felt such huge gratitude and joy in my heart and as I waved Rachel off, with a promise to stay in touch, I felt incredibly positive about the future.

16

'Honestly, Gemma, it wasn't my fault. How was I to know?'

I tried so hard not to laugh but was failing miserably and had to apologise.

'I'm sorry, Occy. And it's not your fault, it's mine, because I didn't explain properly in advance. I never thought.'

Remembering the moment when I had heard a customer raising her voice, I smiled. I'd had my hands full in the kitchen and strained to hear what on earth was going on.

'I just want half a baguette. That's all,' the woman shouted.

'Yeah, I get that. But who's going to have the other half? I need to wait and see if someone else will have the other half before I give you yours.'

'Why? I had half a baguette in here last week.'

'I understand that but if you have half a baguette, that leaves half a baguette behind and that's waste and I've been taught that we don't waste food. So, we need to find someone to have the other half. One second. Let me ask.'

After that, all I could hear was Occy clearing her throat and then in a really loud voice, she asked, 'Does anyone want to buy the other half of this lady's baguette?'

I moved into the doorway to see what was going on more closely. The looks she was receiving from the other customers should probably have told her to quit while she was ahead but she didn't and just went for it again.

'Hi, everyone. Could I have your attention please. I'm so sorry to bother you. But unless someone buys the other half of this baguette, this lady won't be able to have her half.'

Those looks again, and a few sniggers around the room yet still she didn't clock that anything was amiss.

'I'm so sorry, madam, but you might have to wait for a bit to see if anyone else comes in and wants the other half.'

'Seriously, just give me the whole bloody thing. This is ridiculous.'

Time for me to intervene. I washed my hands and wiped them down my apron as I walked out to the main counter.

'Everything OK out here?'

'Are you the owner?'

'Yes I am.' I smiled. 'How can I help?'

'This young lady here said that I can't have half a cheese and onion baguette. I won't eat a whole one and I've bought one before. She says that she must sell the other half before I can have mine.'

'Ah, that's my mistake. I'll get that sorted out for you. If you'd like to take a seat, I'll bring it over to you. Sorry for the mix-up.' I'd had to suppress my laughter as I turned to Occy. 'Occy, can you come through to the kitchen for me please.'

She had rolled her eyes and headed through.

'What have I done wrong? I'm sorry for whatever it is but I don't understand.' Tears appeared in her eyes and started to roll down her cheeks. 'This job is the only thing that's ever meant anything to me. Please don't sack me, Gemma.'

I wrapped my arms around her, pulling her close into my chest and kissed the top of her head, then realised that I'd done this on instinct and that it could be interpreted as being a bit weird, so I moved away. I just wanted to comfort this girl-woman who still seemed to have so much to learn about life.

'Occy, I'm not going to sack you. I love having you around. This is just teaching me that some of the things that adults know are never passed down. We just assume that you know. That's our fault not yours. This is absolutely not your fault.'

She sniffed and wiped her nose on her sleeve. Ew! We'd need to get the anti-bacterial wipes out before she went near food or customers again.

'So if someone asks for half of something, maybe a good reminder is that if it's on the menu then it's OK.'

She nodded in response.

'Ah OK, but it is quite confusing, you know. It might also explain why someone was funny over the Coke I gave them earlier too. He asked for half a Coke, so I gave him half a can and he told me I was stupid and asked for the other half.'

She picked up the menu and pointed out that she couldn't see half a Coke on it.

'Ah, well, when someone asks for half a Coke, they mean half a pint. Not half a can.'

'And I'm supposed to know that because...'

'You're not, sweetheart. These are the things that you pick up on the way. I suppose the pint or half pint thing comes from being in a pub and people normally get asked if they want a full one or a half. It's definitely not you being stupid. I promise.'

'OK, so I understand the half a can of Coke thing now, but half a baguette. Really? It's so illogical. You wouldn't give someone half a sandwich. Adults are just weird.' She turned around in a huff and walked away towards the bathroom. I had to hold back a laugh. She'd made a pretty good point.

After I took the customer's food over and apologised, the lady made the effort to come over to make the peace with Occy, which was really kind of her. We ended up laughing about it – the way that adults assume kids know the same things they do – and she went on to tell us about the time she worked in a pub and someone asked her for a bitter lemon and then looked really confused when she went over with a slice of lemon on a plate.

Occy's expression was totally blank.

'Bit-o-lemon. Get it?'

She shook her head.

The customer and I laughed while Occy just looked at us both as if we'd got two heads, which made us laugh even more. However, it was a lesson to us all to make sure people understand what you are asking of them.

Later, when things had quietened down, almost as an apology but also because I definitely needed to get more on board with the things younger people did so well, I asked her what she thought we could do on social media to promote the café once the refurb was done. After all, this was what I had originally contacted her about, when Jude first mentioned that she was an expert in this area before I discovered that the person he had talked about was a schoolgirl. She became really animated at that, talking about how we could stage the room and take some amazing shots to make us 'proper Instagram worthy'. Lucy was right when she said that it was different when someone who knew what they were doing got involved.

'I've been using a design package in my media class at school. I reckon I could make loads of really sick graphics for our Insta profile. In fact, I have a couple of projects to do over the next few half terms so maybe I could use the café as my portfolio.'

'Only if it's allowed. I can't be getting you to do work for me when you're at school and doing lessons.'

The fact that she had called it *our* Insta profile hadn't gone unnoticed and it made me feel quite warm and fuzzy. I loved that she was feeling part of something.

'I'll ask my teacher but I bet they'll let me because it's a real project; most of the others will just be doing fake stuff. I'm sure it'll be fine.'

'Well, just make sure you do ask please. And if you need anything from me to pass on to the teacher, let me know.'

'Thanks, Gemma. You're the best. So, what are we cooking today?'

'Have you done your homework?'

'I've only got a bit to do. It'll be fine.'

'No, I made a promise to your dad that it would be homework first. This is an important school year for you and you need to make sure you're doing all you can to help yourself. I know you don't realise it now, but you'll thank us for all the nagging when you're older.'

'You sure about that?' She huffed and grabbed her school bag, before plonking herself down at one of the tables in the corner.

After about half an hour, she came into the kitchen saying she was all done, so I suggested we make a huge pot of Bolognese and another of chilli con carne. Occy grated the carrots and chopped the onions and mushrooms, which made me slightly anxious as I had to keep reminding her to stop looking at me while she was talking and concentrate on what she was doing. She then found it highly amusing to do it even more to tease me.

While I cooked a huge pan of minced beef, I taught her how to crush garlic cloves and pointed out which other spices to add in each pot, and she chatted away ten to the dozen when I asked her about school. I had to constantly remind her to keep on stirring the sauces. While she was doing really well with the cooking, doing two things at the same time was still a challenge at times even if only one of them was talking.

'God, this smells absolutely lush! I'm starting to get hungry now. I haven't eaten since lunch at school and even then it was just shoving a quick sandwich down before my next lesson.'

'Well, there's tons of this. You can take some home.'

'You're the best, Gemma.' That big beaming smile once more warmed my heart. 'I like it here.'

'That's good to hear. I'm glad you are enjoying working for me.'

'I don't mean just here. I mean in Driftwood Bay. I feel like for the first time in ages I'm finally fitting in somewhere. It's so much better here than at my last school.' Her light bulb moment came next. 'Maybe it's because I'm feeling happier with life in general. Dad's not quite as uptight lately which is sick. I've got Lizzie now, who is my best mate, and she's also one of the really cool girls, so people want to be hanging around with us and I love working here at the café. Thank you so much for giving me a chance.'

My heart squeezed when she said that. To know that I played a little part in her happiness really did fill me with joy.

'Oh, darling, you are very welcome. I think I need you just as much as you need me. Well, you know the café needs you, I mean.' She grinned. 'I could take you or leave you if truth be told.'

I winked at her.

'Yeah, right. You know you love me, Gem.'

'*Whatevs*, Occy.'

I did my best teenager impression and pulled a face and she laughed. As we potted some of the Bolognese sauce for her to take home for her and her father, I told her how long she would need to cook the pasta for. It might be nice for Jude to come home from work and relax instead of having to go straight into cooking mode. And it was no hardship when I was cooking a huge amount anyway. But it also felt good to be sharing with Occy some life skills and lessons too.

'What do you do with all this food, Gemma?'

You had to love kids of that age. So inquisitive and not afraid to ask questions.

I swallowed a lump in my throat. What I did with the food wasn't anything I'd shared with anyone yet and I wondered now whether to let her into my confidence.

There was a little bit of me that was worrying about letting Occy too far into my life. Even if she and Jude moved away again now, I would really miss her. She was a little ray of sunshine in my day and I was loving having her around and being part of my life. Everything I had been through with Lucas had made me put my guard up, not wanting anyone apart from Lucy to be too close. I wasn't sure if I was totally ready yet, but somehow this girl was cracking through the walls that I'd built around me. I sincerely hoped that I wouldn't regret it.

17

Every day, the progress in the building next door was becoming more and more noticeable and the whole place was really starting to take shape. It was exciting to watch the headway that Clem was making and see my vision start to come together. I tried to pop in at least once a day even though Clem said that I shouldn't be so impatient and should leave it longer between visits so that I could see more of the impact. It was quite genius of him to try to complete one half of the building before knocking through. Closing, even if for a few days, would have a big effect on the business and closing for the least amount of time possible was necessary so that we didn't lose too many customers.

We were hoping that in a short space of time, we could move the café into the other building and get the work done in the existing café before knocking through and making it one big space. That was the plan and in principle it was a perfect strategic move. We now just had to make it happen.

Lucy had invited me round that evening and I enjoyed my walk around the harbour to get there. It was starting to get a lot cooler in the evenings and I was glad I had put my coat on, wrapping it tighter around me.

The glittering sea made me smile as always. I could never decide whether it was prettier by day or night.

I arrived at the B & B and let myself in. Lucy was sitting in the lounge, tucking into a big packet of cheese and onion crisps. She looked really well, if a little tired, but I was sure she didn't need to hear that right then. I leaned down to her, gave her a kiss and grabbed a few crisps from the packet.

'Nice, I'm starving!' I laughed as she gave me a mock look of hurt. 'It's good to see you, sis. You look amazing. Clearly being pregnant suits you.'

'Oh, I feel like shit, so thanks, love. I'm either throwing up or eating everything in sight. James says that our shopping bill has gone up at least a hundred pounds a week.'

Laughing, I flung myself into one of their comfy armchairs, enjoying how it felt like I was being hugged. Their lounge was warm and inviting, with subdued lighting to make it feel calming and cosy. I was so glad that I'd come out. It was good to get away from the café and think about something else for a couple of hours. While I loved it there and was very much looking forward to the future, it was literally filling my every waking moment and I'd recently started to dream about it too. When I wasn't working, I was in my head thinking about it, planning it, envisioning what it would look like or on my laptop shopping for it, marketing it, and I was looking forward to some well-deserved time to fill my brain with something else.

Lucy and I spent a lovely evening together while James made himself scarce – of course, after making sure that all the guests were fed and looked after. She said that he was enjoying an excuse to go to the pub with his mates as he wasn't drinking at home any more, in solidarity with his newly teetotal wife. I wondered whether Jude was one of the people with him in the pub and thought back to a lovely time we'd had all together in the flat a few evenings ago when he'd come to pick Occy up from work. After I'd cooked us some food, we sat and played Scrabble, laughing when Occy kept asking if swear words were allowed. I wondered whether it would happen again soon. I really enjoyed being in their company. The only downfall was that after they left I had felt more alone than ever.

Lucy and I relived many of our childhood memories and laughed a lot. It was cathartic to remember Mum and the good times, rather than just being sad when we thought of her. It reminded me of how good it felt to laugh. Maybe even life-affirming.

There was a time after Mum died that I thought I'd never laugh again. When I just existed in a little bubble of sadness. And then just days later, when Lucas left too, it was like my whole life had come crashing down around me. Not only had I lost my mum and my husband, but I'd lost the future that I thought we would all share together. Lucy was the one who picked me up, both physically and emotionally, and now that I'd given my head a good wobble, I was going to make damn sure that I would be the best sister to her, in the same way that she had been to me.

While we talked about how much Mum would have loved being a grandparent, we also laughed about how much she would have hated being called Granny and we decided that when we talked to their baby about their grandmother in heaven, she needed a more glamorous name. Lucy suggested 'Glamma', which we rather liked and, more importantly, thought that Mum would have loved.

'How's it all going at the café, babe? I've had such a mega busy week so far. These days it's taking all my energy to get up and get dressed let alone look after the B & B guests. I've been falling into bed at night and zonking out straight away, so haven't had any time to pop round to see all the work for myself. I'm so sorry.'

'Don't apologise, you are growing a whole person inside you. That's a miracle in itself and must be completely exhausting.'

'Yeah, I suppose so.'

Lucy seemed to have something on her mind, so I asked her what she was holding back on. She smiled.

'We know each other so well, don't we?' She took my hand in hers. 'I have two things to talk about. I'll wait till James comes back from the pub for one of them. But there is something important that I wanted to say.' She took a deep breath. 'I want you to hear me out before you say anything. OK?'

I nodded, wondering what on earth she was going to say.

'I think you should change the name of the café.'

My eyes widened and my stomach lurched. Wow.

'Don't say a word until I've finished.'

'OK.'

'You know that Mum would have loved the fact that you are having work done at the café, don't you?'

I smiled.

'This is your time now, Gemma, your time to shine. It's not Mum's café any more, so I think that you – and we'll help if you want us to – should think about a new name. You can reveal it at your launch night. Then it's a proper fresh start for you. Your business, your ideas.'

Her pause for thought gave this idea even more of an impact for me. I was a little gobsmacked, a state that was most unusual for me.

'OK, you can speak now, Gemma. What do you think?'

'Gosh, honestly? I don't know what I think. It hadn't ever

crossed my mind. It's always been The Harbour Corner Café. What would people think if I called it something different? Would they think I'm trying to get rid of our memories?'

'Darling, you'll never get rid of our memories. They're in our hearts. And they're in our every day. They're there when I look in the mirror and see our mother staring back at me.' I smiled. I knew exactly what she meant. 'She will be in every cake that you bake, every meal that you prepare, every time you smell something that reminds you of her, every time you see a rainbow, a feather. When you hear a song that she loved. She'll never leave us. You do know that don't you?'

I swallowed a huge lump that had appeared in my throat.

'What if I forget, Lucy? Sometimes I struggle to remember her voice. Sometimes her loss feels like it's so raw I can't cope. The other day I read something in her handwriting in a recipe book at the café, and it literally took my breath away. What if all that stops because it's not her café any more?'

Lucy reached out and wiped away a tear that was trickling down my cheek.

'You'll never forget her, Gemma. I promise.'

'I'm scared that I will.'

'I know. But I really do think it's time for you now. This is your new venture. Your ideas and your vision. You don't have to decide now anyway. It's just a thought that I wanted to share with you. Just think about it.'

'I will. I promise.'

We heard the front door slam and a few seconds later, James was stumbling through the lounge door, clearly a little tipsy and pretending not to be. I saw him and Lucy exchange a glance and she nodded as he sat on the arm of the sofa beside her.

'And the other thing we wanted to ask you, together, was...'

They both placed their hands on Lucy's belly. 'Will you be this little one's godmother please?'

I flung myself at the pair of them. What an honour and a privilege. At that exact moment, I felt like my heart might burst through my body and I hugged them tight.

I might not have the family I had hoped for, with Lucas and the children we would have had, but what I did have was the most caring sister, along with the most amazing brother-in-law who I thought the absolute world of. What they had asked me was the most precious and special thing that anyone could possibly have ever asked me in the whole of my life.

I showered them both with kisses.

'You bet your damn life I will. Thank you, thank you, thank you.'

18

'I'm not going!'

'But you must go. It's an awards ceremony and you're up for an award.'

'I don't care, Occy; I'm just not going.'

'Dad, you can't not go. You're being silly. If this was me, you'd be telling me to go, wouldn't you?'

'Probably.'

'Then think about that. Why don't you want to go? Gemma, listen to this. Dad's refusing to go to the fire awards ceremony where he's up for an award.'

We'd fallen into a comfortable routine of them joining me a couple of times a week for dinner in the flat. Jude would finish work and come straight to fetch Occy after her shift, but if he was going to be later, she would stay and do her homework and then we'd all eat tea together.

It was nice to have company. Jude and I chatted mostly while Occy spent time on her phone messaging with Lizzie. If it was up to me, I wouldn't have allowed her to have a phone at the table, but it was up to Jude. He was her dad and it was his job to set boundaries. He did explain to me that sometimes he just had to pick his arguments with her and give in over some things.

'Gemma, did you hear me?' Occy pressed. 'Dad's refusing to go to the awards dinner. What do you think about that?'

'Oh, sorry, miles away. So, why's that then, Jude?'

'Because I'll be the only one there without a partner, and I'll feel like Billy No Mates. Being on my own never bothers me until there's an occasion like this. People always look at me like there's either something wrong with me, or that they feel sorry for me. Then I'm the one who ends up feeling awkward. I just don't want to go.'

'Sorry, Occy, but I'm going to agree with your dad here. There are loads of things I don't go to because I'd be on my own. I don't blame you, Jude.'

'Thank you, Gemma, I knew you'd understand.'

I looked across at Occy whose face had suddenly lit up.

'You know there's a perfect solution to this don't you, Dad?'

'You think so, do you?'

'Absolutely. Gemma can go with you.'

Crikey, I wasn't expecting that.

I suppose it was a solution but I would need to know much more about it first. That's if Jude wanted me to go with him, of course. I didn't really know much about him at all. He might have a bank of women that he could ask to accompany him.

'No, that wouldn't be right. I wouldn't ask her to do that.'

'You're not asking her though, are you? I'm just saying it's the sensible thing to do. You don't have anyone to go with and Gemma's on her own and lonely, so she could go with you. Sorted.'

'I'm not asking her to come, Occy. I don't want to go. Just leave it.' Jude had started to raise his voice.

'You said you didn't want to go because you didn't want to go on your own. But you don't have to go on your own. Gemma can be your date for the night.'

'Er... I am here you know,' I said, trying to butt into the conversation but it was no good. They were so focused on each other it was like watching an intense tennis match.

'I don't want a date for the night. What sort of a saddo has to beg someone to be his date for the night? Just leave it, Occy. Please.'

I stood and excused myself, saying that I needed to get something. I needed a bit of distance from this deep conversation, although I could still hear their raised voices from the kitchen.

'You need to have a night out enjoying yourself. You stop in night after night and never go out and have fun,' she countered. 'And Gemma would go if you asked her. I know she would. She's bloody gorgeous and you'd be lucky to have her on your arm as your date.'

'Don't swear, Octavia.'

'Bloody isn't swearing. And don't call me Octavia. How many times do I have to tell you that?'

'Bloody *is* swearing and Octavia is your name.'

'Occy is my name and stop changing the subject. Maybe "date" is the wrong word. Maybe just friend would be better, then you can introduce her as your friend. Which is exactly what she is.'

'She's probably not even free on Friday night. And I can't imagine she'd enjoy a Michael Bublé tribute artist anyway.'

God, I bloody loved Michael Bublé. What did either of them know about me in the short time that they'd known me?

Time for me to take back a bit of control here. I headed back to their table.

'Excuse me, you two, but I *am* free on Friday and there's

nothing I love more than a Bublé tribute. But you know,' I said to Jude, eyes meeting his, 'you don't have to invite me.'

Jude and Occy both turned their heads to me in synchronisation, then back to each other. They were literally carbon copies of each other. It made me smile, knowing how Occy would react if I said this out loud.

'Why is it always all about you, Dad? Has anyone ever told you how miserable you are? If they haven't, maybe they should.'

With that, she flounced out, slamming the door behind her.

'Well, that certainly told me.'

'Ah, she's just looking out for her dad,' I said. 'It's nice that she wants you to go out and have fun. Not everyone would be the same. Are the awards something you really wanted to go along to?'

'Well, it might have been nice, but...'

'Maybe you should consider going. Tell me, if you had a partner would you go?'

'Yep.' There wasn't a moment's hesitation.

Bizarrely, I knew exactly how he felt. Someone I knew from my very first job in an office had invited me to their birthday party, which was being held in a social club a few villages away. While it would have been lovely to see her, the thought of going alone was terrifying for me. Who would I sit with? Would I know anyone? Would anyone talk to me? Would everyone be part of a couple? Would everyone be looking at me thinking, *Look at that sad old cow over there on her own.*

I suppose I could have asked Lucy to go with me but she'd never met Jenny so it wouldn't have been much fun for her either. In the end I made an excuse, which was silly because it probably would have been a perfectly lovely evening. I know that if I was part of a couple, I would have had my glad rags and my dancing shoes on raring to go and party.

'Then I'll come with you.'

It wasn't right that he should be missing out when I could help the situation.

'Honestly, Gemma, don't worry about it. You really don't have to come. I'd hate to think that we'd guilted you into coming.'

'You haven't. Where is it at?'

'A big posh hotel near Truro. It's the Devon and Cornwall Fire Brigade Annual Awards Ceremony.'

'And you're up for an award.'

'It's only a regional award but yes I am.'

'So that must be a big thing then?'

'Well, you know.' He grinned. 'It's quite a thing in our field of work.'

'Then Cinders *must* go to the ball.'

'You don't have to come with me, Gemma. Maybe I just need to grow a pair and go on my own. I just get so fed up with all the sorry looks I get from half of the wives, and the flirty looks from the other half when their husbands aren't looking. My station leader's wife accosted me last time and tried to drag me into the disabled toilet. And I don't think she needed a hand with her dress!'

I tried very hard not to feel jealous at this. After all, Jude was just my friend and I had no right to feel that way.

'And my mates... well... they just take the mickey and think it's hilarious.' He tried to laugh it off but I could see how much it bothered him. I knew exactly how he felt.

'Are you saying that you don't want me to go with you?' As soon as I said it, while I meant it in a joking way, I realised how presumptuous I'd been. How vain of me to assume he'd want me to go with him. He might not want to be seen dead with me.

'Obviously, you might have someone else you'd rather ask...'

Not sure why, but at this I held my breath. I didn't quite

know how I was going to react if he said he did have someone else.

'Oh, great work, Adams,' he said to himself. 'Now I've insulted you too!' He smacked his head with the heel of his hand. 'There isn't anyone else that I can ask. There really isn't.'

'Look, Jude, I know I don't have to, but if you'd like me to, I'd be honoured. It's not like it's a date or anything. Just two friends going supporting each other. That's what pals do.'

'Are you sure?'

'Yes, I'm positive.'

'Well, only if you're really sure.'

'I am. Really. I haven't had a proper night out for months. Posh hotel, you say? What's the dress code?'

'Black tie for the men and evening dress for the women.'

'Oh, blimey! My long frocks haven't been on a night out for years. I am definitely up for it. *That*. Not *it*. Obviously.'

'Only if you're sure.'

'Stop saying that. I am. If you are.'

We were both egging each other on to make the final decision.

Jude sat back and chewed the inside of his cheek.

'Well, in that case, thank you, it's a date.' He coughed and rubbed the back of his neck in that way he did when he was feeling a little nervous. 'I mean a not-date. Of course.'

I grinned and he smiled back.

'Here's to Friday's not-date then,' I said.

'There's a car coming for me at seven. Shall we swing by and pick you up?'

'That would be lovely.'

'Thanks, Gemma.'

'No problem. It'll be fun.'

He walked towards the door, and as he opened it, he turned,

about to say something else. But then he seemed to change his mind.

'See you Friday then. Goodnight.' He waved his hand in the air as he walked away.

A night out with a friend would be great. Roll on Friday.

19

Both Meredith and Occy had insisted on coming round to help me get ready for the awards ceremony, even though I told them both that I neither wanted nor needed them to. However, it seemed that my opinion wasn't important as they'd both turned up just as the café closed and ambushed me.

Now, coming out of the en suite, a bath towel wrapped around me, I found both of them sitting on my bed, wines glasses in their hands, and a plate of pizza waiting by their side.

'Er... Personal space, guys! Ever heard of it? And that had better not be alcohol you're drinking, young lady.'

They roared with laughter.

'Told you she'd say that.' Occy grinned. 'Mine has the tiniest amount of champagne and the rest is just orange juice. Honest. Anyhow, you're not wearing that black velvet dress that's hanging up there, are you?'

'Yes I am, what's wrong with it? Don't you like it?'

'It's lovely but it's not as lovely as this one.' She stood and held up a long slinky scarlet satin dress that I had never actually worn. 'That one... well, it's a bit, well... womanly.'

'Well, I am a woman.'

'Yeah, but now this one... It's proper sexy. You'd look smoking hot in it.'

The red dress was one I'd bought for a party we were supposed to go to on the weekend Lucas told me that he was leaving me. It had been hanging up at the back of my wardrobe ever since and, to be honest, I'd forgotten all about it until now. They'd clearly been having a good rummage and I wasn't sure how I felt about them going through my things.

'Oh, I'm not wearing that. I'm not that fond of it,' I said, the memories flooding back. 'I'll go with the black one. Sorry, girls.'

Meredith and Occy exchanged a glance and I could see that they thought I'd made the wrong decision. However, I really didn't want to wear the scarlet dress. There was just too much attached to it.

Occy said that she wanted to do my make-up and, much as I worried about what I might look like, it was easier to not argue. At that moment, I understood what Jude meant about picking his arguments. And so, Occy sat me down and began to do my face. She talked all the way through, telling me what she was doing. Apparently, the smoky eye make-up would bring out the colour of my eyes and the dramatic scarlet lips would stand out against the black dress. I had to put my trust in her, and she kept promising to make me look 'sick'.

After that, Meredith assured me she would be able to trans- form my poker straight hair to that of a film star, with waves that would tumble gently over my shoulders. I wished her luck as it was something I'd never succeeded at despite trying many times.

When I looked in the mirror, to my complete surprise, I was quite delighted with the result.

'Maybe you'll find yourself a nice firefighter there tonight.'

'Ha! Thanks, Mere, but the whole reason in me going is because everyone else is going to be married. Anyway, I'm too busy for anyone in my life right now. I'm just not interested.'

There it was again. A look, between Meredith and Occy that I couldn't quite decipher.

'OK. Let's get you out of that dressing gown and into your dress then.'

'You do know I'm an adult and can dress myself, don't you? Can you pair at least give me some privacy while I get dressed, please?'

They both grumbled their disappointment, and after they'd left, Meredith shouted through the door, 'I hope you've shaved your legs!'

Occy cackled and then yelled, 'And your pits. And your lady bits too!'

This pair egging each other on was not how I had planned to spend my time getting ready.

Of course, I had shaved parts of me that hadn't seen a razor since the end of summer, when I'd retreated back into mainly jeans. No real need when you lived alone anyway, there was no way that either of them, or anyone else for that matter, was going to get that close. It had been a good while since anyone had seen me in my bra and pants and that was not changing anytime soon.

Quite out of character for me, this evening I had decided to wear a nice set of underwear. Normally these days, with nowhere special to go, I'd just grab the nearest bra and knickers from my drawer and if they turned out to be the same colour that was a bonus. But tonight, I decided to wear a matching lacy M & S set that I'd only worn once before. I'd lost a bit of weight, and as I looked at myself in the mirror, for the first time in a while, I didn't feel like the frumpy old thing I normally did. I thought I looked OK.

I slipped into the black velvet dress and went through to the lounge.

'Wit-woo! Look at you!' Meredith grinned as I walked in.

'Can one of you do me up please.'

Occy jumped up to help, with a slice of pizza hanging out of her mouth, yelling as she caught her foot on the corner of the chair. In what felt like total slow motion, I saw her falling towards me and before I could stop it from happening, the pizza landed smack bang on my left boob as we both fell to the floor.

While that was pretty crap in itself, what was worse was the sound of material tearing as I went to get up.

'Shit, Gemma, I'm so sorry.'

I knew I probably should have told her off for swearing, but I could tell she didn't know whether to laugh or cry and, to be honest, neither did I. Meredith didn't seem to have that problem however, finding it particularly hilarious and she didn't hold back in showing it.

As I turned, I could see that the dress had split right up to the backside.

'You can't wear that now.'

I heard the doorbell ring at the side door and heard Jude shout up, 'Are you decent?'

'Put the red dress on, Gemma. There's nothing else for it.'

I hesitated but could hear Jude's footsteps mounting the stairs.

There was literally nothing else I could do so I dashed into my bedroom hoping I'd get there before Jude saw me with my arse hanging out. As I slid the satin material over my head, the memories that I thought I would associate with the dress slithered away.

I smoothed it down over my hips and looked in the mirror. It fitted me perfectly.

Taking a deep breath, I walked back into the lounge and their faces stared at me agog. Oh no. They hated it. I looked at them each in turn. I knew this dress was a mistake.

Occy and Meredith both said 'wow' in unison and grinned. Meredith even wolf-whistled. I thought I saw her wink at Occy but it was so slight I wasn't sure if I'd imagined it.

'So. Will I do?'

I turned to Jude who had just walked into the room and did a very nervous twirl, holding my breath.

'Fucking hell!'

20

'Right then... Are you ready? Shall we head off?'

We reached the bottom of the staircase, me gingerly holding the hem of my dress in my hand and taking each step as carefully as I could in my sparkly high heels. Jude opened the front door and turned to me.

It was only then that I realised that he looked... well... bloody hot. Obviously if you liked that 'film star, ruggedly handsome man in a uniform' type of look. Which, of course, I did not.

He was however, looking particularly dapper in what I suppose you'd call a dress uniform. A tunic or maybe even blazer it might possibly be called, with a white shirt and black tie and formal trousers. A variety of medals hung from his top pocket.

'I didn't want to say anything in front of...' he looked upstairs and saw Meredith and Occy hanging out of the window waving, enthusiastically '...those two.'

They had refused to leave with us, saying that they would tidy up before heading off so I didn't have to come back to the chaos they'd managed to create all over my bedroom. Occy was staying at Meredith's for the night, so that Jude didn't have to clock watch all night and worry about getting back for her. They were looking forward to having a girls' night in, with a film, and some popcorn if they had any room left after the massive pizza they'd devoured.

He crooked his arm for me, in which I hooked one arm, while scooping up the hem of my dress with the other.

He whispered into my ear as he opened the car door and I felt his warm breath on my neck.

'You look stunning.'

A shiver trickled all the way down my spine.

'Thank you. You're not looking so bad yourself, Fire Safety Officer Jude Adams. You scrub up well.'

'God, imagine if we were on a *proper* date, I'm not sure we'd get much further than the back seat of this car.' He tutted and ran a finger round the inside of his collar. 'I think I'm a bit out of practice at this dating – or even not-dating – lark, Gemma. I'm sorry. I feel a bit nervous.'

'Get a grip, kiddo. It's only me.' My flippant words did not match how I was feeling and, with shaking hands, I fumbled with the clasp on my silver clutch bag.

I looked over at him with a grin and he took a deep breath and grinned back. And suddenly we were able to both settle into a more relaxed conversation about the café. Time flew by and, before we knew it, the driver had pulled up at the entrance to a very grand hotel that looked more like a stately home. Jude came round and opened my door and once again offered his arm.

We walked the short distance to the door where we were welcomed by a gentleman in full fire brigade regalia who ticked our names off the list on his clipboard. Once inside, another uniformed officer offered us a glass of bubbly each and invited us to go through to the main bar area where people were mingling.

Even the entrance foyer was spectacular; a huge sweeping staircase with elegant mahogany bannisters on which I envisaged children of years ago, sliding down, squealing with delight. The ornate carved wooden ceilings drew our eyes upwards and I reached out for Jude's arm, starting to feel a little anxious, feeling out of place and well out of my depth in a place such as this. I hadn't been in a room full of people that I didn't know for a very long time.

Jude squeezed my hand and I knew he was reading my mind.

'OK?'

I blew out a big breath and nodded.

'You'll be great. I'll be right beside you. And if I forget to say this at the end of the evening, thank you for coming with me tonight. I really appreciate it. There's no one that I'd rather be on a not-date with, but you.'

I grinned back at him.

'And if I forget too, thank you for bringing me. I've had a lovely time.'

He laughed.

'We're like Richard Gere and Julia Roberts in *Pretty Woman*.'

I blushed as I thought about some of the things that Richard and Julia got up to in that film and tried to erase that picture from my mind.

'Let's hope you're not saying, "big mistake", to me later and still feel like you've enjoyed yourself at the end of the evening.'

Jude introduced me to several of his colleagues from his current station, along with some other people that he'd worked with before at other places. When the gong rang, its loud echoing sound reverberating around the room, he grabbed my hand guided me over to our table, holding my chair out for me as I sat down. The perfect gentleman.

'It's good to see you tonight, Adams. Finally, we get you along to something.' A woman who seemed to be sitting to my side turned to me. 'And you are?'

'I'm Gemma. I'm a friend of Jude's.'

She grinned and shook my hand.

'Nice to meet you, Gemma. Any friend of Adams' is a friend of the fire brigade. I'm Steph and it looks like you might be stuck with me tonight.'

I noticed that Jude had become caught in conversation with the person on his other side and, without him, I felt a little out of place, but Steph made polite chit-chat and it wasn't long before the first course was served. Once we finished, Steph leaned across and whispered to me.

'Any chance you can come to the loo with me, Gem? I've just necked three glasses of bubbly on an empty stomach and I'm feeling a bit squiffy already. I might fall over on these bloody great heels if I don't have someone to make sure I'm steady. Us girls have to stick together, don't we?'

I looked across at Jude who was deep in conversation but he seemed to be in tune with me as he glanced up and smiled, then mouthed, 'Are you OK?' I nodded before walking away with Steph to the ladies' room.

When she came out of the cubicle, she moved towards the mirrors and pouted, re-applying her lipstick which already looked perfect. 'So, give me all the goss on Adams then, Gemma. How long have you two been...' She mimicked speech marks in the air. 'Friends.'

'We *are* just friends. I've not really known him that long to be honest.'

'Well, I've known him for the best part of ten years and there's definitely something, or someone, who has been putting a smile on his face for the last few weeks. I'm presuming that someone is you.'

'That's nice of you to say so, but honestly, we're just good friends.'

'Yeah right. And I'm Lady Gaga.' She winked. 'There's going to be a few hearts breaking in the fire station when the rest of the crew meet you. There's a whole lot of love for Adams going on. A lot of women who wouldn't mind sliding down his pole, I can tell you. A few men too come to think of it.'

I could feel the heat rise up my neck and was pretty sure that the colour of my face would soon match that of my dress.

'We're just friends.'

'OK, if you say so. But since you arrived tonight, I've been watching and he's hardly taken his eyes off you.' She put me right on the spot and, as she held my gaze, I couldn't hold hers back for long and was the first to look away. 'Just saying. I don't blame him by the way, you're fabulous! Come on, let's get back. I'm starving and need something more than a prawn cock to soak up this booze before I'm totally shit-faced!'

She hooked her arm in mine and staggered back to the table.

After she said that, I couldn't help but notice that Jude did keep looking at me. I wondered if I'd got something on my face but I discreetly looked in the mirror of my clutch bag and couldn't see anything, so I must have been imagining it. He was clearly just making sure I was OK like he promised. I appreciated it.

The meal was delicious and the wine flowed. Well, it did

when you were sat next to Steph. I had to keep covering the top of my glass to stop her refilling it. I had work tomorrow, although I had arranged to have a late start, and I didn't want to have a massive hangover to deal with. Luckily as she turned away to talk to someone who had approached the table, I managed to pour myself another glass of water; luckily, she hadn't seemed to notice that I'd drunk more water than wine. A little trick that Mum told me and Lucy about years ago to pace ourselves. The last thing I wanted to do was show myself up, but, more than that, show Jude up.

Once the meal was over and the tables cleared, there was an announcement to say that the award proceedings were due to start. Numerous commendations were handed out and the final accolade of the night was given in recognition of a special act of bravery. When the chief fire officer told of the tense situation Jude had been involved in, describing the bravery of the single-handed rescue of four children in a house fire, tears streamed down my face. I felt ridiculously proud when they announced him as the winner and he walked to the stage to a standing ovation to collect his prestigious award.

Steph put her fingers in her mouth and gave a piercing whistle, which dogs in the next county must have pricked up their ears at, and our whole table winced. As Jude returned to the table, he was surrounded by colleagues who were all shaking his hand and thumping him on the back in congratulations. He was clearly well respected and loved. A bottle of champagne had been placed in front of him and one of his station officers opened it and poured.

When the crowd finally dispersed, he sat and breathed a sigh of relief.

'Crikey, that was intense.'

'That was amazing more like. I didn't realise you were so hands-on.'

'I was, but since moving down here, less so. It was quite traumatic at the time and the service are all about mental health and well-being so wanted me to be doing a less active role for a while.'

'You're amazing.'

'Ah no. Just doing my job.'

He was so humble. This whole evening had reminded me that there were very special people in the world – doctors, nurses, paramedics, police, firefighters, and many more angels without wings – regularly saving lives, thinking it's all in a day's work, while I was making cakes and cooking full English breakfasts. Food for thought for sure.

'Oh, I love this one!' Steph jumped up. 'Come on, you two. Don't be boring. Get up and dance with me?'

As she pulled us both up, Jude leaned towards me and said, 'Now do you see why I didn't want to come alone?'

I giggled. 'She's lovely. Just a bit... well... tipsy?'

'Loud and off her tits I think is the expression you are looking for.'

Steph literally dragged us onto the dance floor but I was thankful she did. It had been absolutely ages since I'd been out dancing and it felt good to let go and lose myself in the music. Mum, Lucy and I loved to dance around the café. Whenever we were feeling down or stressed about something Mum would insist that we all got up and had a good old sing and dance to let off some steam whether we wanted to or not. She alleged that dancing released the endorphins in your blood which make you feel good. I truly loved a good old dance.

Suddenly, the tempo changed and a slower number came on. I turned to walk back to the table but Jude grabbed my hand.

'Where do you think you're sneaking off to? You're here to be my partner tonight, you know. Not leave me standing around in case someone's wife feels sorry for me. Come on. Let's dance.'

I took his hand.

In hindsight, it was a 'big mistake'.

21

Pinned close against his body, I could smell the spicy tones of his aftershave. Closing my eyes, I tried to breathe in deeply without him noticing that I might be a crazed lunatic, but God! He smelled *so* good. One thing about living alone after living with a man is that I missed the smell of a clean, fresh-out-of-the-shower, aftershaved male.

Being that close to him should have felt weird, but it didn't. Our bodies fused together seamlessly and swayed to the music, perfectly in harmony with each other, and I had to remind myself that we had committed to being just friends. I buried my head against his shoulder, not trusting myself to look up at him. Doubting myself. I thought that being alone was what I wanted. That I didn't need to be part of a couple, but tonight reminded me that it was nice to be part of something again.

'Are you OK, Gemma?'

I looked up and felt my stomach flutter as his eyes locked onto mine and then flickered to my lips and back. His tongue licked his bottom lip and my stomach flip-flopped. I desperately wanted him to kiss me right then and I hoped more than anything in the world that he was feeling the same and that I wasn't misreading the situation. His head bent towards mine, I could feel his breath on my face, his lips mere millimetres away. I closed my eyes and surrendered myself in anticipation of what would happen next.

'Fuck! Sorry!'

Steph's body slammed into us, forcing us apart. Jude raised his eyebrows at me.

'Bit pissed. Well, super sozzled actually. You've had him enough tonight. It's your turn to dance with me now, Adams. He's hot property you know, Gemma. All the ladies at the station lust after him more than anyone else. And he's a huge hit with the gay guys too. It's that aloof single man vibe that he gives out.' She pinched his cheeks the way a granny does to a baby. 'He's irresistible.'

She lunged at him and I laughed, walking back to the table where I raised my glass and smiled. The last thing I saw before she whisked him away was him rolling his eyes and mouthing, 'Help.'

I'd drank way more bubbly than I was used to and it had very nearly got me into a whole lot of trouble just then so I stopped drinking it, reverting to water.

When the lights came on fully and as people started to bid their goodnights, we gathered our things together, me grabbing my bag and Jude grabbing his award and we fell into the car for the drive home, both shattered by our big night out. Sitting side by side, with his thigh pressing against mine, felt like yet another intimate moment that shouldn't be happening. If we would have been a couple, we might have snuggled up with each other and I was certainly feeling quietly nervous about being in such close proximity after our near kiss earlier. I tried to shuffle a little nearer to my side of the car and he looked over and gave a little tight-lipped smile.

The gentle movement of the car must have caused me to nod off because the next thing I knew, we were outside the café and I had woken up to find I'd been leaning on Jude's shoulder and had dribbled all over his tunic.

'Oh God. I'm so sorry!'

'That's OK, it needs dry-cleaning anyway after Steph spilt red wine all down it. Twice.'

'She's quite a character.'

'She is that.'

We both got out of the car and Jude walked me to my door, unbuttoning the top button of his shirt and unfastening his tie.

'So are you going to make me a quick coffee before bed?' Even though it was late and dark, the silvery moonlight illuminated his face and I could see him blush. 'I mean, before I go home. To my own bed that is. I didn't mean...'

I bit my lip. This needed to be handled delicately.

'Yep, I'm not on the early shift but will still need to work when I'm up, so it'll have to be a quick one.' It was then my turn to blush. 'Coffee that is. And I do mean coffee only.'

'Yes, ma'am.' He saluted me and we laughed in relief as I fumbled in my clutch bag for my keys and unlocked the door. His face must have been right behind my backside as we climbed the steep stairs but there was nothing I could do about it and he had the good grace to be looking down when we reached the top and I turned round.

'Have a seat and I'll go and put the kettle on.'

Instead of sitting, he removed his jacket and walked towards the window. I had to tear my eyes away to go through to the kitchen. When I returned with two coffee mugs, he was still in the same spot.

'It's so beautiful up here. I could just sit and stare at that view forever.'

I unbuckled my shoes and sighed when my feet sank into the sumptuous carpet. It had been a while since I'd worn three-inch high strappy sandals for that length of time and my feet were throbbing.

'I rarely close the curtains. Too beautiful a sight to shut out. There are times even now, when I still find it quite overwhelming, even though I've lived here for a while.'

'I'm not surprised. Our house is on a hill, and you can just about glimpse the sea, if you stand up and lean out of the skylight. I'm sure the estate agent told us it had sea views.'

'Ah, surely you know most estate agents elaborate on the truth to sell houses. And if yours was called Russell, then he has quite the reputation for manipulating the truth to suit his needs. Ask Meredith about the lighthouse next time you see her.'

'It feels weird that I can see the lighthouse from here and my daughter is in there, sleeping. I can't remember when I last spent a night away from her. Don't tell her this because she'll call me a freak, but I sometimes stand and just watch her sleeping at night before I head off to bed myself. Wondering what she's dreaming about, thinking about how amazing she is and how she doesn't realise it. Hoping that I'm enough for her. Whether one parent is enough.'

My heart went out to him.

'I'm pretty sure that one parent who loves you deeply is way better than any parent that doesn't have their child's best interest at heart.'

'That sounds like it comes from a place of experience.'

'Maybe it does. School was hard for me because at that time it was less common to have one parent. These days, it's more unusual if you have two. Anyway, tell me about Occy as a young child.'

I was always good at changing the subject when anyone mentioned my father.

'I hope you've got a while. She's my favourite topic to talk about.'

* * *

'Morning, sleepyhead.'

I handed Jude a cup of coffee as he stirred on the sofa. He looked a little befuddled as he took in his surroundings.

'Oh God! I fell asleep. I'm so sorry.'

'Hey, it's fine. It was a long night and we'd drank quite a bit. I did try to wake you, but you were dead to the world.' I pulled my kimono dressing gown slightly tighter around me, feeling a little self-conscious being in this situation.

'You must think I'm awful.' He rubbed his brow and raked his hands through his hair, tousling it even more. I dragged my eyes away.

'Not at all. It's honestly not a problem. There's some water and some headache tablets there if you need them. I bet Steph also has these for breakfast this morning.'

He sat up, swung his legs round and yawned as he looked at his watch.

'I feel like I've had the best night's sleep I've had in years. Can't believe it's nearly nine. You don't need to go and open up do you? I think you said not last night.'

'No, I arranged for Pat to do that this morning, knowing we'd have a late night, although I should probably get dressed soon and go down and help her. It feels a bit strange not doing the early morning shift. First time in ages.'

'I'd better make a move then. I'm honestly mortified that I fell asleep on your sofa.'

'You looked so peaceful and comfortable, I just threw a spare duvet over the top of you and left you there when I went to bed. Did you not wake up at all?'

'Not once. I think at home, I'm constantly listening out for Occy. She... please don't tell her I told you this, but sometimes she has nightmares and wakes herself up. The worst thing is that she's shouting "Mum" out loud sometimes. It's heartbreaking.'

'I won't say a word, but that must be hard for you.'

'I just go in and comfort her but when she wakes up the following morning, she never mentions it and neither do I. I'm not even sure if she even remembers. I've never asked her.'

'Bless her.' We were both silent in our thoughts as we sipped our coffee, side by side.

'Right, I'd better get off.'

'I'll walk down with you.'

When we reached the bottom of the stairs, Jude stepped outside and stood on the doorstep, before reaching in to give me a peck on the cheek.

'Thanks for... well... everything, Gemma. I had a lovely night. You were the best company. You were amazing.'

'Morning, lovebirds!'

Clem and Meredith had stopped opposite us, Alice the dog at their feet, both with huge grins on their faces. Jude and I both turned scarlet.

'It's not what you think.'

'That's what they all say.'

Clem winked as he headed into the shop next door.

Jude shuffled off up the street to do the walk of no-shame.

Meredith walked off in the opposite direction. 'I'll see you later, lady! And be prepared. I want to hear *everything*.'

22

'So, come on! Dish the dirt! I want to know everything. And I mean the whole shebang. Don't hold back.'

It would take some convincing that nothing untoward had gone on between me and Jude.

Meredith had come into the café later that morning, and I was still struggling to get going, probably because it had been a late night, though there were also lots of thoughts going around my head. Starting later had been quite hard.

It did me good to keep on telling Meredith that we were just friends, nothing more. Re-telling myself as well along with all the reasons why.

'There's nothing to tell. You've got the wrong end of the stick. Totally. There is absolutely nothing going on between us.'

'So, you don't fancy him then?'

'Well, that doesn't really come into it, does it? If we've decided to be just friends, then I can't think of him in that way.'

'You do fancy him then?'

'I never said that.'

'You didn't say no either.'

'Oh, shut up, Meredith.'

She grinned back at me, loving the fact that while she was teasing me, I was cringing with embarrassment.

'He did look quite hot this morning though,' she continued, 'doing the walk of shame with his jacket slung over his shoulder and his tie hanging out of his pocket. With you standing on your doorstep in your dressing gown waving him off, it definitely looked like he'd been rogering you senseless all night.'

'Enough now. Haven't you got anything else to do with your life but badger me about a non-event?'

'Not really, to be honest – no! And it's so much fun to see you blushing like a teenager. Sorry, I will stop now.'

'Thank God for that. Now, are we going to look at those fabric swatches you've got or not?'

'OK, but don't think I haven't noticed that you've just changed the conversation.' She grinned and opened her portfolio, pulling out the mood boards she'd made up with the palettes we'd discussed.

With our joint vision and Clem's renovation skills, the new and improved café was coming along nicely. The warm, earthy colour tones would complement the walls where the brickwork was going to be left exposed. The original floors would be sanded back to their original state with a distressed varnished look. There'd be brightly coloured comfy sofas with big squishy cushions for people to sit back and relax, with low coffee tables mixed up with more formal oak dining tables and high-backed chairs.

In winter, it would be warm and cosy and I could light the fire. The sound of a crackling fire and the smell of burning wood always filled me with joy and I was looking forward to it all coming together. And in summer, it would feel cool and calm. Everything would be perfectly placed to make the most of the amazing view that the café was blessed with. We just needed it to happen now.

Next up was finding a suitable date to go and have a mooch at some final pieces of furniture and accessories. Most of Martin's stock had been sold off when he moved out but he had told us about a place that might have what we needed, so we tried to sync our diaries.

'That's a Monday, can't do that.'

'Why are your Mondays so inflexible, Gemma? Why all the mystery?'

'No mystery.' I scratched the back of my neck. 'It's just my day to do stuff for me. I mainly just meet old friends. Nothing more than that.'

Meredith scrunched up her mouth and narrowed her eyes. I changed the subject once more.

'How did you get on with Occy last night by the way? You haven't said and I'd totally forgotten to ask.'

'Oh, she was great company. After we'd tidied up at yours, we went back to the lighthouse and watched *Dirty Dancing*, which I can't believe she'd never seen. Poor child. I left her in bed this morning while we went out for a walk with Alice. She said she was nice and cosy and didn't want to leave the spare room. Said her room was nowhere near as nice and she'd love hers to be like it.'

I tapped my lip, deep in thought, and Meredith asked what was going through my mind.

'Let me get back to you on that, when I've had more time to think an idea through.'

'That sounds interesting.'

'Mmm, I think it will be. So, what was Occy's favourite part of the film?'

We spent the next ten minutes discussing the merits of *Dirty*

Dancing and which line was the most memorable. While I voted for 'Nobody puts Baby in the corner', Meredith's vote was for 'I carried a watermelon', and we talked about how sexy Patrick Swayze was in that film and how we wished we could dance like that, with him.

I loved the friendship I had with Meredith. We'd become such good friends since she'd relocated here. She was just over fifty and with me being thirty-nine, there was a good age gap between us but it never mattered. When she had first moved to Driftwood Bay, she was quite reluctant to admit her feelings for Clem because he was nearly ten years younger, but age was but a number. They clearly adored each other and got on like a house on fire, so why shouldn't they be together?

But the great thing was: they weren't joined at the hip and Meredith still purposely made time for her friends. She'd said this was really important as it was something that she hadn't done in her previous long-term relationship, prioritising her husband's wishes over her own, and as a result, her friendships had waned.

We agreed a date later that week and I asked Pat if she could cover. She was grateful of the extra hours, with Christmas looming and presents to buy for her family. And then, much as it would have been nice to sit in the café chatting with Meredith all day, it was starting to get busy so I thought I'd better get a shimmy on and help.

Since Lucy had suggested the idea, I'd been constantly racking my brains for a new name for the café and was still considering whether it was the right thing to do at all. I was swaying towards a change. It felt like it was time for a fresh new start for The Harbour Corner Café but it had to be the perfect name. It almost felt like that was the most important part of the whole project. I was trusting in the universe again and hoped that it would come to me. Lucy and James were also trying to think of something suitable, although the name of my business was probably not as much of a priority to them than the name of their child.

Everything was slowly coming together. A call from Rachel, the woman who had got in touch about the job, confirmed that she'd be in Driftwood Bay a couple of weeks before the launch, which worked perfectly. She said that she'd arranged some rental accommodation and was looking forward to her new adventure. The timing couldn't have been better; she could get used to the systems that we had in place before everyone got trained up together on the new equipment I was having to install – hopefully a good way for the staff to all get to know each other.

That evening, I put the finishing touches to the menu and emailed it over to Lucy for her thoughts. It was important to me that, even though it was my business, she felt that she could still have an input. She also had a great business brain and had offered me some fabulous advice over the years – tips that she'd picked up at the B & B.

It seemed like everything was coming together nicely and all was on track. Time to sit back and relax, breathe a little and enjoy life.

23

The next few weeks flew by and it was an exciting yet terrifying time waiting for the big launch event. Jude and Occy continued to come over for tea and having Occy there meant that Jude and I had returned to how our relationship had been prior to our big night out, slipping back easily into our roles as friends. It felt safe and the right place for us to be.

Finally, Clem was ready to knock through and the time had come for us to take the biggest step of all. The Harbour Corner Café would be closed for a couple of weeks to pull it all together. Furniture was ready to be delivered and we'd left two clear days before the launch to make sure everything was spot on. There were a lot of changes taking place and Clem was working his backside off, along with a couple of his pals who he'd called in favours from to help, to ensure that the business was impacted as little as possible.

Luckily Geoff, the landlord of the Harbourside Hotel, had very kindly lent me a converted horsebox which he'd bought years ago and intended to use as a catering trailer for events but never quite got round to apart from at the annual beach party. It was all set up on the front patio and we were able to serve limited food and drinks and people would still be able to sit on the outside furniture. I'd bought plenty of blankets which people could wrap up in if they were cold, but they seemed to enjoy the temporary outside experience and the weather was being incredibly kind to us. Thank goodness.

Geoff was quite glad to not be doing so much food at the pub. He was getting older and we'd come to an agreement that he was happy for us to become the dining venue in the village and the pub would become more of a drinking establishment. It was an understanding that suited us both and importantly let him wind down. He needed less stress in his later years and wanted to enjoy his business as well as his life.

The hospitality trade is a hard one to be in. You can't just not bother to turn up one day and not open. Opening regularly is a necessity and not only that, but you also have to do it all with a smile on your face too, even sometimes, when people aren't being the nicest to you. So many people in the industry were burning out and businesses closing down due to lack of custom so it was nice to think that we were helping him to continue in a trade that he knew and loved.

Life is precious and sometimes cut short unexpectedly. Losing loved ones certainly teaches us that. You always think you have all the time in the world to do the things you want, but life can sometimes tell us differently and it's important to live our best lives while we're here. The future isn't promised. The past is gone. The present is a gift that not everyone is blessed with and we should spend our time wisely. I knew that I was blessed to love my work and was excited about the future.

* * *

The day that Rachel came to Driftwood Bay was a memorable one. I was working on my own from the catering trailer, and the large hiking group had come back, wanting food and drinks. When I saw that she'd arrived, I asked her to grab a seat and bear with me. She did better than that: two minutes later, the door opened and she threw her bag on the floor under the counter, her words music to my ears.

'Right, tell me what I can do to help.'

We worked in harmony, moving around each other in perfect symmetry, ensuring that our customers were satisfied. When all the orders had been completed and we'd got time to breathe, I turned to her.

'I think I love you already!'

'Well, nothing like being chucked in at the deep end. I hope I was helpful.'

'Helpful? I don't know how I've managed without you. You were like my fairy godmother sweeping in to save me.'

'I've found throughout the years that if you make yourself indispensable, it's harder for people to want to get rid of you.'

We both laughed.

'Excellent tactics. I like it. I've got Pat and Occy coming down to meet you later. It's so important for me that we work together as a team. That you guys bond, support each other and have each other's backs.'

'That sounds great, Gemma. Sounds like a really good work ethos to have.'

'Fab. Let me show you around inside.'

Every time that I'd come into the building recently, I had felt a little shiver run down my spine. Clem was working utter wonders, my vision was unfolding before my very eyes and the change was stratospheric. He'd suggested that we cover the windows for the last couple of weeks so it all remained a secret and, as a result, the anticipation of what we were doing was the talk of the village. I couldn't wait to unveil the place on launch night and was excited to reveal the new name too. Only Clem, the signwriter and I knew what it was – he'd even sworn not to share it with Meredith.

* * *

When Rachel returned later, after settling in at her accommodation, I introduced her to Pat and Occy and they got on like a house on fire. Occy and Rachel seemed to form an easy rapport, laughing easily. Occy was old for her years and Rachel appeared quite youthful in hers so they really did bond well. While I sat back and watched them, I felt like Pat would take the 'Mamma Bear' role and that, as a team, they would work well together. It was a huge relief.

After I talked through my plans for the launch event, they all chose their own roles for the evening and made a couple of tweaks to my schedule – all of which made sense –and raised some points that I hadn't even thought of.

'I bet Lizzie would help out, you know. She's always saying that if any jobs come up here, she'd love one.'

'That's a good shout actually. If Lizzie could help you with the serving of the food, and the clearing of tables, that would be great. An extra pair of hands is always helpful and if we get too busy in the future, we might need someone on a more permanent basis.'

Occy beamed.

'I'm not promising anything though. Until we know how busy it will be, recruitment of staff will probably be gradual. We might have some hectic days before I decide that we have to take on more staff.'

'That's OK, it's nice that you'd consider her.'

'Well, if you say she's OK then I'm happy to take that as a recommendation.'

The guest list was huge. I'd originally tried to put some names together, but it had felt awkward to invite some people and not others, so we'd basically given an open invitation to the whole village. The local paper had very kindly included a brief report about us, but without a business name or any images, they couldn't really say a lot. However, they had promised a full-page feature once we were fully open, which was exciting and would be most welcomed. Any free publicity was much appreciated.

Patio heaters had been borrowed from everywhere possible and there would be sheltered space in the little courtyard garden, as well as some on the patio which overlooked the bay. Hopefully people would mingle in all areas and I prayed for a dry night. We wouldn't want wind and rain stopping people coming out and enjoying themselves.

We'd worked really hard on making the outside spaces as lovely as possible and wanted everyone to enjoy them as much as they enjoyed the inside areas.

What was giving me the biggest headache was that there was a lot of cooking to be done beforehand, as well as on the day, along with my normal Monday cooking duties. I didn't want to renege on that agreement; people relied on me and I didn't want to let anyone down. It would be an early start, but I was used to that. Hard work never bothered me and it would be worth it.

Full meals wouldn't be available to order on our launch evening, as I thought we would be making it difficult for ourselves. Instead, Lizzie and Occy would be wandering around with taster samples from the new menu which would hopefully give people an insight into what we would be doing going forward. Lucy had been brilliant and had made some amazing suggestions, knowing how easy and difficult certain dishes were to cook. My favourite appetisers were the mini fish and chip tasters served in cones, and the miniature toad in the holes, which used locally sourced pork sausages and a scoop of mashed potato in a Yorkshire pudding. We had cranberry and brie bites for the vegetarians and vegans, as well as caramelised onion and goat's cheese crostini. Rachel also reminded me that some people are gluten free so I'd have to look up something special for that option too.

Poor Occy and Jude had been my guinea pigs on a couple of occasions although they didn't seem to mind sampling the various choices I'd been experimenting with. It was nice to have someone help me make those final decisions instead of doing it alone. We'd spent several lovely evenings together languishing and putting the world to rights and trying out the new menu, and Jude said he'd never seen Occy look so happy.

Before now, the refurbishment had always seemed like a long way in the distance but now it was nearly here, and I was amazed at how the time had flown by. It was going to be all hands on deck to pull everything together but it was exciting, giving me a fuzzy feeling in my tummy.

24

'Ready?'

'You bet!'

It had always been important to me for Lucy to be the first to see everything completed and in place. There was an hour to go and she'd walked round to the harbour and knocked on the door as I'd requested.

Standing behind her, I covered her eyes with my hands and guided her over the step.

I removed my hands.

She gasped. 'Oh, Gem.'

'What do you think?'

She turned to me and then back to the room.

'Gemma... It's...'

'Do you hate it? Oh God! Have I got it all wrong?'

She turned to me once more.

'My darling Gemma. I couldn't be prouder of you if I tried. This is amazing. *You* are amazing. This is just incredible.'

The relief was indescribable and I breathed out loudly.

'It was so important to me that you liked it.'

She meandered around the room, gently running her fingers across the huge, gilded mirror that hung above the fireplace and turned to smile at me. It was the mirror that Mum used to have in our lounge and looked perfectly at home above the fireplace where the wood burner was gently crackling away.

The main serving counter had been completely revamped, and the huge clock that Mum used to keep in her kitchen took pride of place above the two huge coffee machines at the back. A tall glass cabinet sat to the left, with a display of soft drink bottles and cans, and, on the front, a low-lit cabinet in which the cakes we'd been busy baking were displayed. Colourful gingham bunting ran around the counter, intertwined with glimmering fairy lights.

'If she could see this... do you know what Mum would have said, Gem?'

We laughed as we said her catchphrase in unison: 'Just the job!'

'You do know that she would have loved it, don't you?'

'Oh, I hope so.'

'I *know* so, lady. God, if she could be here now, she'd be beside herself with excitement.'

'I wish she was, Luce.'

'Oh, darling. Me too. More than anything in the world.' I noticed that she put her hand to her stomach as she said this and I had to swallow a lump in my throat.

'Look at us. Two successful business owners. And one about to be a mum.'

'And one about to be an aunty too. How exciting.'

She pulled me tightly to her chest.

'I love you, Gemma.'

I squeezed her tight.

'I love you too, Lucy. Now there are two more things we need to do, and I want us to do them together.'

Lucy looked puzzled.

Because I didn't want anyone outside to see the sign before Lucy, it had literally been under wraps and I'd had the sign-writer make a video reveal. I held up my iPad for her to watch. She gasped and held her heart to her chest, tears appearing in her eyes. She whispered the name.

'The 5 O'clock Somewhere Bistro'.

'You like it?'

'I absolutely adore it, babe. You are wonderful, you know. She'd love – and most definitely approve of – the new name.'

When Lucy and I were younger, every time Mum fancied a tipple, she used to have a little saying, one that we've always used all our lives. That was the name I had decided to call the business, and instead of calling it a café, we'd upgraded it to a bistro. I was so happy that Lucy approved.

'Just one more thing, Luce. Something for the back wall.'

I put my hand under the counter and passed her a parcel wrapped in tissue paper.

She unfolded it carefully and removed a photograph of her, Mum and me. I remembered the day so vividly even now. It was from one of her days off and we'd gone to have a picnic on the beach. Lucy and I had made all the food and put the whole picnic together. We are all laughing hilariously at the camera because I'd not long bitten into a Scotch egg which was revoltingly gritty and Lucy confessed to us that she'd dropped it in the sand and applied the five-second rule. Mum had always said that it was one of the happiest days of her life so it seemed the right photo to have on display.

We took one side each, and hung it up on the back wall, where it could be seen from every angle in the room. I poured us both a glass of Buck's Fizz – I'd checked beforehand that she could have a small amount of it – and we clinked our glasses together, then raised them to the photo.

'To Mum.'

25

Everyone had their designated jobs and after a little pep talk, where I made everyone stand with their hands on their hips, reciting the words, 'we are superheroes' to much laughter, we were finally ready to open the doors.

I would be front of house, and chief welcomer, with Occy and Lizzie mingling with plates of appetisers and Pat ensuring that the welcome drinks were flowing. Rachel was in the kitchen, keeping on top of the steady stream of food coming through. She said that she loved the behind the scenes work more than being front of house.

'Honestly, Gemma, I'll be fine. It'll be a bit overwhelming if the whole village is out. Remember that you know everyone round here, but they're mostly strangers to me.'

I did understand. I forget sometimes that living here nearly all my life meant that I knew the locals nearly as well as I knew myself.

Occy had such a huge grin on her face and kept wandering around telling me, 'It's *vibe*, Gemma, totally vibe.' I had no idea what that meant, and didn't want to show my total uncoolness, but thankfully Pat put me out of my misery: apparently, it was the latest phrase to express that something was really good and that I should be flattered. I was truly honoured.

At bang on 7 p.m., I removed the screening from the window panels and switched on the lights to a loud cheer. I'd been worrying that there would only be a few people turning up but it seemed that we'd attracted quite the crowd. My heart squeezed when I realised that pretty much the whole town had come along to celebrate.

I opened the door and moved outside to switch on the festoon lights and remove the material that had been draped over the sign.

Lucy and I stood hand in hand while Pat struck a metal ice bucket with a knife to get everyone's attention. When the crowd simmered down, I cleared my throat, took a deep breath and made my announcement.

'Ladies and gentlemen. I would like to declare the "5 O'clock Somewhere Bistro" open.'

Once the name could be seen from behind the material, there was a huge round of applause and we turned to grin at each other.

The village really had turned out in droves for our opening night. I wasn't sure whether that was because they were joyous in celebrating the launch night or whether it was because there was free grub and booze on offer.

Surprised to see Geoff in the throng, I headed his way with a glass in my hand and when I reached him I raised a questioning eyebrow.

'One night off a year won't hurt, cherub.' He winked and took the glass from me. 'I wasn't missing this night for nothing. I've known your ma since we were kids and I've been a customer in her café since the first day it opened. She would be mighty proud of you, young lady. You've done an amazing job. I just can't be arsed to do food these days. The kitchen would have needed a big renovation and I don't have the energy and I've got better things to spend me money on. I'm so glad you are taking over as the food place in the village and we can concentrate on being a good old-fashioned boozer.'

We'd be running evenings like the book club and I'd agreed that the local WI group could have their meetings here once a month, and Geoff had mentioned that he'd be keen to be running proper pub quizzes and pub nights. It seemed like an arrangement that would suit us both.

As I thanked him, I kissed his soft bristly cheek and could see him blushing. Pat grinned at him as she walked past and, not for the first time, I saw him wink at her. She, in turn, got just a little bit too girly for it to be a nothing response. Interesting!

It was an hour later when I finally got a chance to speak to Jude. I'd spotted him earlier but had told myself I hadn't *really* been looking out for him, but when Meredith whispered in my ear, 'I think you just need to admit that you fancy the pants off him and are perfect for each other,' I realised that it was probably time to admit it to myself. Maybe in the future at some point, he might even find out for himself too.

Since the evening he'd stayed on my sofa, my mind had frequently drifted away into daydreams much akin to the plot of a romcom movie: single independent woman meets hot single fireman dad and we lived happily ever after. Sometimes I'd dream of him and it all got a little steamy, making me wake up in a bit of a fluster, and then when I faced him, I had to pretend I hadn't been dreaming about rolling around in bed with him.

But life wasn't always like a fairy tale sadly, as I was about to find out.

Jude made his way over to me, through a little break in the

crowd and handed me a glass of bubbly from the tray that Pat was carrying.

'Bet you haven't even had chance to have one yourself yet, have you?'

The cold bubbles hit the spot perfectly, and he kissed my cheek.

'Congratulations, Gemma. This, is... well... it's...'

He didn't seem at all himself this evening. I had to excuse myself to talk to some customers, and when I turned, he was still hovering around, shuffling from one foot to the other.

'Is everything OK, Jude?'

'Have you got time to take a short break? I know it's a daft question but do you think you could join me outside? I won't keep you long.'

Looking around the bistro, I could see that everything was in hand. Occy and Lizzie were both laughing as they were still handing out appetisers and napkins and Pat was in her element going around the room chatting and filling up glasses. For the first time in a while, I didn't feel needed.

'A breath of fresh air would be perfect right now. I'm a bit hot and bothered from all the rushing around as well as all the adrenaline coursing through my body.'

Side by side with him on one of the benches that overlooked the harbour, I couldn't help but feel his warm leg resting against mine.

I took a huge breath and blew it out slowly, releasing all the anxiety I'd been holding on to for days.

'Gosh, what a relief that it's gone so well.'

'It's amazing, Gemma. Well done. I'm super proud of you.'

'Ah thank you. But just look at your daughter.'

Through the windows, which were just starting to steam up from all the bodies inside, we could see Occy milling about. She looked like the cat that got the cream, taking it all in her stride as if she was involved in events like this all the time.

'Look at her. Happy, smiling away and chatting to people.'

'I know. Who would have thought it? You giving her this job has been the best thing anyone could ever have done for her. She's gone from being a surly miserable child to a pleasant young lady who's been a pleasure to be around. It's all thanks to you. I'm so grateful to you.'

'Ah not just me, Jude. Rachel and Pat have been a great influence on her too. She gets on so well with them both. My little team have come together beautifully.'

'Well, talking of coming together, I have something I'd like to say.' He turned to face me and took the glass out of my hand, reaching down and placing it on the pavement beside the bench. 'I didn't know whether to say anything or not but I don't think I'm being true to myself if I don't.'

My heart started to beat a little faster. I had absolutely no idea what he was going to say, but the butterflies in my stomach were telling me that this was going to be something I might not want to hear.

He took one of my hands in his and cleared his throat. 'Gemma.'

He sounded so serious. What on earth was he about to come out with?

'Since the other night, I've not been able to get you off my mind.'

'Oh!'

That was *not* what I was expecting to come out of his mouth.

'I may have got it all wrong and I know that we both said that we weren't interested in getting involved with someone else but I just want to make sure that I haven't got the wrong end of the stick.'

I looked down at my hand in his and back to his face. It had come as such a bolt out of the blue when it hit me recently, but deep down in my heart, I knew that I felt the same. I went to speak but he held his palm up and asked me to let him continue before he ran out of courage. I smiled at the thought of this big brave handsome fireman who flung himself into dangerous situations every day being scared of stringing a sentence together.

'When you were sleeping on my shoulder in the car that night, I wanted to pull you to me. I wanted to wake you up and kiss you. I wanted to take you home and have you lie in my arms and... well... you know... more too. I don't know if I'm imagining that you feel the same, and if you don't, I'd rather you just put me out of my misery and embarrassment and maybe we could agree to never mention this unfortunate moment again. OK, so that's it. I'm done.'

He smiled a crooked smile and raised his eyebrows anticipating my response, looking more nervous than I'd ever seen him before. He looked down at his hands as I spoke.

'But you said that you didn't want anyone in your life. That you weren't looking for love. You made it perfectly clear.'

'Totally and that was absolutely the case, but that was until I met you. Sometimes you find something that you didn't even know you were looking for.' He mumbled this, still looking down at his fingers which he'd started to twiddle.

With trembling hands, I put my finger under his chin and raised his head so it was level with mine. We locked eyes. I leaned forward and dropped a gentle butterfly kiss on his lips and heard him sigh. I pulled away. His face literally lit up with a huge smile. I couldn't help but grin back. Who knew that just one tiny kiss could set off a million fireworks in my stomach?

He squeezed my hand.

'So, you do feel the same then?'

I felt my nose wrinkle. 'Yep.' I was still grinning from ear to ear. 'But you were adamant that you didn't want to get involved with anyone, Jude. What changed?'

'I could ask you the same thing. But I didn't want to get involved with anyone. I still don't want to get involved with *anyone*. I do, however, want to get involved with *you*.'

'Now that I rather like the sound of.'

Jude's brow furrowed.

'I don't know what I can offer you right now. I'm a single dad who works a lot, with no real plans for a future of my own, and a hormonal fifteen-year-old daughter who takes up most of my time and energy. But I do know that I want to get to know you better and spend as much time with you as I can. And see if this could take us somewhere. Maybe it will. Maybe it won't. But what do you think?'

He held his palms up and tilted his head to one side.

'You old romantic, you.' I nudged his shoulder and scooted even closer to him. 'I'm not sure my prospects are much better. I'm a divorcee and have just thrown myself into a business where I'll be working all hours trying to make it a success. My sister is going to need me because she's having a baby. Shit! It's only just occurred to me that that might be why I'm throwing myself into this project – because I can't have children of my own.'

'You think?'

I laughed.

'OK, so maybe I am; my heart is ever so broken because of that fact as well as my ex-husband having an affair behind my back, and when he got his girlfriend pregnant it nearly finished me off. Still want me now?'

'Yep! You've not put me off yet.'

'So where do we go from here?'

'I might have an idea.' He leaned forward and threaded his

hands through my hair, pulling me closer still. My heart was hammering against my chest. Surely, he must be able to feel that. Maybe even hear it. His soft lips met mine and this time we kissed even more slowly than before. Passionately. Deeply.

Until I heard a voice shouting our names with urgency. It was Occy.

'For God's sake, will you pair of lovebirds stop snogging like you're my age and get yourselves over here please. I don't want to panic you but the kitchen is on fire.'

'Shit!'

I ran to the kitchen door with Jude hot on my heels. When we reached the building, he told the two of us to stay out front and he'd go and assess the situation.

When he called me into the kitchen thirty seconds later, he had put out what appeared to be a small chip pan fire and opened the back door to let out the smell of smoke.

'No need to panic here. Everything is fine. Your staff member had it all under control and Occy was just being her normal dramatic self, telling her that I was a fire fighter.' He spoke to the figure who was turned away from him. 'Sorry, you must be Rachel. You must think I'm dreadfully rude. I'm Jude. Are you OK? That must have been a bit of a shock.'

Rachel turned and faced him head on.

'Hello Jude.'

He literally jumped back and clutched his hand to his chest.

'Oh my God! What the fucking fuck are you doing here?'

26

Seconds felt like minutes as we all took turns staring at each other, open-mouthed, waiting for someone to break the silence. As I should have expected, it was broken by Occy, who steam-rollered through the kitchen door.

'I could really do with a hand out here, you know. It's getting quite busy again and we've nearly run out of food.'

You could literally cut the atmosphere with a knife. I was super confused about how Jude and Rachel knew each other. She'd not long moved into the village.

'I'll be out in a sec, Occy.' Jude smiled but it didn't reach his eyes, though I'm not sure she even noticed as she huffed out loud and flounced back into the main room. 'Do not say a thing,' he barked at Rachel. 'And don't move. I'll be back to deal with you in a minute. Gemma, I need a word.'

He grabbed my hand and led me out of the kitchen's back door. There, he bent double, his hands on his knees and taking deep breaths.

'How on earth do you know Rachel and why are you so

furious with her?' I asked. 'I can't have you speaking to my staff that way. It's just not on.'

He straightened himself up and started to rub at his temples, blowing out through pursed lips. It was quite hard to believe that just seconds ago those same lips had been kissing mine.

'Jude? What the hell is going on?'

'That woman in there. That's not Rachel. That's Amy. And she's Occy's mother.'

27

A chill ran through my bones.

'Jeez, Jude. What the hell.'

'Tell me about it. I haven't seen her for thirteen years. Thirteen fucking years and then, all of a sudden, she's here. Oh no!' His hands flew to his cheeks. 'Do you think Occy knows that Rachel is her mother?'

'She can't surely!'

Footsteps behind us alerted us to the fact that we weren't alone and we turned to see not one but two people stood watching us.

Occy screamed out loud and collapsed to the floor.

'She does now...'

28

After coming round, Occy moved herself into a seating position, Jude rubbing her hand.

'It's OK, darling. You fainted. You're fine.'

'Fine? *Fine*, really?' She looked straight over the top of him at Rachel. 'Do you honestly mean to tell me that I've been working beside you for a couple of weeks now and you didn't think to tell me that you were my mother? Seriously? What the fuck?'

'I'm sorry, Octavia, I thought it was the right thing to do. I wanted to get to know you first.'

'My name is Occy. Not Octavia. Dad! What is she doing here? Also, my mother's name is not Rachel. It's Amy. I'm so confused.'

'Your guess is as good as mine. I literally found out about two minutes before you did. And her name *is* Amy. Not Rachel.'

'I've been going by the name of Rachel for a long time,' the woman – Amy/Rachel – said. 'I decided I needed a change. Do away with the old me.'

'Oh nice. You needed a change.' Jude was now shouting at her. 'A bit like the change you needed when you left Occy and I all those years ago, you mean? You don't just walk out on your family when you fancy a change, Amy.'

'Oh, Jude, stop with all the self-righteous bullshit, will you? Some things don't change, do they? I'm here now and I would like to spend some time with my daughter, getting to know her. We've been getting on great, haven't we Octav—Occy?'

'Well, we were, but that was before I knew who you were. God, this is so messed up. I can't think straight.' She rubbed at her temples.

'Honestly, Amy. Rachel. Whatever your name is these days. If you wanted to see Occy, you should have got in touch with me and arranged something.' He was literally yelling in her face. This was a side of Jude that I'd never seen before and hoped I wouldn't ever see again.

'And run the risk of you not letting me see her? Not a chance.' I saw a bit of spittle leave her mouth and just miss him. She was giving as good as she got.

'I've never not let you see her, Rachel, and I never would and you know it. You've had every opportunity to be part of her life, for years. *You* chose not to. *You* made that decision.' He started to poke the air near her neck and she sensibly backed away from him, sensing his rage.

When she spoke next, her voice was calm and controlled.

'You made it perfectly clear that you didn't want me anywhere near her, Jude. You hardly made it easy for me.'

'Easy for you? It was about her. Not you! You can't just waltz in and out of a kid's life when you feel like it. Why would I ever want to make it easy for you? You don't pick and choose when you are in a kid's life. You *are* a kid's life. How many times did you think you could let us down and get away with it? God, you're despicable. How could you do this to us? To her?'

He was bellowing now with what seemed like years of frustration coming out. While I didn't want to interfere, I couldn't let this continue and let everyone at the launch hear what was going on. Not through embarrassment, but I didn't want everyone knowing Jude's private business. It wasn't doing anyone any good and I thought that I was the only one of us who had the ability to diffuse the situation a little.

'Look, why don't you all go home and cool off?' I suggested. 'Have some time to think about things and work out where to go from here. Have some space to get your heads around everything. You could all go back to Jude's and talk.'

'She's not going anywhere near our home. I will not allow her to contaminate it with her... her... rottenness!'

Jude looked across at me, scowling like he did the first evening I met him. He was like a completely different person to the one who had earlier taken my face in his hands and kissed me tenderly. Was that really only just a few moments ago? It seemed like a whole different lifetime.

'I don't need space. I need to spend some time with my daughter. I'm her mother after all. I have rights.'

'You gave up the right to be a mother to her years ago, Amy.'

'Rachel.'

'Rachel then. You can change your name but you can't change who you are.'

She lowered her head and stared at her feet for a few seconds, breathing slowly. When she raised her head again and looked back at Jude, it was with steely determination in her eyes.

'I've spent years changing who I am so that I can be a good person for Occy. So that I can come back and be in her life. And there's nothing that you can do about it. So if it's all about her, let's ask her what she wants. Occy, do *you* want me in your life?'

We turned round to get Occy's answer, but she'd disappeared.

'Occy? Occy love?' All the colour drained from Jude's face. 'Where are you?' he called out, but the only sign that she'd been there in the first place was the scrunched-up apron that she'd left on the floor. This was not good at all.

'You see, Amy? You just can't help yourself, can you? Once again you just waltz in and create complete and utter chaos for everyone. You really didn't think this through, did you?'

'Jude, the last time you saw me was thirteen years ago. You know nothing about me. You have no right to tell me what I can and can't do.'

'To be honest, right now I couldn't give a shit about you. Somewhere out there is my daughter and I'm going to find her.'

'Well, she's *our* daughter and I'm coming too, whether you like it or not.'

Jude and Rachel disappeared around the corner and their voices, shouting Occy's name, soon got fainter before disappearing into the night air.

I shivered and wrapped my arms around myself, feeling a chill down my spine. Looking behind me, I noticed someone step back into the shadows but I couldn't see their face. I couldn't even work out if it was male or female. I moved closer but the door chimes rang out and Pat called out to me.

'I could really do with some help in here, guys.' She looked surprised to see only me.

I picked up the discarded apron from the floor, totally discombobulated. How things can change in a heartbeat.

'Everything OK, Gemma?'

'Just bloody perfect, Pat. I'm on my way.'

* * *

With Rachel and Occy still missing in action, Lucy and James, and Meredith and Clem stepped in to wind everything down and to help Lizzie and Pat see the guests out while I hovered in the kitchen area not ready to face everyone. They all worked wonders, helping me to clean up. I owed them big time. When the last of the crockery had been either washed up or loaded into the final dishwasher run of the night, I waved them off at the door and took one last look around at the bistro, feeling proud of how everything had come together. As I turned off the lights, I smiled at what we'd achieved.

But then my smile turned to a frown, thinking about the other events that had unfolded tonight. It really had been an unexpected roller coaster of an evening, from the minute I showed Lucy around before the grand opening.

All I fancied doing was sitting and looking out to sea for a few minutes to ground me, to download my thoughts and to calm my racing brain, but the black bin bag tied up by the back door caught my eye. The bin men were due the following morning, so I grabbed my jacket from the hallway and headed out, picking up the bag on the way. I dropped it into the big bin in the yard area and made my way to the bench on the corner of the harbour. The same one on which, only a couple of hours before, Jude had told me that he felt something for me.

Did it really happen or was it all in my imagination? I pulled the lapels of my jacket together, feeling the chill in the air. The inky black sky was peppered with twinkling stars, and as I looked for the main constellations, finally a calmness came over me and I felt a sense of tranquillity.

Glancing at my watch, I gave a huge yawn and stretched. Today had been one hell of a day and I needed my bed. But first I needed to find out whether Occy had been found.

I felt the presence of someone behind me and immediately swung round, expecting to see either Occy or Jude – or even Rachel. I'd hoped for Jude, of course.

I certainly wasn't at all prepared for who it was – the second person to sit beside me on the bench that night.

29

'What the—'

'Hey, Gem.'

'What on earth are *you* doing here?'

The very last person I thought I'd be talking to right now was my ex-husband.

'I saw a feature about the refurb in the local paper and thought I'd come over.'

My eyebrows drew together and I could feel all that tension from earlier return to my shoulders.

'Why would you do that? I'm not part of your life any more, Lucas. You made that perfectly clear two years ago when you went off with Julie. Remember?'

'Of course, I remember. It's the worst decision I've ever made in my life.'

'Well, that's tough, because it's the decision you made. How are your girlfriend and your child by the way? I'm sure they'd be happy to hear you talk about them being a crap decision.'

'They're fine but they don't need me. They don't want me.

I've left her, Gemma. There's no one I'd rather be with than you. I've come back to you.'

He smiled at me and took my hand, which I immediately snatched away. The words that two years ago I longed to hear meant nothing to me. It was way too late.

'Jeez, Lucas. You really think that after everything that's happened you can just swan back into my life? What is going on in that head of yours?'

I thought back to Jude ranting at Rachel earlier and felt total sympathy with him. Here, in this situation, Lucas thought he was only affecting me but he was also affecting Julie and their baby too. Rachel was impacting on both Jude and Occy. What was wrong with these people?

'I'm not interested, Lucas. I have nothing to say to you. I'm going in now. Goodnight.' I stood to walk away but he grabbed my hand again.

'I've got nowhere else to go. Please. I'm begging you.'

I should never have hesitated. I should have walked away. Kept my head held high. But that one moment of hesitation gave him the opportunity to get into my head. He jumped up and stood in my way, maintaining eye contact.

'What if it was always meant to be this way, Gemma? What if we were always meant to find our way back to each other? I love you and don't want to live without you.'

He was planting 'what ifs' into my head and I knew that I should never have said the words that next came out of my mouth, but I did.

'You'd better follow me.'

* * *

As I handed Lucas a mug, I purposely sat in the chair opposite him to keep my distance. My arms were folded and I felt very defensive of my surroundings, especially when he said he'd forgotten how nice it was in the flat above the café.

'Why are you here Lucas?'

We could sit and pussyfoot around each other, making polite conversation or we could get to the crux of the matter.

'I've told you. I'm not happy without you.'

'And it's taken you two years to work that out.'

'No, it's taken me two years to do something about it. I've known since the beginning but I was too ashamed to admit that I was wrong, to beg you to have me back.'

'So why now?'

'I suppose it's just all come to a head. I thought that I couldn't live without having a child and, yet, I don't feel like that any more. I've been waiting to get those paternal feelings, but they just never came. Julie and the baby are a unit together, and I feel like an outsider looking in. I suppose at first, I was flattered that she showed me interest and then when everything happened with us, she was there for me. Then when I found out she was pregnant and you weren't, I was stuck in the middle. Damned if I left you because of what we'd gone through and damned if I left her pregnant and alone. I thought I was making the right decision, but it turns out she didn't need me all along; I was just surplus to requirements. Once she'd got the baby that she wanted so badly, she didn't want me any more.'

'Wow. So, you thought, I know. Poor Gemma will still be so heartbroken over me that she'll have me back in a heartbeat? Is that about right?'

'Well, I thought you might still love me and give me a second chance.' He leaped up from his chair and came to sit on the arm of my chair. 'I know how much you loved me. Please think about it. We were good together, weren't we?'

Over the years since we'd split up, I'd thought about our relationship a lot. We did have our wonderful moments of course. But I also remembered some really crap ones too. When we first got together, Mum said he loved himself more than he loved me and I recalled the nickname she called him, Mr Flash and Fly-by-night. Lucas thought it was flattering. Mum did not consider it to be a compliment.

Anyhow, we were both different people now. I'd grown much more independent. I'd had to be. I wasn't that weak, pathetic wife he knew me to be.

'We could move to another part of the country. We could do anything we want. As long as we're together.'

'I've just invested in my business, Lucas. You know that. That's why you're here. Because you saw the feature about it.'

'Yes, I did and you can call it a bistro but it's still just a café in the middle of nowhere, isn't it? Who has even heard of Driftwood Bay? It's never going to be on the map properly, is it? I could see whether there's any jobs going in any other of our regional offices. We could move and have a fresh start.'

My heart pounded. I felt totally offended. I'd poured my heart and soul into this business venture. The same business that had saved me when Lucas had left me broken-hearted. I wondered just how far Lucas would go to satisfy his own needs. He was only really thinking about himself. Again.

'You have a child now, Lucas. Have you thought about that?'

'Of course I have, but to be honest, babies and toddlers aren't that entertaining, are they? I could arrange to see her at holiday times. And it's not like you can do much with a girl as a dad anyway. It would be different if it was a boy...'

There was so much to unravel in that, particularly when you

were saying it to someone who could not have children. I thought back to lovely Jude and how he tried to be the amazing father he is every single day, putting his daughter ahead of everything. The things that he did for his daughter, and that he'd do even more if she let him. These two men were poles apart.

That then got me drifting to thoughts of Jude, Occy and Rachel and wondering what was going on with them tonight. I grabbed my phone and dropped Jude a text, asking if he'd found Occy. He responded immediately, briefly telling me that he was still out looking.

Lucas took my phone from my hand and put it on the arm of the chair. He turned my face towards his.

'I love you, Gemma, that's what is important here. Please give me another chance.'

'I think you should leave,' I said stiffly. 'You can't just turn up here and throw all of this at me and expect to just slot back into my life.'

'I've literally got nowhere to go, Gemma. Please can I just stay here tonight then I'll look at finding somewhere else tomorrow? I've got no chance of getting anywhere at this time of the night.'

Glancing at my watch, I couldn't believe it was already well after midnight. I couldn't even call Lucy as I knew she'd be asleep by now. She was knackered when she had left earlier and she needed all the sleep she could get. And, thinking about it, James had arrived late to the launch because he said that they were fully booked at the B & B and couldn't get away. So, there wasn't even the chance for Lucas to get a room anyway.

Misery was written all over Lucas's face. This was the man that I'd spent years with. Living in the same house as. Sleeping in the same bed as. Doing far more intimate things with than I didn't want to think about right then. I remembered how much I'd once loved him. How I thought we had a future together. What if we were where we were meant to be right now? Were we always meant to come back together in this way?

Julie's face suddenly popped into my head and I remembered that he'd got another woman pregnant and left me. This was completely messing with my head.

I stomped off to the airing cupboard and fetched the spare duvet.

And for the second time recently, I threw it over a man who was on my sofa, and declared that I was going out.

30

Hearing Jude before I saw him, I walked towards his voice. He was yelling Occy's name and I literally banged into him as we both rounded a corner from different sides.

'Oh God, I thought you were her then.' His shoulders slumped and he looked thoroughly despondent.

'Sorry, Jude. Where have you looked?'

'I've looked everywhere. Of course, I've looked everywhere. I can't bloody find her.' He raked his hands through his hair and I could see that he was shaking, quite near to tears. 'Sorry, Gem. I didn't mean to snap at you. I'll bloody kill Amy for this. Where on earth can she be hiding?'

The word 'hiding' prompted a childhood memory.

'Come on. I've just had an idea. I might know a place she could be.'

I grabbed hold of Jude's arm and pulled him along with me down onto the sand and towards the far side of the bay. When we were children, there was a cave that all the local kids used to play in, totally hidden from view. The stories about Smuggler's Cove in years gone by used to scare me to death but it was somewhere that I had a feeling Occy would know about. I'd heard that a lot of the local kids still went there now to smoke and drink.

As we reached the rocks near to the cave, we heard the murmur of voices. I pulled Jude back out of view and put my fingers to my lips. I couldn't hear what they were saying, but I could distinctively hear two female voices. I tugged Jude down to the side of me and crept up to the top rock where I knew we'd be able to get a better view without being seen.

Sure enough, there was Occy at the end of the water, kicking at the gentle waves with Rachel about five feet behind her. Being that little bit closer meant that we could hear some of their words even if they were very quiet.

'I just wanted to get to know you first. Get you to like me as a person before I told you who I was. I was always going to come back for you, Octavia.'

'It's bloody Occy. I've told you that.'

I looked up at Jude and he smirked despite the circumstances. He made to move forward and I could see that he was about to head down to where they were and launch into a tirade, but I held him back and shushed him again.

'And how was I supposed to know you were always going to come back for me? I'm not a mind-reader.'

There was a huge part of me that was incredibly proud of Occy for not being a pushover. Another part of me was wondering exactly what Rachel's motive was for coming to see her now. Or were her words completely genuine?

'Surely you've thought of me over the years. Wondered if I'd ever be in touch?'

'Of course I have. That's why I got the job at the bistro. So I could save up.'

Jude turned to me, puzzled. I put my fingers to my lips again.

'What do you mean? What does that have to do with anything?'

'I was going to save up. Then, when I was eighteen, I was going to try to find you. When I could afford to.'

Jude gasped and I thought they might hear him. But they continued to chat.

'I never wanted to upset Dad, but I did want to find you. Ask you why you left me. So, I'm asking now. Why did you leave?'

Rachel exhaled. 'I thought it was the right thing to do. I'm sorry, Occy, I really am.'

Occy kicked at the waves. You could have heard a pin drop. Not a murmur from either of them.

This was all my fault. I was the one responsible. The conduit for all this mess happening. If I'd never offered Rachel a job, then none of this would have happened. I hoped that Occy and Jude wouldn't point the finger of blame at me. I'd been racking my brain to work out whether I could have stopped this happening but there was no way that I could think of that I could have done it differently, some way to ensure Rachel's real identity was revealed to me at any point.

'Occy, I'm your mum and there's never a day gone by that I haven't thought of you.'

Jude huffed out loud and again I had to shush him. If they knew we were here, they might stop talking and there were things we might never find out.

'Really. I didn't even get birthday cards from you for half the years you've not been around.'

'I've been a crap mum. I know that. But I'm back now and I want to make it up to you. I want to be in your life all the time. I'm here to stay. Unless... Well...'

'What?' Occy turned to face her.

'Unless you wanted to come and live with me somewhere else.'

'Right, that's it.' Jude stood from where he'd been crouching behind the rock and marched over, yelling at Rachel before he even reached where they were standing.

'You've been back in our lives for less than a few hours and are causing complete and utter pandemonium. You have no right to do this, Amy. Occy! Grab your things. We're going home. It's late.' He pointed at Rachel. 'I'll get your number from Gemma and I'll call you to arrange to meet. When *we're* ready to talk to you. And not until then.'

As Jude thundered past, with Occy in tow, that flirtatious smile from earlier a distant memory, Rachel had the good grace to hang her head. Dithering about whether to stay or go, I suddenly remembered that if I went back to the flat, I'd have to deal with Lucas. Jude and Occy were disappearing into the distance so I turned to Rachel, who was sitting on the sand with her head on her knees. I couldn't help but feel sorry for her whatever the circumstances.

'Fancy a cuppa?'

She nodded and gave a wistful smile, before pulling herself up from the ground and slowly walking towards me with sunken shoulders.

Lucas being in the flat meant that we couldn't go up there, so I opened the front door to the bistro and flicked on one of the lights at the back of the room and put the kettle on. It didn't seem worth firing up Betty for just two cups.

'Do you want to talk about it?' I plonked the cups down on the table, suddenly feeling totally overwhelmed. What a day. Was it ever going to end?

'Where on earth do I start?'

Two hours and two hot chocolates later, Rachel was completely spent after pouring out her heart to me. She said that she would always regret the way she'd handled everything, and that she wanted to make sure she had the chance to make amends with her daughter. She felt she had to try, even if Occy didn't want to hear it, or Jude wouldn't allow her the chance. That Occy deserved to have a better mother than she'd been and that she wanted to try to explain her side and somehow move on.

I said I'd walk her back to where she was staying. She looked shattered, as was I. Ironically, the place she was renting was only two streets away from Jude and Occy. They could have bumped into each other at any point.

'Rachel, I don't normally offer advice unless I'm asked, but right now, I think I should. Just give Jude some time. He might come round.'

'Don't be fooled by Jude's self-righteous behaviour, Gemma. There's a lot of things you don't know about him. Even though you think he's a saint. I can assure you he is not. And thank you but no, I didn't ask for your advice.' The door closed behind me.

I stared at the door incredulously for a second or two, then walked back down the hill to the harbour.

My phone pinged to signify a text.

You awake?

Jude.

I am.

What a night!

You can say that again. You both OK?

Sorry to leave you at the beach. I just needed to get Occy back. My head just won't let me sleep right now. How come you're still awake?

I can only imagine. I've had quite a night myself. I've been sat in the bistro with Rachel since you left and have just taken her home.

The three dots appeared, then disappeared. I waited. And waited for a response but there was nothing until I reached the bottom of the hill.

I can't believe you are siding with her, Gemma.

Jude, I'm not siding with anyone. She was upset. I listened. That's all.

I'll speak to you tomorrow. Goodnight.

No kiss to end his message. He was clearly in a mood with me.

Taking in a deep breath and then puffing out my cheeks, I approached my front door. I glanced over at the bistro, the lights now out, the doors locked. It felt like the launch event had never happened. Was it really only a few hours earlier? Such a lot had happened since.

I crept up the stairs to the flat, not wanting to wake Lucas. Ridiculous that this was my home and I was the one creeping around. It used to really annoy him when I came in late at night and woke him. Suppose old habits are hard to break.

I needn't have worried. He was sat up, in just his boxer shorts, the duvet I threw at him earlier on the floor.

'Where've you been?' He didn't sound very happy.

'Sorry?'

'You've been gone ages. Where've you been?'

Courage rose within me. He didn't know the new me but he was going to meet me now.

'Where I've been is absolutely nothing to do with you. I have a life here, Lucas, if you hadn't noticed. I have friends and I have family. You are not part of my life any more. You walked out on me two years ago!'

'Of course I haven't forgotten that. That's why I'm back now to make amends.' His voice softened. 'Come here, Gemma.' He held his arms out to me. 'Come here, love.'

While I could have done with a bloody big hug right then, Lucas was not the person I needed it from. And if I did, would it give him the wrong idea? Would it make me waver and feel like I should forgive him? If I hugged him, would it lead to something more? I looked over to a picture of me, Mum and Lucy on the mantelpiece. We're smiling with our arms wrapped around each other. What would Mum advise me to do right now? I closed my eyes and, in my head, asked her to help me.

My decision came to me in a flash.

'Go to sleep, Lucas. I'm going to bed.'

As I walked to the bedroom, I heard him mutter something under his breath.

Looked like this was the night that I was going to piss everyone off.

31

Leaving Lucas fast asleep on the sofa, I crept out past him and down the stairs to the bistro. I didn't want him there. He was making me feel uncomfortable in my own home. Getting used to my own space was one of the hardest things I'd had to do over the last couple of years and now I had, I was feeling completely claustrophobic. I hadn't even been able to have a shower that morning for fear of waking him up. The last thing I wanted was for him to start a whole new conversation. I could not give in to him. Feeling sorry for him the previous night had already made me wobble.

As I opened the door to the bistro, I thought about the launch event. All the shine had been stripped away. Last night was supposed to be *my* night. The night that the business was relaunched with a new name and a new future. But how could it be when the past was still hanging over me in this way?

I dropped Lucy a text, asking her if she could talk and she said she'd call me in ten minutes. I knew she was an early bird, even more so now she was pregnant as she was struggling to sleep. In fairness, I didn't know where to start with her. Did I tell her about Jude and his declaration? I'd have to tell her all that I'd found out about Rachel then too. And what if she ran into Lucas before I had chance to tell her he was around?

Why was my normally simple life, suddenly in turmoil? I'd not long started the day and already had a monster of a headache.

When the phone rang a few minutes later it all came tumbling out.

'Oh my God, Lucy, first Jude told me he liked me, then Rachel turned out to be Occy's mother, then Lucas turned up and—'

'Gemma, stop. Breathe.'

Years ago, Lucy had taught me the art of square breathing, where you imagined the four sides of a square. If you inhale in and then out, using the corners of the square as a counter, your breath slows down and you feel much calmer. I used this technique now and immediately felt better.

'OK, now start at the beginning.'

Explaining everything from the night before took a while but Lucy listened intently, waiting for the right moment to comment. I could hear heavy breathing while I was talking, which made me think she was doing stuff at the same time. Then there was a tap at the window and, lo and behold, there she was.

As I opened the bistro door to her, I burst into tears.

She held me to her chest and soothed my sobs by rubbing my back.

'OK, are you opening up today?'

'Well, yes, we're meant to be. It's our first day but who knows what staff I'll have. Everyone is due in at eight, and I know Pat will be here, but who knows if Rachel or Occy will turn up. It was gone 3 a.m. by the time I got back last night. And I have no idea if Jude will even let Occy come in...'

'OK, let's take things one step at a time. James is holding the fort at the B & B and he can manage without me for an hour or two.' She rubbed her belly and gave me a nervous smile. 'Have you eaten? Have you had a drink yet?'

As I shook my head, she waddled her way behind the counter and flicked on the kettle.

'I can't work that blooming thing.' She pointed to Betty the Beast. 'But I'm sure you have a tin of instant somewhere, don't you?' She rummaged in the cupboards until she found a jar. 'This'll do.'

A couple of minutes later she handed me a coffee and sat down beside me with a camomile tea.

'I'm sorry. You don't need this stress, Lucy. I shouldn't have called you.'

'I'm your big sister and if you can't call me when you need a shoulder to cry on then who can you call?'

'Thanks, love.'

She patted my arm.

'So firstly, what are you going to do about Lucas? Have you got any thoughts at all?'

'There's a bit of me that wants to give him, us, a second chance. He's my husband. Am I stupid?'

'He *was* your husband. Before he started shagging that old slapper behind your back. Then he left you and had a baby with her. And all of this while our mother was dying of cancer. And then he left you just after we lost her. Do tell me you haven't forgotten all of that.'

'And I've never been sorrier about anything in my life,' came a voice from the doorway. Neither of us had heard Lucas come into the bistro from the interior door. 'Hey, Lucy.'

'Lucas!' She gave him her best ice queen stare.

'I'll spend the rest of my life making it up to you all, if you'll allow me to.'

'It's up to Gemma what she does, Lucas. She's her own woman. But if she's asking for my advice, then I'll be sure to give it to her. And my advice will be to steer clear of you because you are a lying, cheating scumbag who doesn't deserve to clean my sister's boots, let alone ask for her forgiveness.'

'I understand that you want to protect her—'

'I'm her sister. Of course, I'm going to protect her. Which is incidentally what you should also have been doing as her husband. Remember those vows you took? To love and to cherish? For better, for worse? Sound familiar at all?'

'Stop! Please!' I yelled at the pair of them. I rubbed my temples, looking at the clock. Fifteen minutes till opening time and I still hadn't prepared a thing.

'Lucas, please just go. I can't think straight with you around and I have a bistro to open.'

'I don't have anywhere to go, Gemma.' He looked down at the floor.

'You should have thought about that before you double-crossed my sister, shouldn't you?'

Lucas tutted at Lucy, rolling his eyes. That was the last straw for me. She was right.

'You are not my problem. Now just go.'

He walked towards the door then paused.

'Can I have a word in private please,' he asked. 'Just one more minute of your time.'

I walked towards him and shooed him outside.

'Gemma. I love you more than anything in the world.'

'And...'

'I will make it up to you every day for the rest of my life. I swear to you.'

'Your promises are pretty shit to be honest. How do I know you won't change your mind when the next pretty girl comes along and bats her eyelashes at you?'

Out of the corner of my eye, I could see Jude and Occy walking towards the bistro. *Great, that's all I need right now.*

Jude's eyes widened as he got closer and even more when he saw Lucas pull me towards him and – before I even knew what was happening – kissed me, full on the lips.

'I'll call you later. I love you.'

And with that, Lucas walked away, leaving me staring at his back.

Jude shook his head at me.

'Can any of you women actually be trusted at all?'

'It's not what you think, Jude. Let me explain.'

He held his palm towards me.

'Save it, Gemma. I'm not interested. Occy wanted to come to work and I brought her because I didn't know whether Amy would be here or not. Is she working today?'

I swallowed the lump in my throat. The way Jude just looked at me was full of disgust and disappointment. And who could blame him? Last night we were talking about exploring us and maybe the chance of building a future together. I know that, as a parent, that's not a decision that's taken lightly. Not only do you risk your own emotions should the relationship not work out, but also the emotions of your child too. And now, he just saw another man kiss me and tell me that he loved me. I could only imagine how it must have looked.

'Jude, please let me—'

'Just leave it, Gemma. It's fine. What's the score with Amy?'

I still couldn't get used to him calling her Amy.

'She's meant to be in at 8 a.m., same as Occy and Pat. She's not arrived but there's still five minutes yet.' I looked up. 'Oh actually, here she is now.'

Pat and Rachel were walking down the high street together. When they reached us, Pat nipped inside discreetly.

'Amy, we need to talk,' Jude said sternly.

'I'm due to start work. Can we chat later?'

'No! Now.' His voice was cold and hard, not the loving, caring voice that I'd heard the night before when we sat together on the bench. She looked towards me and I nodded my approval before taking Occy inside the bistro. She didn't need to see this.

I noticed that she looked awful. Her eyes were red and puffy and she looked absolutely shattered. In the space of a few hours last night, the poor kid had had her world totally and utterly turned upside down. When we got inside, she fell into my arms and burst into tears. I held her close to my chest, stroking her hair, soothing her.

'Oh, Gemma. I just can't believe it.'

'Do you want to go home?' I asked.

'God no! I want to work to take my mind off everything. Dad is walking around like a bear with a sore head and snapping my head off. I dread to think what he's saying to her out there.' She nodded to the area outside where Jude and Rachel were clearly having a heated discussion.

I made a decision. We were strong capable females. And we would get through this one way or another.

'Right, lady. Get yourself up to my bathroom and wash your face. You've got mascara all down your cheeks and look like a panda!' Occy laughed. It was good to see her laugh again. 'Chop-chop. We've got a bistro to open.'

Lucy asked if I needed her to stay and help but I said that she should get off. The last thing she needed was to be on her feet working. She should be resting and saving her energy for when the baby came. She looked tired and I felt responsible for dragging her out.

'Call me when you've got some time.'

I nodded and she leaned forward and kissed my cheek.

'We'll talk about...' she pointed to Jude outside '...the other stuff. You'll be OK, you know. We've gone through worse.'

She was right. Yes, going through the whole Lucas-leaving-me debacle was truly awful, but it was nothing compared to losing our wonderful mum. Grief literally exhausts you. It's like a constant sad cloud hanging around you. And you try to shake it off but it's like a rucksack full of rocks that you carry around. You can move it from one shoulder to the other, and temporarily it feels a little better, but then it gets heavy again. Because it is. But you get used to it being heavy and eventually you accept that's exactly what it is and always will be. Some days it'll feel heavier than others but it'll never get physically lighter.

It was only when the counsellor talked to me using this analogy that I truly registered what grief was.

Nothing could have prepared us for losing Mum. We both thought that because we knew it was coming, it wouldn't be so bad, but, God, it was awful. We'd had to carve a new life for ourselves without the one person in it that we'd never known life without. Mum was always there if I needed her. To pick up the phone, to ask her advice, maybe just to listen to me when I needed her to, and then she was just, well, gone. And I was still so very sad. Sad for a future that we wouldn't have together and sad that she wasn't here to see what was going on in her girls' lives. That she didn't know what was happening in the bistro, that she didn't know about Lucy and James having a baby.

Meeting Jude finally brought sunlight into my day. My days were better when he was in them, and once I'd admitted to myself that I did like him in that way, when he told me he felt the same, I was totally elated and thought it was a huge turning point in my life. That things were starting to look up and I – we – had a future to look towards. Yet that world had come crashing down around me within minutes.

Maybe I was right all along. It was easier not to get involved with anyone, not to fall in love; then you wouldn't get hurt.

Jude and Rachel were still out on the patio, both looking like they'd calmed down a little, and were now deep in conversation. I didn't think she'd be able to break away to help us to open up any time soon. She looked like she had far more important things to sort out.

Occy looked around the door furtively. 'In all the fuss this morning, I've forgotten to bring my make-up bag with me. One false eyelash fell off upstairs so I've had to take them off. Can I go home and sort my face out? I can't face the world looking like this.'

'Darling, you look so much prettier without all that shite on your face.'

I flipped my head around to see who'd just spoken and gasped out loud when I saw Pat's face. Occy looked horrified.

'I'm sorry but it's the truth. You are such a natural beauty and you're hiding it under too much make-up. You don't need it. You are truly beautiful. Inside and out and if anyone says anything different to that, you tell them to come and see me.'

'What do you think, Gemma?'

'The truth?'

She nodded, and with her eyes wide in anticipation, she looked so vulnerable.

'You look beautiful, Occy. You are lovely. Pat's right. You don't need it.'

That smile that was capable of lighting up any room returned.

'Do you think, she... Rachel... Amy... Mum... shit, what on earth do I call her? Do you think she'll work here today? I don't know what to say to her.'

'I honestly don't know, but what I do know is that I can see a group of early morning walkers heading this way and they look hungry. We need to get our arses into gear and get this place open. Occy, would you like to do the honours?'

She seemed delighted to be the one to turn the closed sign round to open. On its first proper day of business, it was Occy that declared the bistro officially open.

'Let's get this show on the road!'

32

The walking group was a lovely bunch and great trade for us, even though they kept us on our toes. Rachel had come in to work after she and Jude had parted company, and for the whole of her shift, she and Occy were pussyfooting around each other, saying nothing but everything at the same time. The poor kid shouldn't have to be put through this. The situation would be hard enough for an adult to cope with. Look at what a tizzy Lucas had got me in returning after two years, let alone a mother turning up after thirteen.

Occy looked every bit a little girl today, without her warpaint, quite pale and her eyes were still a little red. I wondered what on earth was going through her mind.

Because it was a gorgeous day, we had the bifold doors open; those who wanted fresh air sat out on the patio and those who felt the cold, stayed indoors. Seagulls squawked and swooped to pick up any crumbs that had dropped to the floor, and as I went out to clear the tables, I took a moment to take in my surroundings and do my daily appreciation of the beauty of Driftwood Bay.

Boats bobbed in the distance, at the pub on the opposite corner Geoff was taking in a beer delivery and along the harbour there was a general hustle and bustle going on, with the sunshine bringing lots of the neighbours out for walks. It felt good to be here. There was no way I could leave, even if Lucas and I decided that there could be a way forward for us. I couldn't believe I was even considering it, but I had loved him once. Very much. And that was a lot to forget.

As I looked out towards the bright sunlight, I saw Jude walking around the harbour. He was looking down at his feet and just looked defeated.

Should I approach him or leave him to it?

What I really wanted to do was to wrap my arms around him and make everything better. But I knew I was unable to make what was hurting him go away. It was something that needed to be dealt with, somehow in the best way possible for everyone. Maybe I could just be his friend. He looked like he needed one right now.

As I stepped down from the patio to go to see him, I heard shouting from indoors. Thank goodness we'd gone quiet and all the customers had left for the time being. I'd been dithering, which had delayed me from going to see Jude. Now that decision had been taken away; my attention was clearly needed inside.

'Hey, hey, hey. What's going on?'

Rachel and Occy were squaring up to each other, their faces inches away from each other's. Pat was busying herself behind the counter, not knowing whether to get involved or leave them to it. However, we all were already involved, one way or another.

'Gemma, she keeps saying she wants to talk to me, but Dad has told me not to talk to her without him being here.'

'I'm your mother, Octavia. And if I want to speak to you, I will.'

'How many times do I have to fucking tell you? It's *Occy*!' She was practically screaming at her. 'You can't even get my name right.'

'That's enough,' I said, feeling it right that I intervene. 'Come on Occy. Let's go for a walk and get some air. Rachel, are you happy to stay? Or do you need to finish for the day?'

She nodded back at me. 'I'll stay.'

I tucked Occy's arm in mine and we headed to the beach, where luckily, her dad was no longer around. It had been a few days since I'd walked on the sand and when I suggested a paddle, she looked at me as if I'd gone mad.

'Come on. Shoes off. The cold will be invigorating.'

'Fucking freezing more like.'

'You need to stop swearing, young lady.'

'I'm sorry, Gemma. It feels like it's my only outlet for anger at the moment.' She hung her head. A carbon copy of her father. The likeness took my breath away. I couldn't see one bit of Rachel in her.

We leaned on each other as we removed our trainers and socks, and when her feet hit the water Occy squealed like a toddler.

'Oh, get in there, you big wuss.'

As she got used to the water she got braver, and as she was wearing knee-length cut-offs, she went in a little further than me.

'Who's being a wuss now? Come on!' she teased, grabbing my hand, and pulling me further into the water which was now splashing around my ankles. Shit the bed! It was cold. I was worried about my skirt getting wet but it was also good to see Occy smile even if it was temporary. I had achieved my aim.

Glancing behind and not seeing another soul on the beach, I hoisted up the bottom of my skirt and tucked the hem into my knickers. When I turned round, Occy had her phone out and was snapping a picture.

'If you ever show anyone that, you and I will fall out!'

'Ha. I'll put it on the bistro's Instagram feed. What do I get if I don't share it?'

'You get to keep your job. How's that for starters?'

'Are you allowed to say things like that these days?'

'Probably not, but you've got no evidence that I said it.'

She threw back her head and laughed, pulling me in even further with one hand, while tucking her phone in her back pocket with the other. After last night, I didn't think any of us thought we'd be together today and certainly not that we'd be laughing.

We allowed the gentle lapping waves wash over our feet and held our faces to the winter sun, which still felt like it had healing properties. The distant chimes of the boats could be heard in the harbour, a beautiful background sound along with that of the crying gulls. Breathing in deep the fresh, salty sea air was so good for your soul, even if you felt that your toes might drop off at any second with frostbite.

'Come on, it's going to get busy soon. We'd best head back to help Rachel and Pat.'

Occy followed on behind.

'I wish *you* were my mum, Gemma.'

I stopped in my tracks and swallowed a huge lump that had appeared in my throat. I turned to face her and tucked a wayward strand of hair behind her ear. A pointless exercise as it just popped back out again anyway. I couldn't speak.

'I just feel like you, well you know... You get me. Also, I think my dad has the proper hots for you.'

I reached forward, still not finding the right words, and kissed her on the forehead. 'Come on.'

* * *

You could cut the atmosphere in the bistro with a knife. Thank goodness the customers didn't know what was going on and it was only us insiders who could see.

Every time I wandered past the window, I looked out to see if Jude was around. I'd noticed him walk past a couple of times throughout the day, and would have loved to pop out but we were so busy I didn't get the chance. The last time he'd passed, I sent Occy out just to let him know she was OK. He must have been in turmoil.

We were so busy, and with Occy and Jude so much on my mind, I hadn't had time to think about Lucas, so when his text came through asking what I was doing later that night, it came as a surprise. I really didn't have the time or the energy to think about him or us, or whether there even was the chance of an us, so I just put my phone to one side. He'd have to wait.

Rachel left around three, after the lunchtime shift, but Occy said that she didn't want to go home yet and asked if she could stay on. I didn't have the heart to say no but only agreed on the condition that she worked on our social media profiles and if she got the OK from her dad first. She showed me his text back to her, saying that it was fine and he'd be back to pick her up from work at five.

It was a quiet couple of hours, but it was all still so positive for the business. Compliments about the work we'd done at the bistro kept on coming in from all our visitors, we took a booking for a baby shower, and quite a big group for afternoon tea for the following week.

I didn't realise the time when the door went at five and I turned round to see Jude standing before me. He looked so forlorn and sad. I wanted to reach out and touch his face.

Comfort him. Make everything better. But it wasn't my place. I didn't know what he wanted from me right now, or even what I could give.

'Any chance of a word, Gemma?'

I nodded.

When he refused the cup of coffee I offered, I told Occy we'd be outside for a few minutes. Just because he didn't want one, didn't mean I couldn't. I'd not sat down for hours and couldn't remember the last time I'd had chance to have a drink or some food.

I sat down opposite him at one of the tables, and cradled my cup, focusing on the swirls on the top of the froth as I waited for him to speak.

'You know I like you, don't you, Gemma?'

I nodded. 'Same.'

He smiled but it didn't reach his eyes.

'If this was a different time, I'd be doing everything I could to win you over. But right now, I can't make you any promises. I have to prioritise what's going on here and now and sort out this shitstorm that Amy has created. You do understand that, don't you?'

'Of course. And what you saw wasn't what you think.'

He shrugged as if he didn't care. It cut me to the core.

'Is there anything I can do to help you?' I asked.

'Not take sides maybe?'

'I won't be taking sides, but... and I say this as your friend... there are three of you involved in this. You. Occy. And then Rachel aka Amy. I find it so weird that we know her as something different.'

'I know.' He looked down at his hands.

'As someone who doesn't have a mum in her life and would do anything to have her back, all I'm saying is that maybe you have to put what Occy wants ahead of everything. Surely as a parent, that's what you must do.'

'I appreciate your candour, Gemma, but as someone who has never been a parent, I think I'm the best person to know what's best for my daughter, don't you?'

It cut through me like a knife. Obviously, I was perfectly aware of the fact that I had never and would never be a parent. It was the cruellest thing he could possibly say to me. Knowing how much I'd been affected by my infertility, he couldn't have hurt me more.

I stood abruptly. However much he was hurting, it didn't give him the right to talk to me this way.

'OK, Jude. I'll leave you to it.'

As I turned to close the door behind me, he was raking his hands through his hair. I knew that he was going through a lot right now but if he wasn't careful, he was going to lose everyone who cared about him and end up with nothing and no one.

33

I turned the ringer off and flung my phone on the chair, not wanting to deal with it pinging yet again with another message from Lucas. It wasn't sorting out the dilemma I was now in, but I didn't want to talk to him. I still hadn't responded to his message from earlier. I didn't know how to. What on earth did I say when I didn't know how I was feeling?

It felt as if my flat had been contaminated by him. An unwashed coffee cup sat on the breakfast bar and the top was off the biscuit tin. This reminded me of how he used to be. Untidy and expecting me to run around after him. Even when he was trying to win me back, couldn't he have tried just that little bit harder? Maybe old habits were hard to break.

Throwing myself into cleaning everything I could still didn't take my mind off all that was going on.

If he'd been unfaithful to me once, would he do it again? And if I went back to him, how long before things slipped back to how they'd been before? Or would he have learned his lesson? He said he'd changed, but how could you know? So many thoughts were spinning through my head and I had an absolute blinder of a headache.

I lay on the bed for a while but sleep couldn't have been further from my thoughts, my mind flitting from one scenario to another. One where Lucas and I were together and then another where his child was calling him away and he had to go. When I thought about the fact that the man I once loved so much had a child with another woman, it wrenched at my heart. After all we'd gone through trying to conceive, he'd gone and done it anyway. Not only that, but he was also throwing all of that away, walking away from his family, saying that he wanted to be with me.

Mum always used to say that she would do *anything* for her children. I know that she had been wounded when our father left us, but she made up for us only ever having one loving parent by being the most amazing mother ever. We came first for her; she even put us above her own happiness. I couldn't imagine having children and not doing the same. A tear rolled down my cheek at the thought of not being able to feel like this about a child that I had carried in my body and brought into this world. While I had accepted that it would never happen for me, it still made me sad. It also made me sad for Lucas's child, that he didn't seem to feel that way about his own flesh and blood.

The thumping sound in my head made it feel like it was going to explode. Then I realised that it wasn't my head, it was someone pounding on the front door. Luckily, from my bedroom window, I'd be able to see who was there and I wanted to look because if it was Jude or Lucas, then I was going to ignore them both.

But no need to worry. It was Meredith. She grinned up at me, waving a bottle of white wine. I opened the window and shouted down to her.

'I'm not really great company at the moment, Mere.'

'Yep, I know. Lucy told me.'

'God, is nothing sacred around here?'

'Not when you're friends. So, are you going to let me in or not?'

'Suppose so.'

'Thanks for the enthusiasm.'

'I'm sorry! It's just... all... well a bit too much at the moment.'

'And that's exactly why you need a drink with your mate. Now, where are your wine glasses? This bottle of Pinot isn't going to drink itself.' She grinned at me again from her spot on the pavement outside.

'Just a small one for me though. I don't really feel like drinking and I really fancy an early night.'

* * *

Two bottles later, I did feel better. Talking it through with Meredith had helped. I still didn't have any definitive answers, but I did have more substantial pros and cons for getting back together with Lucas or binning him off altogether. And Jude, well... She did bring Jude up and after the first huge glass of wine went down so quickly, my feelings for him came tumbling out so we discussed that too.

As Meredith left, she hugged me on the doorstep.

'You're so lovely, you know, Gemma. You're kind, you're honest, and you have so much to offer someone. Lucas doesn't know what he's thrown away and Jude doesn't know what he could have if he played his cards right. You wear your heart on your sleeve. There are no secrets with you.'

'Oh, I'm not so sure about that, Mere.'

Only two nights ago, I'd left Driftwood Bay to head off to

Truro to carry out my weekly secret mission and this thought didn't make me feel particularly honest right now. However, I still wasn't ready to share about that just yet so I pushed it back down.

'It'll all work itself out in the end,' she said. 'Either way. But don't be forced into making a decision by someone who let you down so badly. I know I don't know Lucas and all the ins and outs of your relationship and there are always two sides to every story, but I do know that he destroyed your life and that's not something that you can do to someone and then just expect to jump back into their lives when it suits you. Especially when that person is someone as lovely as you. *And* when that person has not only rebuilt their life but is living a bloody good one, fulfilling their hopes and dreams. You've become someone who is not just surviving, but thriving.'

'Thank you. Maybe I just needed to hear all of that tonight. I really do appreciate you coming round and forcing me to be in company. It's so hard when you have a customer-facing business; you feel like you must paint on a smile and show everyone that it's all OK. All I've really wanted to do today is curl up into a little ball and cry.'

'I get that, mate, I really do.'

'And what the hell I do about Occy and Rachel working together is another thing to worry about. I can't have them squaring up to each other all the time.'

'Maybe you need to suggest that the three of them, Jude, Rachel and Occy, sit down and sort out something. It's not fair on you otherwise.'

'I don't think that Jude is up for hearing advice from me right now.'

'How on earth have you managed to find *two* stubborn men?'

'God knows. Maybe at least the fact that I know Lucas is the way he is is good. It's come as a big surprise about Jude though. Maybe it's a case of better the devil you know.'

'I'm just asking you to remember that he was the one that started all this. But you're the one that gets to make the decision now. You know we'll all stand by you, whatever you decide, don't you?'

'I'm not sure Lucy will.'

'She will. If you choose Lucas, then she'll come round in time. Maybe not straight away and I think he'll have to prove himself to her but only because he broke your heart, Gemma.'

'If you don't love, you don't get hurt. Maybe I just need to go back to that idea of being on my own and then no one can hurt me. It's safer.'

'I totally understand that, but the risk there is that you might also never have great love. What if Jude turns out to be the love of your life and you turn him away because you're scared to get hurt?'

'But what if I invest two years of my life with him and then it doesn't work out? Wouldn't that be a total waste of time?'

'You could look at it like that, or you could look on it that you would have lovely memories from those two years together.'

'But when someone has a child, you become attached to them too. So that would be a double whammy.'

'I get that, Gemma, but you can't go into a relationship wondering what might happen when it doesn't work out. You can't protect yourself from life.'

'Can't you?'

She kissed me on the cheek.

'Just think about everything and you can make your choice in your own time, if and when you're ready, but you shouldn't make a decision based on nostalgia Gemma.'

* * *

My phone had been sat on the side, ringer off and face down for the last three hours. When I picked it up, with blurry eyes, I noticed that there were thirteen missed calls from Lucas and four text messages asking me to ring him.

Plucking up some courage that Meredith had instilled in me, I sent one simple message back saying that I'd call him when I was ready. Then I turned off my phone and went to bed.

Sleep was fitful and I dreamed that we were in the olden days. Lucas and Jude were dressed in long jackets with tails and riding boots and were engaging in an old-fashioned duel. I ran towards them, hearing a gunshot and my own voice yelling, 'No!' One of them had fallen to the ground and I fell down too. From the ground, I saw the other walking away, but I couldn't see which one it was. Which one was still alive.

When I woke, my heart was pounding and it took a while to get back off to sleep again.

34

The following morning, I could see Jude was walking along the beach, kicking at the sand. He looked up at the flat, and I stepped back, hiding behind the lounge curtain. It was a glorious day and a walk on the beach would have done my hangover the world of good, but there was no way that I would go out there while he was there. I couldn't face him right now.

When I noticed that he'd gone, I grabbed a fleece and a blanket from my coat cupboard and went downstairs to make a coffee, popping my head out of the door to make sure that the coast was clear before heading out.

Breathing in the salty sea air always warmed my heart. I loved listening to the rhythmic sounds of the harbour and it never failed to soothe me. I dusted sand from a flat rock before laying down the blanket and I perched on the edge, watching the hypnotic ebb and flow of the gentle waves. It was a lovely sunny start to the day with blue skies overhead and my head was starting to clear.

'Budge up!'

I looked sideways. Bugger.

'Hi, Gemma.'

My heart began to race. Still, he had this effect on me.

'I know I have no right to ask you this but I wondered if you'd do me a favour?'

'You know I will, Jude.'

'Thank you. I wondered if you might allow Occy to stay over after work tonight for tea. Amy and I need to talk and, while we need to talk to her too, I think our initial chat should be on our own.'

I sighed. I was clearly a soft touch where this family was concerned.

'Sure.'

I wanted to say that I thought it was a good idea but after his outburst yesterday I didn't want to comment or offer anything that could be misconstrued as advice.

'Thank you. I really do appreciate it. How are you?'

I gave a brief derisory laugh.

'That good, eh?'

'Oh, I'm OK. It's just been a bit of a week.'

'You can say that again.'

I wasn't used to there being an awkward silence between us. We had spent weeks constantly filling time with chatter. I looked down at the ground not knowing what to say.

He cleared his throat.

'I owe you an apology, Gemma. I should never have said what I did yesterday, about you not being a parent. In the short time you've known her, you've been more of a parent figure to Occy than Amy has been her entire life.'

'You were upset.'

'I was, but it's no excuse. I was hurting and, in response, I hurt you and that's never the right thing to do. I'm sorry.' He looked down into his hands which were linked loosely on his lap.

I placed my hand on his, and a little shiver ran up my spine when my skin touched his. He looked up and our eyes met.

'Can you believe all this happened just when I'd told you how I felt about you? Talk about great timing. What a bloody mess.'

'Yep.'

'And what about you? Do you mind me asking what's going on with you and the man I saw kiss you yesterday?'

'Lucas.' There was a moment's silence. I drew a breath. 'He's my ex-husband.'

'Oh. I see.'

'You can see what you want to see, Jude.'

'I know that I saw him come out of your flat first thing in the morning, kiss you and tell you he loved you. I presume that means he spent the night and that you are back together.'

'Did you see me kiss him back? No. Did you hear me tell him I loved him? No. If you'd have walked into my flat yesterday morning, you'd have seen that he slept on the sofa. You should never assume anything, Jude. Surely you know that.'

'God, I wish things were different right now.'

'Me too. Then you wouldn't have just insulted me by insinuating that I slept with the man who broke my heart the minute he walked back into my life. Maybe you don't know me at all. I will have Occy tonight, but it's for her sake, not yours.'

Gathering the blanket from beneath me, I stood and walked away, holding my head high. I walked away from someone who I had hoped just a couple of nights before might feature strongly in my future.

* * *

Occy arrived for her shift after school but was quiet and not herself at all. She was back to wearing a full face of make-up, false eyelashes, false nails, and clearly fake tan, even though she knew she shouldn't be wearing any of it while she was at work. Rachel had not long finished her shift but I'd managed to work the rotas so that they didn't even cross over and risk seeing one another.

When we'd finished work and cleared everything away, I asked her if she'd like to do some cooking and when she nodded her approval, I asked her to close the bistro's blinds.

When I told her what I was thinking of making, her eyebrows raised just as I'd hoped. It never failed to be a conversation starter.

'What on earth is a frisky pudding?'

'It's something that my mum taught us to make as children. Something that used to cheer us up when we were feeling a bit down. We used to cook together as a family. You'll like it, I promise.'

We threw together the ingredients and Occy asked me lots of questions about when Lucy and I were younger. It was nice how she was interested in listening to me talking about our lovely mum. There was a little bit of me that didn't want to tell her what a wonderful lady she was, because I didn't want her to be sad that she'd missed out on this type of mother, but at the same time, she needed to know that there were different types of mums and even mother-figures in the world.

'She sounds great, your mum. I wish I'd have met her.'

'She would have loved you, Occy. But we don't choose who we get. We were just incredibly lucky that our mum chose to be the type of mum she was.'

'That's what it's all about though, isn't it, Gemma? A choice.

And my mum chose to leave me and Dad. Nobody made her do it.'

'Well, I'm not defending her, but sometimes we feel that the choices we make are the only ones we have. It's not always as cut and dried as we think it is. Is there anything I can help with? Do you want to talk about it?'

She sighed. 'I'm worried about telling Dad how I really feel, because I don't want to hurt his feelings. And I don't know how to deal with that. He's everything to me, Gemma, and he's put his whole life on hold for me.'

She looked so desolate. I hoped with all my heart that a solution could be found for this situation.

'But remember,' I said. 'He chose to do that. Because he thought it was the right thing to do. Tell you what, while I get these into the oven, why don't you make us one of your hot chocolate specials and then you can tell me all about it.'

* * *

'I don't really know where to start,' she said once we'd sat down.

'Maybe you just let it all out and then we can start to unravel it. How does that sound?'

She gazed out of the window, seemingly focusing on a boat, out on the horizon. I knew that if I stayed silent, she would talk when she was ready.

'OK, so I know she's been a shit mum but I want to get to know her, Gemma. Before I knew she was my mum I really liked her and we had a laugh.'

'Well, that won't change. You can still have a laugh with her.'

'What if Dad won't let me?'

'Well, maybe when you've said all this to me, we can work

out a plan of how to let your dad know how you feel without hurting his feelings.'

She nodded.

'I love my Dad. So much.' A tear plopped onto the top of her hot chocolate.

We both smiled.

'Your dad is a lovely man.'

She raised an eyebrow. 'I knew it. You fancy him.'

'As I said, he is a lovely man. He's kind, generous, loving.' That eyebrow stretched even higher. 'He's a great dad and a really good friend, that's all. That's all we can be right now.'

'But that's another thing,' Occy said. 'I think he'd like more than that with you. He's scared to show his feelings. Mum leaving damaged him more than he'd ever let on. He's a big brave fireman but I think he's scared to be with someone else. He's trying to protect himself.'

I gulped. That all sounded rather familiar.

'He's had "lady friends"—' she mimed speech brackets in the air '—but when they've wanted more, he runs a mile. I've never seen him with anyone else the way he is with you. He's always happy and smiley these days. You turned his frown upside down.'

I smiled. 'That's nice, Occy, but I think you and your dad need to think about you and your mum right now. Concentrate on you. I'm not going anywhere.'

'Thanks, Gemma. Maybe Mum and Dad might get back together.'

She looked at me as if she was expecting me to answer this. Or say how I felt about it. It had crossed my mind more than once. Even if Jude didn't want to do it for himself, it might be something he chose to do for the sake of his daughter. And if he did decide this was the best option, then he couldn't really be blamed. Mum probably would have done the same for us.

'How would you feel about that?' I asked tentatively.

'I suppose it might be all right. God, they could be talking about that right now. But also, what if she's not sticking around and wants to go and live somewhere else and wants me to go and live with her? She mentioned that before. Will he want to give me up? Oh my God. What if they make me choose?'

Occy started to sob and quite suddenly her breathing started to get extremely erratic. She began to thump her chest. Her face was going red and she tried to reach for her bag. She managed to whisper the word 'inhaler' to me and I delved into her bag until I found a blue inhaler and handed it to her. After a couple of puffs, she was less red and seemed a little calmer.

I sat and rubbed her back as she nestled into me. Finally, her breathing returned to normal.

Just as we'd settled back into the moment, a loud noise began to sound off from the kitchen – the smoke alarm. An acrid smell was beginning to seep out and it was progressively getting worse. We looked at each other and Occy wrinkled her nose.

'Fuck!' she yelled out.

'Occy!'

She smiled despite the situation. 'I think I'm allowed that one.'

As I flung open the back door, I saw the smoke billowing from the oven. I grabbed the oven gloves and removed the baking tray full of very burned frisky puddings.

'Well, they were a huge success then.'

Occy laughed. 'Call the fire brigade.'

'Christ, they're the last people we need to see right now! They'd probably send your dad.'

We started to laugh and then when Occy snorted loudly, it

made us laugh even more. I threw the baking tray into the yard and wafted a tea towel at the smoke alarm.

When the smoke had cleared enough for the beeping to stop, I put my arm around Occy's shoulders and said, 'Come on, let's go and watch a film upstairs.'

She dipped her head to one side. 'You got popcorn?'

'Of course.'

'You got Netflix?'

'Of course!'

'Can we watch something with Ryan Reynolds?'

'Hell, yeah!'

'I love you, Gemma. Race you!'

I stood dumbfounded and watched the back of this brave, sassy, spirited teenager that I'd become dangerously fond of over the last few weeks. As she took the stairs two at a time, I whispered, 'I love you too.'

35

It was nearly ten o'clock and still no word from Jude. Occy stretched her arms above her head and yawned. This was excruciating for me let alone for her, although I do think watching the film had taken both our minds off the situation – Ryan Reynolds was a rather lovely distraction!

And at least Lucas had adhered to my request of him not contacting me; I was glad that was one complication I didn't have to deal with right now.

A thump on the front door made us both jump and I headed downstairs. Jude put his fingers to his lips and in a low voice asked if he could come in. I nodded and closed the door behind us but he didn't head for the stairs. The size of my tiny entrance hall meant that we were in very close proximity, and as we touched arms, I flinched when a static jolt shocked us both.

'Can I talk to you for a minute before we go up?'

'Yep, of course.'

'I just wondered how she was?'

'She's scared that her life is going to change. She's scared that she's going to lose you and she's scared that she doesn't know what her future holds.'

'I thought she might be.'

'Have you managed to sort anything out tonight?'

'I hope so. I just hope Occy approves of our suggestions.'

I picked up on the fact that he said 'our'. That sounded hopeful.

'Can I ask you one really important thing, Jude?'

'Anything.' He tilted his head and when he looked into my eyes my heart melted to mush. He was just so lovely, and in that moment I knew that I was totally and utterly head over heels in love with him. What a time to realise.

'Do I call her Rachel or Amy?'

He grinned. 'Funnily enough, we talked about that tonight. Is it OK if I go up?'

'Yep, I'll make myself scarce for a minute or two. Are you getting straight off or can I get you a cuppa?'

'You haven't got anything stronger, have you? I think we might need it. I'd love to stop and have a drink with you. Would that be OK do you think?'

'Sure.'

Despite me worrying about what he was going to tell me, I needed to know and the sooner the better so we could all move on.

'I'll never be able to thank you, Gemma. You've done so much for me and Occy and I can't tell you how much I appreciate it. You've been such a good friend to me. To us both. You're a superstar, you really are, and I'm sorry I've been a bit of an arse.'

For some reason, the way he phrased his words made it seem like he was talking about the past and not about the future. I wondered what he might be about to divulge to Occy.

'Just a *bit* of an arse?'

'OK, a huge twatting twat then. More like it?'

I grinned as I retreated to my bedroom but I left the door open. Despite my wanting to give them some privacy, I must admit I hovered outside the door to see if I could hear what was going on. Sadly, their low whispers were out of my hearing range but it wasn't long before Jude called my name.

I took a deep breath and joined them.

'You got that drink now?' he asked.

'I'll grab us a bottle.'

Occy was on the sofa, snuggled in close to her dad who was sitting in the spot that I'd been in just a few moments ago. Bless her, she looked so comfortable and she was trying so hard to keep her eyes open but within seconds was gently snoring. I covered her with a blanket and she turned the opposite way, nestling into the corner of the sofa on a big squishy mohair cushion.

'You must have the comfiest couch in Cornwall, you know.'

'I know. It's seen more action in the last month than it's had in the last two years.'

I blushed as Jude raised an eyebrow. 'Is that right?'

We locked eyes again until I blinked and looked away.

'So. How did it go?'

'As well as it could, I think. I've just checked with Occy and we've said that the three of us will meet up tomorrow. Rachel – and to answer your earlier question, she will from now on be known as Rachel – would like to spend some time here in Drift-wood Bay, getting to know Occy. So, we're going to discuss them doing that with a view to maybe it increasing to an overnight stay – if and when Occy is comfortable, and then maybe at some point even a whole weekend.'

'How do you feel about that?'

He looked down.

'Honestly, Gem? It scares the shit out of me. What if we do all of this and she decides it's all too much again and clears off? Occy doesn't really remember much about the first time her mum left, and none of us know what the future holds. I don't think even Am—Rachel knows, but if we don't try it none of us will ever know.'

'Maybe this could be the best thing that's ever happened to either of them?' I said. 'I know you're worried about Rachel being in her life, but what if she really has turned over a new leaf and wants to make amends? It could be the best thing for Occy and really that's what matters, isn't it?'

'Yes, you're right. I know you are, but it's bloody hard. It's been me and Occy for so long. We're a team. I know we've not always been perfect and she hated me when we first moved to Driftwood Bay, but since she started working for you at the bistro, it seems like life is on the turn for her. She's made friends at her new school. She talks to Lizzie nearly every hour they are not at school together. She's a different kid. She smiles all the time. She's eating better, sleeping better even. She's *happy*.'

'That's great to hear. But she's also growing up, Jude. She needs a female influence in her life. I'm not saying that you don't do a great job, but there are things that girls go through that she might not want to discuss with you. Things only a woman can answer. And I know you have women at the station, but it's not the same, is it?'

'I've got you, Gem.'

'You have and I hope we'll always be friends. And I'll be here for Occy as much as I possibly can.'

Jude bristled slightly and I wasn't sure if I'd been too abrupt. I felt like we were really pussyfooting around each other.

'It all feels like it's the right thing to do. For Occy. You're the one who has helped me to see all of that. Even if I was too much of an arse to realise it at the time.'

'And Rachel, what has she said? Do you really think she's turned over a new leaf?'

'Who knows. I don't think she knows herself, but chatting with her tonight has made me realise that maybe you can't always have the answers that you want. Rachel yelled at me earlier, saying I can't go on punishing her for something she did more than thirteen years ago. That if we want to move forward for Occy's sake, I must forget the past. She knows I'll never forgive her, but I can move on.'

'Maybe it'll be good for you as well, Jude. Holding on to everything that happened in the past can't be good for you either. This might free you too.'

'Possibly. But when I saw Rachel breaking her heart tonight, over the amount of time and things she's missed out on in Occy's life, I felt sorry for her, Gem. I'd built her up to be some sort of a monster over the years but she's not. She's just a woman who's beaten herself up for the last thirteen years for leaving her daughter. Perhaps she doesn't need me constantly reminding her of what she did and how it affected everyone's lives. And, after all, Occy's not so bad, is she? Not now?'

'She's lovely, Jude. You've done an amazing job with her, whatever you think.'

'Who knows what will happen? None of us can predict the future. Maybe Rachel *will* try to be the best mum that she can be and it'll work out brilliantly and we'll all be happy. Or maybe she'll try and she'll fuck it up again, and we'll have to pick up the pieces once more, but I suppose none of us are ever going to know until we try... It's all about Occy and her happiness, and that's all that matters.'

'And you've explained all that to Occy? She's happy with all that?'

'She wants to give it a go. I must let her be a part of the decision-making in this situation. It's her life as much as mine. She knows that there's a possibility that it might not work out the way she hopes and she's as nervous as hell about it, but she wants us to try. She likes the idea of us trying to be co-parents. She did just say though, before she fell asleep, that she's worried that if she's with her mum more that I'll have nothing else to do. If I don't have to spend all my time looking after her, I might get lonely. Bless her.'

In that instant, I felt a moment of courage. Maybe Occy wasn't the only one who had to take a leap of faith and try something to see if it worked out. We all have the power within us to change our lives. We don't need to wait for someone else to come along and do it for us. It's not anyone else's job to make us happy, it's ours. Sometimes we must be brave and empower ourselves. We just need to be prepared to take a chance once in a while.

I moved over to where he was sitting and knelt before him, took the wine glass from his hand. After taking a deep breath, I leaned forward.

'Maybe I could help you with that. After all, none of us should be lonely, should we?'

Our lips brushed, and I heard Jude sigh. Just as our kiss became more intense, more passionate, Occy spoke.

'Oh, thank fuck for that. About time, but what are you two like? Get a room!'

36

Lucy came waddling up to the bistro the next morning and I smiled as she approached. It was such a lovely day and I was having five minutes outside. She seemed to be suddenly acting and looking very pregnant and I could tell that she was loving every minute. Her bump was beginning to be quite prominent and she looked radiant, despite her telling me that she'd been throwing up nearly every morning for most of her pregnancy so far. She said it was a total swizz that it was only for the first few weeks. Almost squatting down on the chair, and sighing louder than anything I've ever heard, she subconsciously rested her hand on her belly as I made her a ginger and lemon tea.

'How you doing, love?'

'I'm OK. Feeling fat and frumpy. I'm tired and tetchy. And bloody James won't leave me alone. Says he feels horny all the time with a pregnant wife and constantly wants to put his—'

'Whoa. Too much information. Stop please!'

She laughed. 'You're a prude.'

'She's really not, you know.' Occy just happened to stroll past at that time, on her way to school, grassing me up big time. 'You should have seen her and my dad snogging the faces off each other last night.' She chuckled and walked away.

'Oh, thanks, Occy.' Lucy laughed. 'Good to know. Anything you want to share with your sister, Gemma?'

She turned to me and my face was on fire.

'Penny for them?'

I'd drifted off for a few seconds, thinking of the night before.

Jude and I had parted company a little awkwardly when he and Occy went home, and then a little later had been texting each other. He said that he and Occy had sat up talking for half an hour and were meeting Rachel today to make some arrangements.

I'd been a little concerned that we'd gone from kissing one minute to him talking about Rachel again but then he'd asked me if I'd like to go to the cinema tonight. This time on an *official* date. Not a *not-date*.

The excitement I felt at this was like nothing I'd felt before. Lucas and I had been friends before we got together but this newness with Jude, this huge thrill that I was feeling was brand new to me and I liked it. Maybe it was hope, maybe it was anticipation, even a little nervousness.

I had fallen asleep with a big grin on my face and a warm heart.

'When I have something to tell you, I will,' I said, to which Lucy raised an eyebrow. 'It's just something we're taking slow and seeing how it pans out.'

'And Lucas?'

'I've not spoken to him for a few days. While he was messaging me and hanging around it felt like a cloud lingering over me. I'm enjoying the break from him to be honest.'

'Well, hopefully this will give you some perspective. Do you miss him? Does Jude know about him? And does Lucas know about Jude?'

I pondered my sister's questions.

I realised that I didn't miss Lucas. I was more annoyed with him for coming back into my life and disrupting it than happy to see him, though I wasn't sure if it was just because of the circumstances. I was maddened by his arrogance to think that I'd just accept him back without much question after all he'd put me through.

Jude did know about Lucas, but not really everything. It was probably something that I should discuss more with him. I didn't want to start our relationship with any secrets so I would have to ensure that we spoke before we took anything any further. Honesty is always the best policy in my book, so things don't come back and trip you up later.

And did Lucas know about Jude? Did he deserve to know what was going on in my life? I didn't think he did. He had assumed he could just step back into a life that he had stepped out of. He hadn't asked if I was with anyone else. He didn't actually care. It was all about him and what he wanted. However, there was always still a little voice in my head saying, *What if you are meant to be with Lucas? What if he has changed? Remember how much you loved him once. Maybe you should give him another chance.*

It had all been quite confusing, but all I knew right now was that I was looking forward to spending time with Jude tonight.

For the second time that morning, a question from Lucy pulled me away from daydreaming.

'So what was this about Christmas that you dragged me out to chat about? It's come around so quickly, although I'll be glad to shut the B & B down for a few days and have a bloody good rest.'

'Good, because I've been thinking. I was considering doing Christmas dinner here?'

'Thank Christ for that. I was dreading cooking this year.'

We both laughed.

'Well, you do it every year but now I have more space and I was thinking about getting everyone together. You and James obviously. Mere and Clem, and we could invite her mother and Clem's dad Martin too if he wants to come. Oh and Vi too. I bet she'll be on her own for Christmas, she normally is and says it never bothers her, but it would be so lovely to have a big meal together with all the people around that are a big part of our lives.'

Vi lived in one of the houses in the harbour with her dog Gladys, and after a fall, had been building her confidence again, getting out and about following weeks of not being able to walk. It was lovely to see her back to her old self, with a great deal of help from Meredith, instead of being sent off to an old people's home which is what her grandson thought would be for the best. She had proved him wrong and had a new lease of life.

'And Jude?'

'Well, yes. If all works out between me and Jude, then Jude too. And Occy, of course. Maybe even Rachel.'

Lucy pulled a face at that part.

'Hear me out. This could be Occy's first Christmas with her mum but if we did a big dinner here, it could mean that she doesn't have to choose who to spend it with. She could have her mum *and* her dad.'

'Is that not a bit weird though?'

'I think maybe we all have to behave as grown up as we can in a situation like this. If it means that everyone is happy then it's the perfect solution. Blended families are all the rage these days, don't you know?'

She dipped her head to one side and stared at me.

'So, you have it all worked out then. When did you get so wise, Gemma?'

'I had a good teacher.' We both looked across at the picture of Mum and smiled. 'Let's make it a Christmas to remember. One that Mum would have done if she'd been here and one that she'd be so incredibly proud of. And I promise you won't have to lift a finger.'

'Now that I do like the sound of, although I suppose I could, like, sit on a stool and stir the gravy or something.'

'That would be a huge help. Thanks, sis.'

She grabbed the menu off the table and batted me on the arm.

'No need to be sarky! I think it sounds perfect, Gemma. What are you thinking? Around two o'clock-ish?'

'Well, it's still a while away but, actually, I have something else to do around midday so I was thinking more around four or even five o'clock. I'm also going to open the bistro first thing for a couple of hours to do bacon and egg sandwiches and other stuff like that. The local hiking group have said that they do a massive walk on Christmas Day morning and wondered whether we might be open. Not sure I fancy doing a big fry-up, so might keep it quite simple, but I reckon I'd be daft to turn that down. And I think it might be a cracking start to our Christmas Day.'

'It sounds like a belter of an idea. But what's so important that you have to do on Christmas Day at midday? I know you are my sister, but, honestly, you are quite mysterious at times, you know.'

'Maybe I'll share it with you soon. Just something that I must do. Please don't ask for more than that right now.'

She scrunched up her face and narrowed her eyes, holding my gaze.

'OK. I'm sure you'll tell me when you're ready.'

'Thanks, Luce.'

'Anyway, your nephew or niece is bloody starving. Don't suppose there's any chance of a full English today?'

I grinned.

'I am eating for two, you know.' She winked at me.

I'd never seen my sister look more happy or more beautiful as she did when I watched her tuck into her breakfast. She deserved this so much and I felt proud of myself for overcoming my selfish feelings and no longer experiencing that pang of jealousy that I first had when she told me she was pregnant. Now, even though I was envious of what she had going on in her life, I was simply truly grateful to be part of it.

Maybe we just had to live in the here and now, forget about the past and not worry about what the future holds. Just enjoy the moments we experience each and every day. Some people aren't lucky enough to wake up. Some people are breathing their last breaths and it's our duty to honour those people by living the best life we can.

Wow. That was profound. Perhaps, I'd just found the meaning of life.

37

'So, how do you feel?'

'What, you mean because my daughter is spending the evening with her mother for the first time in thirteen years?' He blew out a long, loud breath. 'Not sure really. Not sure how I'm supposed to feel.'

'Are you happy to go to the cinema still? We don't have to.'

'No, I'd like to go. Maybe it'll take my mind off things. Sorry, that makes me sound like I don't want to go with you. God, now I'm making a right hash of this.'

'Before we go, I wondered if I could just have a minute or two. There are some things I really want to share with you if that's OK.'

He looked worried, but I reassured him that it was nothing mega serious – just some stuff to know before he decided whether he wanted to take things further with me. I told Jude that Lucas wanted us to get back together and that I'd seriously considered his proposition, but that after giving it a lot of thought I'd decided it wasn't what I wanted. I just didn't want to go into whatever we had together without him knowing that I had considered it. I felt that it was only right.

'Is that it?'

'Yep, that's everything.'

I suppose once I'd said it out loud, it didn't seem as much as it did in my head.

'I just felt that you deserved to know what I'd been thinking. I had to be sure. And I am. Never been surer of anything in fact.'

He stood and pulled me to my feet. As he moved closer, his gaze was intense and long, and everything else seemed to melt away. He bent his head towards mine and my breath caught in my throat as I closed my eyes and moved towards him too, not a millimetre of space between us. His body pressed against mine, he gently threaded his fingers through my hair, then ran a finger slowly down my cheek. My whole body tingled with anticipation. When he pressed his lips to mine, warmth flooded through every part of my body. God, if this is how I felt when he kissed me, I could only imagine how he might make me feel when we were naked. He suddenly broke away.

'Shall we go to the flicks then?' He winked and I knew that I'd fallen harder for this man than I ever thought possible. Hook, line and sinker.

* * *

We came out of the cinema holding hands and laughing. I had made him watch a romcom, under duress of course. But we were laughing because he admitted that he did have a little tear in his eye at the point of the climax, the moment when it feels the two lovers were fated never to be together. But, as in all good romcoms, they got their happy-ever-after.

'If only life was so simple, Gemma.'

'Ah, but where's the enjoyment in that?'

'I've surprised myself to be honest,' he said. 'I didn't think I'd be able to switch off at all but snuggling up to you on that double sofa-seat, holding hands tightly, seemed to do the trick. Thanks for tonight. I've really enjoyed it.'

He dropped a tender kiss on my lips. I shivered. I had no idea how he did that to me.

'Me too. So how are you feeling now?'

'Interested to see how Occy's evening went. Intrigued to know how much she will tell me. Wondering what happens next?'

'Maybe don't press her, let her tell you in her own time. She'll be feeling all sorts of emotions right now. Throw into that her teenage hormones and she's probably ready to spontaneously combust with overwhelm. This has been a lot for her, Jude. She's not taken it lightly. Just let her take it at her pace.'

At that moment, I decided to backtrack slightly, knowing I was doing that thing again of offering advice when it wasn't asked for. Sometimes when someone told you something, they just want you to listen, not to fix things.

'Just my opinion obviously. But that's just what I'd do. She's your daughter and you know her best.'

'I do, but you're also quite wise too and you do throw another perspective at the situation. A female one too. Come on, let's go and pick her up.'

We drove the short distance to Rachel's; her curtains twitched as the car pulled up and, soon after, Occy came running down the path with her rucksack over her shoulder.

'OK, love?' her dad asked and she nodded.

'How was the film?'

Jude had clearly been paying attention to the film as he began to witter on about the plot, taking the mickey out of me for crying at the end. I grassed him up by telling her that he was quite moved by one scene in particular.

They dropped me off at the harbour. Jude and I exchanged a quick but tender goodbye kiss on the lips – with Occy saying that she would look the other way. Then she squeezed my shoulder from the back of the car and said, 'Goodnight.'

I'd hoped I might hear from Jude after Occy had gone to bed but I didn't get a message or a call so I settled down in bed and picked up a novel from my bedside table. It reminded me of my plans to organise a book club at the bistro so I grabbed the notebook and pen I also kept beside my bed to make a note. Otherwise, I'd be worrying so much that I'd forget, I wouldn't sleep and then would probably be so tired the next day that I'd forget what I was supposed to remember anyway.

I wasn't particularly worried that I'd not heard from Jude, it just might have been nice to get a goodnight text. Funny how when you are older, you feel less anxious about things like that. I wasn't sure if it was because you feel less pressure for everything to work out so you don't let it bother you so much, or because you've actually got to an age when you have been through so much other crap in your life that it's not really the end of the world when things don't quite work out how you thought they might.

But as I drifted off to sleep, I heard a text message come through. A message from Jude to say that all seemed fine and Occy had wanted to stay up and watch TV for a bit, curled up on the sofa with him, so he'd made the most of it. I sat and thought about how it would feel if we were all doing that together, playing happy families. Or would they do that with Rachel? Because *they* were a family.

I was too tired to think about it any more so just sent a heart emoji back, put the phone down on the bedside table and nodded off. I had a big day ahead of me and I needed to have my wits about me.

* * *

'I'm so glad that you invited me to meet you, Gemma, it's so good to see you.'

I wrapped my hands around the mug of coffee I was holding, trying to stop them from shaking. When he texted me to tell me he had gone away, I felt relief that he wasn't going to pop up from around a corner unexpectedly, like he had before. That told me a lot so I asked him if we could meet up when he was back.

'Did you enjoy your holiday?'

'It was OK. Bit strange being alone, but I needed to get away and, to be honest, I didn't know where else to go. Abroad and away from everyone and everything for a week seemed like a good plan.'

'It's the right time now, Lucas, for us to talk.'

'Gemma, please let me go first.'

'But I—'

He held his palm up to me, determined to say what he needed to say.

'I've been an idiot. I don't know what came over me. You were just so focused... Sorry... *we* were just so focused on having a baby that I felt like that was all that mattered to you. It felt like I could have been anyone. When I met Julie, I never meant it to go as far as it did. At first, it was just a bit of fun; she made me feel good at a time when I was feeling a bit shit. None of it was even her fault. I didn't tell her I was married until after she found out she was pregnant. And when I confessed it to her and told her that we couldn't possibly bring that baby into the world, she was distraught. She threatened to tell you everything. She was determined that she was going to have the baby come what may and said that if I didn't tell you she would. You know the rest.'

I breathed in deeply and then blew out the air through my cheeks. Wow. I'd been blaming the wrong person all along. Yes, Julie had wrecked my marriage but she'd been in an awful predicament herself. The poor woman.

'I want to do the right thing, Gemma, I really do. I love you and I would do anything to have you back in my life. I tried to make it work with Julie. After all, if it didn't work, then what was it all for? But we drifted further and further apart. I felt like I was an intruder in their life and that they didn't need me. She told me that after the split she took over all the child-rearing duties because she didn't want to impact my life too much. What she saw as helping me, I saw as shutting me out.' He hung his head.

'You know I'm not going to take you back, Lucas, don't you?'

He gave a brief nod and we locked eyes.

'I'm so sorry. For everything.'

'Life moves on. People move on. I loved you. So very much. But when someone hurts you that much, you can't always repair the relationship. It's like a plate that you've dropped on the floor and it gets smashed into pieces. You can put the pieces back together but the cracks are still there. They'll never really go away and the plate is never as strong as it was before. It could crack anytime.'

'I should have talked to you more. I wish I had.'

'The past is the past, Lucas. Let's all look forward now.'

'Are you and that Jude bloke together now?' He tried hard but couldn't help but spit the words out, his eyes pleading with mine to know the answer.

I nodded. 'We are.'

A loud breath escaped from his body. He looked down at his hands, then back up into my eyes.

'Does he make you happy?'

I smiled as I thought about the feeling I got every time I saw Jude. The way my heart flipped and my tummy felt like a million butterflies were fluttering around in it.

'Yes. Yes, he does. Very.'

'Is he kind?'

I thought back to our plans for Christmas dinner and how he had offered to help me – not just because he knew I would welcome it but also to allow Occy and Rachel to spend a few hours together alone.

'Yes he is. Very.'

'And is he kind to you?'

Without hesitation, I nodded.

Lucas took my hands in his.

'I hope you'll be happy together, Gemma. You deserve nothing more than the best. I know that might sound strange. I'm sorry that things have worked out this way. I should have behaved better towards you and I'll spend the rest of my life making sure that I never do that to anyone else.'

I squeezed his hands back. 'Thank you. Now you need to go and find your own happy. I wish you good luck and love in your life. Goodbye, Lucas.'

As I walked away, I felt a tear trickle down my cheek. But it wasn't from sadness. It was from the overwhelming sense of relief that I felt, knowing that I could now move on without the past overshadowing the future.

38

As I drove to Truro that evening, I realised that everything was now sorted, that this was a fresh start for me and Jude.

I unloaded my car and went into the soup kitchen where I was welcomed warmly with a hug from Mike, who had been managing the centre for several years. He sent two of the centre workers out to help me to unload the car. The boot was full of boxes of leftover food as well as meals I had made specifically for the centre.

'Fancy a cuppa?' he asked.

'Would love one, especially before I make that journey back again.'

'You really do go out of your way for us, Gemma. We really do appreciate it, you know. What you do for us makes such a difference. Not just to the centre, but...' He swept his arm around at the room. 'To all of these people too.'

The hall was busy. It was packed full every time I came, which was normally at night, after the bistro was closed and I had more time to spare to help out. But what I couldn't do here I did back in the bistro where I could prepare food in advance. It was nice to know that I was helping someone; I felt like it was all worthwhile.

I bade everyone goodnight, said I'd see them later in the week and headed back to the car. But as I was leaving, I could sense someone was behind me.

I felt the hand on my arm and screamed out loud.

Mike came running out, asking if I was OK.

'Yes, I am. Sorry for screaming. I was just taken by surprise. Thanks, Mike.' As he returned to the emergency exit, I eyed up the hand that was still on my arm, and then up to his eyes. 'What the hell, Jude? You scared the shit out of me.'

'Sorry, Gem, but what on earth are you doing here? You told me you were going to see an old school friend.'

'Mike *is* an old school friend.'

'Is that all he is?'

'He's also the manager of this soup kitchen.'

'So, you've come to see him? Is there something going on between you two?'

'Is that what you think of me? That I'd be seeing you *and* someone else. If that's what you think, you don't know me very well at all. You can trust me, you know.'

'But why did you never tell me you were coming here? Why all the secrecy?'

'I can't tell you. It's just... It's not something I've ever shared with anyone. I... just... can't.'

'Gemma, you're scaring me a bit now. What on earth are you hiding?'

'Why are you even here? Where's Occy?'

'She's gone to Rachel's. She rang and asked if Occy could have a sleepover. I couldn't really say no, but couldn't get it off my mind, wondering how it was going for them, so I headed round to yours and I don't know what made me do it and please don't shout at me, but I saw you going out so I followed you. I knew you were keeping something from me, but I didn't know what. I wasn't *planning* to follow you but I did. What's going on?'

'Is Occy staying over at Rachel's then?'

'Yep. Why?'

The biggest sigh escaped from my whole body.

'You'd better meet me back at mine and I'll explain everything.'

'OK, Gemma.' He paused before asking quietly, 'Are we OK?'

I smiled at him. Now I was going to have to tell the truth about a secret I'd been harbouring for the last two years. Once the truth was spoken it could never be unsaid and everything would change. And if Jude knew, then perhaps he'd encourage me to tell Lucy too. Maybe I was stupid to think that it was something that I could keep from everyone forever.

That night, the drive back to Driftwood Bay, normally a time that filled me with joy, felt like one of the longest drives I'd ever done.

* * *

'Drink?'

Jude nodded and took the bottle of brandy I'd been carrying from me, along with the two glasses, and poured two huge measures.

I took a deep breath before I sat beside him, perched on the edge of the sofa. This was going to be one of the hardest things I'd ever done. But if I faltered now, it would be harder than ever.

'When my mother died, I found something out that she'd kept from me and Lucy, a secret she'd kept for years.' Jude's brow furrowed as he listened. 'Years ago, my father left us. We were told that he'd moved away and didn't want to be part of our lives.

We were young and, I suppose, I just accepted it. However, once a year Lucy and I received a letter from him, saying that he was sorry he couldn't be with us but that he thought about us all the time and wished us well for the year ahead.'

My mouth felt dry and I took a glug of brandy before continuing.

'When I was sorting through some things at Mum's house before she died, I found a box she'd left at the back of the wardrobe. I found a letter in it from Mike, who as I said, is an old school friend but it was addressed to Mum. In the letter, he introduced himself as my school friend and that he'd been working at the soup kitchen for about six months. He went on to describe a man who had queued up for food who looked famil-iar. He said he'd been wondering for days where he remem-bered this person from, and then when he appeared again, Mike instantly remembered that he was mine and Lucy's father. He introduced himself, asked if he could join him and they began chatting. He learned that my father was terminally ill and that his biggest regret was that he never got to apologise to his family for abandoning them and that he was sorry he hadn't got in touch at all over the years. So, together, they sat down and wrote to my mum, doing just that.'

I sipped at my drink again and took another deep breath, wiping away a stray tear that had run down my cheek.

'I found the letter when Mum was poorly and didn't know what to do, whether I should bring it up or not, but it totally consumed me, Jude. I couldn't stop thinking about it. I knew she wasn't well but I had to ask.

'Because what confused me about the letter was that he said he hadn't been in touch, but he had. He wrote to us, every year. That's when Mum told me that those letters weren't from Dad at all, that she wrote them and sent them to us because she didn't want us to think that he'd abandoned us.'

'Oh God, Gemma. What did you do?'

'She was so ill and we knew she hadn't got long left to live, so I couldn't be angry with her for long.' Tears rolled down both cheeks freely now, as I remembered the night that I had stormed out on Mum. I'd sat staring out at the sea, wondering what on earth I'd do with the information I now had.

I sniffed and Jude handed me a tissue from the box on the coffee table.

'I couldn't stay away from her. She was so ill, Jude, and she asked me to promise her something – something that I didn't know whether I could do. She asked me never to tell Lucy. To protect her from the truth.'

Jude moved closer to me and took the glass I was cradling and placed it on the table. He pulled me into his chest.

'Gem, that must have been awful. So, did you ever tell Lucy?'

'No, but it's been haunting me ever since. Sometimes she mentions the letters and I have to change the subject quickly, hoping that I don't let on that there's something untoward. Lately, I've really felt the need to tell her. I know Mum was protecting us both from hurt. She also said that she was protecting our memory of Dad. That we didn't need to know that he never got in touch. She said that she only ever meant to do it once, but that we were both so pleased to get the letter from him, that she thought maybe another time wouldn't hurt. Then she felt that she was in too deep and knew that with her death, the letters would die too so that she would have to tell one of us. I'm sure she was glad it was me who happened across Mike's letter, because Lucy was more of a daddy's girl, and she didn't want to shatter her illusions for the rest of her life.'

'So, what's happened since your mum died? Surely the letters must have stopped?'

I hung my head in shame.

'I'm an idiot, Jude.'

'Why do you say that?'

'Because after Mum died, I carried on sending them.'

'Oh, Gemma.'

'I know! I know!'

'Hang on. Surely she'd notice the handwriting was different?'

'Mum had written a couple more, and was planning on having her best friend post them. But seeing as I knew, I took them on instead. I should have just come clean but Mum didn't want me to upset Lucy any more than she needed to. So, I've been posting them for the last two years. Lucy gets so excited when she sees them. But I don't know what to do now. You're right. His writing can't just suddenly change, can it? I think I'm going to have to come clean. Do you think she'll ever forgive me?'

'She's your sister and she adores you. I think even if she's a little bit pissed off with you, she'll still love you and in time will forgive you. Sleep on it. See how you feel again tomorrow.' He paused and looked at me closely. 'The one thing that still confuses me though is why have you been helping at the soup kitchen?'

'Truth?'

'The truth is always best, Gemma. I always remember my own mum saying to me that if you tell the truth, it becomes part of your past, but if you tell lies, it becomes part of your future.'

'She was so right. I'm sorry, Jude. I shouldn't have kept any of this from you.'

'I hate to think of you carrying this burden alone. To be

honest, I thought I was going to see you throwing yourself into another man's arms, so this is definitely not what I was expecting. So let me ask again. Why the soup kitchen?'

I hung my head.

'I was ashamed.'

'Ashamed of what?'

'Of what people would think. My own father had to end his days getting food from a soup kitchen. That's how he lived. Mike told me that he lived in a local hostel most of the time, he'd had mental health problems all his life and his only outlet was other women, because they made him feel good. Mum gave him a choice to sort himself out and be with us, or to move out and that's what he chose.

'No matter what he did, he was still my dad and I decided to help at the soup kitchen because...' It was so hard to say this next part. It'd been in my head for so long and saying it out loud was almost confirming everything all over again. 'I might not be able to help my own dad, but I might be able to help someone else's. Kindness costs nothing and Mike's kindness helped mine. I wanted to repay him by helping the centre and other people just like my father. So, there you go. That's it. You know everything now.'

'Oh, darling. Come here.'

Jude held me close and my shuddering sobs reverberated through his body.

'I'll be right here by your side if you decide you want to tell Lucy the truth.'

'Thank you. I do want to tell her. I know she'll be hurt, but I think she should know. Then we can all truly move on and she won't be waiting for the next letter and I won't be sitting worrying myself to death about why I can't send it.'

Jude gently cupped my face with his hands and wiped away my tears with his thumbs.

'You are the kindest, sweetest, most beautiful person both inside and out that I've ever met. You've changed my life, Gemma. Mine and Occy's lives. You really have.'

Our eyes locked. Right there before me I had a wonderful human being and I knew that I wanted him by my side forever. With him I felt like I could do anything and everything. I knew it was time to tell Lucy, and I would do it as soon as I got the opportunity.

He kissed me gently at first and then more intensely, running his fingers through my hair. The kiss became deeper very quickly and I knew that I wanted him then more than I'd ever wanted anyone before. I tugged at his hand and led him through to my bedroom where the light of the silvery moon cast a warm glow across the room. The moon wasn't the only thing experiencing a warm glow and our lips hardly left each other's as we moved across to the bed. And then he gently pushed me backwards and showered my face with tiny, butterfly kisses that made my whole body tingle.

'Occy is staying out for the night, you say?'

He grinned and nodded. As I nuzzled into his neck, he closed his eyes and I could feel his body shudder in response.

'She is.'

'What are the chances of you staying out for the night too?'

'I'd say that the chances were pretty high to be honest. You thinking of anywhere in particular?'

'I might have an idea.'

'Gemma, if you do that thing you just did to my neck again, I'm not sure I can be held responsible for what happens next.'

So, I did it again!

39

'Is everything OK, Gemma? You sounded so strange when you asked if you could come round.'

'It is, Luce, but I do need to talk to you and you might not like what you hear.'

'Gemma, just spit it out.'

'It's not that easy Luce, it's something I've not told you about before but I think that now is the right time to tell you. I reckon we both need a fresh start, and with you having your little one coming into the world soon and me having the business and well... Jude and Occy in my life now, then it's time.'

'God, Gemma, just tell me.'

Lucy's lounge was warm and cosy, as was the whole of the bed and breakfast, but her and James's private quarters were particularly inviting. When my marriage ended and I'd lived here, before I moved into the flat, it had been a wrench to leave. They'd always made me feel so welcome and part of their family.

I looked over at a photo that was on her mantelpiece of me, Mum and Lucy and took a deep breath.

'The letters that we've been getting from Dad.'

'Er... yes...'

'They're not from him.'

She looked at me blankly and then tilted her head to one side. Her expression was so hard to decipher.

'I—'

I held my palm up to stop her speaking. If I didn't get this out now in one go, it would be harder still.

'Let me explain please.'

I went on to tell her everything. From Mum keeping it a secret from us, to me continuing the lie and keeping it from her. When I'd told Jude, it was the first time I'd said it all out loud. Hearing myself say it again, this time to the person who mattered the most in the whole universe, made me feel awful. I just wanted to tell her as quickly and painlessly for us both as I possibly could.

'So, that's everything. Do you think you can ever forgive me? I'm so sorry I kept it from you but it was only because I was trying to protect you.'

Her vacant expression left me wondering how she was really feeling. I could see her mind working overtime, trying to process everything that I'd just told her. What I wasn't expecting was what she said next.

'I know.'

40

'What do you mean you know?'

'I've known for years.'

My hands were trembling and my heart pounding. What the hell was going on?

'Years ago, I came downstairs after having a nightmare. It was late at night and Mum was sitting at the dining room table writing and she put the pen down and left the room to get me a glass of water. I saw the letter on the table. When she came back, I moved away and made out that I'd never been near the table or seen anything. She shuffled all her papers together and put them away quickly after that. But I saw it, Gemma. I saw that it said, "Forever in my heart, love you always, Dad."'

'Oh my God, Lucy. Why didn't you tell me?'

'Because you were always so happy to get those letters. You thought that Dad wrote to us every year and how could I hurt you by telling you the truth? It would have shattered everything you'd ever known. My job as an older sister is to protect you from harm and upset. And then when we lost Mum, at the same time as you were going through the break-up with Lucas... I couldn't have told you then. I wanted to shelter you from any more hurt. Not replace Mum, because no one ever could do that, but as your older sister, I wanted to do all I could to protect you. I did bloody wonder how they kept on coming after Mum died, but I thought she must have asked someone else to post them. What I didn't ever think of is that the someone else would be you.'

We both laughed through our tears.

'I should be the one asking you for your forgiveness, not you asking me. I wonder why Mum never told us though all those years ago.'

'She told me she didn't want our illusions of our dad shattered. When she got the letter from Mike, she thought that she could continue that protection. If we thought she'd been lying for years, we might not have forgiven him or her. At that point, she was already ill and didn't want us to fall out with her for the last few months of her illness.'

Just thinking about this reminded me of what a painful time of our lives that had been and tears flowed down my cheeks as realisation set in. Jude was so right about lies being a burden. What a pickle we'd all got ourselves into, just to protect each other.

'Come here, you daft old tart!'

I burst into tears as I moved towards my sister and she pulled me close into her chest.

'God, your boobs are fucking huge, Lucy.' I half laughed, half sobbed and then realised I'd got hiccups.

'Ha! I know. James says he loves to—'

'No! Too much.'

She laughed and wiped away my tears.

'We've all hidden this from each other for so long because we didn't want to hurt each other.' She smiled. 'Each of us were trying to protect the other two. I couldn't have ever wished for a better mum and I couldn't wish for a better sister. If my child is an only child then so be it. But my hope for him or her is that they get a sibling and they have the same amazing relationship that we do. I know we have our moments but we've always been there for each other, haven't we?'

I nodded and sniffed.

'We always will be. I love you so much, Lucy.'

I squeezed her tightly.

'I love you too, Gemma.'

41

'Occy, can you do me a favour, love, and pop upstairs into the stockroom and grab me a box of napkins please? We need to replenish what we have down here and while it's quiet, it's a nice time to top everything up behind the counter.'

'Sure, just the one?'

'Please.'

Occy clomped up the stairs. It still amazed me that someone who was a size six in clothes, and as light as a feather could make so much noise. Funny, isn't it, how some people are naturally quiet and others are not? Occy, since the moment I met her when she burst through the door like a whirlwind, slamming the door behind her, had always had an unignorable presence in my life. Yet Pat, who was worth her weight in gold and admitted herself that she could do with losing a stone or so, glided around as if she were on castors, always appearing out of nowhere in stealth mode.

Pat and I both stood at the foot of the stairs and listened to Occy squeal as she went stampeding across the roof above us and ran down the stairs, descending them two at a time. She flung herself at me, grinning like a Cheshire cat.

'Oh my God, Gemma, thank you, thank you, thank you.'

'Well, if you're going to be staying over from time to time then you're going to need somewhere you can call your own.'

'Can I go back up and look properly now?'

Her face lit up and it was so good to see that smiling seemed to be her default setting these days. It was Rachel who had given me the idea to give her the spare room I'd been using to keep stock in and it was Rachel who helped me to clear it out. And Mere had helped to design and convert it into a gorgeous room which she assured me Occy would love to stay in; a room that was grown-up but not too serious. After all, even though Occy was a young woman, there was still a little girl in her, as there is in all of us.

I followed her upstairs and stood leaning up against the door frame as she walked around the room, touching surfaces lightly with her fingers. The walls had been papered in vibrant multi-coloured jungle paper, and there was a three-quarter-sized bed with oodles of cushions bursting with colour scattered on top of the white linen in the centre of the room. The dressing table, which also doubled up as a desk, was surrounded with twinkling fairy lights, creating a beautiful space to both study and apply make-up.

'It's amazing, Gemma. I absolutely love it. So totally vibe.'

Jude appeared behind us.

'Now, do you see that thing in the corner? That is called a wardrobe, Occy. Have you seen one of those before? It's a bit like your floordrobe at home but the clothes are kept inside it instead of on the floor.'

She came across and batted his arm playfully and he grabbed and hugged her. It made me realise what a long way they, as a twosome, had come. When I first met them both, they were like distant relatives who just lived in the same house, butting heads all the time. Now, even though her mum was back in her life, instead of growing apart, which we all worried might happen, they'd become so much closer. He was letting her stand on her own two feet a lot more, and the mature way that she had incorporated another parent into her life, as well as accepting me as her dad's partner, was highly commendable.

Seeing her standing with her arms round her dad's waist totally overwhelmed me and I had to walk out of the room for a moment. I stood looking out of the lounge window, taking in everything that had changed over the last few weeks.

Footsteps behind me let me know I was not alone.

'I can't ever thank you enough for all you've done for me, Gemma.'

'You're welcome, sweetheart. I'm glad you like it.'

'Not just for the room, even though it's proper vibe. But for all the other stuff too. The giving me a job, listening to me, getting Dad to give me the chance of getting to know my mum. It's all down to you and I will always be thankful to you.'

She flung herself into my arms. Over her shoulder, I saw Jude stood in the doorway, watching us, a melancholy smile on his face.

'I love you, Gemma.'

'I love you too, Occy.'

I kissed the top of her head and breathed in the smell of teenage girl, a heady mix of fake tan, vanilla and cheap make-up. I loved it.

'Are you sniffing me?'

'Er, yeah.'

'I might love you, Gemma, but that's just weird.'

She grinned as she pulled away.

'Can I go and grab Lizzie and show her?'

'Of course you can.'

She practically leaped down the steep stairs two at a time. Because the building was so old, every time she did it, I expected to hear her yell that she'd fallen, but she was becoming a master.

Jude strode across the room.

'Thank you for all that too, Gemma. I hope you know how much I love you.'

He pulled me towards him and held me close against his chest.

'Are you sniffing me?' I asked.

'Er, yep.'

'Weirdo.'

'Thanks, babe.'

'But you're my weirdo. I love you too, Jude. Thank you for changing my life too.'

EPILOGUE

As I walked towards the dinner table, I took in my surroundings and thought about how my life over the last few months had changed so dramatically and how we'd arrived at today.

This morning couldn't have started more perfectly, with the first rays of sunlight lighting up the room and the sunrise casting a pink and orange glow over the harbour. Jude and I gazed out while sat in bed drinking coffee, Occy's snores coming from the spare room and sleepy snuffles from the foot of the bed, reminded us of the new addition to our family. Reg was a gorgeous little eight-month-old working cocker spaniel, a tiny brown bundle of fluff and energy. When we heard that he needed a new home, we went to meet him and he completely melted all of our hearts. He was the perfect Christmas present for us all.

When we dragged ourselves from the warm bed downstairs into the bistro, we welcomed the hiking group, who were all up bright and early and in high spirits in their Christmas jumpers and Santa hats. Some even poured whisky from their hip flasks into their morning drinks to warm them through to accompany their breakfast sandwiches.

We welcomed many of the neighbourhood before they headed off to church for the Christmas Day morning service with Reverend Rogers, who we found out later had already had one sherry too many before he faced the congregation and was a little tiddly. Apparently, he'd needed a little Dutch courage before he declared that it would be his last service as he was moving on to pastures new and the church would be closing down. He hadn't been brave enough up until now, choosing to save his news for today.

While Occy and Reg enjoyed some time alone with her mum, Jude and I spent three hours over at the soup kitchen dishing up a cracking Christmas dinner. The atmosphere was jolly and festive, the queues never seemed to diminish and we were exhausted but fulfilled. I knew that when I got some time to spend with Lucy over the next few days, I would tell her the reason why I felt that I had to be involved and why I didn't feel like I could share it with her before then. Now I was at peace with the truth, it was time to share it with her too.

The Christmas tree lights twinkled on the eight-foot tree which stood in the corner of the room. I'd allowed Occy and Lizzie to decorate it at the beginning of the month. It wasn't quite how I would have done it myself but the squeals of delight we heard from them when hanging tinsel and gaudy baubles was worth the sacrifice. When Occy showed her dad, he said it was a stunner and had tons of character, after which he had raised his eyebrows and winked at me over the top of her head.

* * *

I took in the vision before me.

Lucy, my dearest most darling precious sister, looking more radiant than I had ever seen her look. Due in the spring to breathe new life into the world with her husband; the brother I never had, James. I could not have asked for a better brother-in-law and someone I knew would make the most amazing father to my nephew or niece.

Meredith, someone I know truly will be a friend for life. Brave, dependable and adventurous, and although she'd only moved to Driftwood Bay quite recently, had already proved that she would be there for me whenever I needed her. And her lover Clem, clever, super skilful and another wonderful human, who without him, the 5 O'clock Somewhere Bistro wouldn't be the thriving business that it is today.

Meredith's mother Lydia. Someone who had realised that it didn't matter how late in your life you discovered that you could change, and then did. She had decided and proved that we all deserve and can have a second chance at life. Lydia had been helping Rachel a great deal in accepting that motherhood came in all shapes and sizes. She knew this because she was determined to spend the rest of her life making up for her own shortcomings over the years to Meredith.

Martin, a lovely man, who without him letting me buy his building, I wouldn't be in the position I'm in today, and who I reckoned was getting closer with Lydia every time I saw them together. I don't know if I was the only person that spotted what I felt were special glances and smiles at each other.

Dear Violet, who was sat with a party hat on, laughing and joking with Occy as they pulled a cracker. Violet was a grandmother figure to everyone in Driftwood Bay and loved dearly by us all. Under the table, by her feet, were Gladys, Alice and Reg, in prime position, ready in case a scrap of turkey dinner might fall onto the floor where they would hoover it up quicker than greased lightning. Living in Driftwood Bay made all dogs fast at foraging, as they had to beat the scavenging seagulls.

Lucas. My past but also maybe a tiny part of my future. Watching him and Julie share a moment, over the head of their little girl who was squealing at the present she'd just unwrapped, made me smile. They weren't together any more but were working out their future, which was inevitably linked now, whether they liked it or not, by the gift of their child. Lucas needed to find his own kind of happy now. Sometimes what we think we want isn't what's the best thing for us. But he was a big boy and had to work it out for himself. And Julie, well, she was rather lovely and had been super grateful for the invite to share dinner all together.

Rachel. Someone who had owned her mistakes and was trying to make up for them every single day. We don't always do the right things in life, but we do what we think is the right thing at that time, with the information we may have. I hoped she had found peace by finding Occy and I hoped that one day she'd find it in her heart to forgive herself. I think that until she does that, she can't truly be free. She was a work in progress, but then aren't we all?

Occy. My darling, feisty, brave, fearless, kind, forgiving Occy. Beautiful inside and out. The daughter I might not have given birth to, but one I loved with all my heart. I might have not had the past with her, but I did have the pleasure of being part of her future. And with all those fantastic qualities she had, the world really was her oyster. I knew that she would go far.

And finally, Jude.

The kindest, most thoughtful, handsome, wonderful man I could ever wish to meet and someone I was so lucky to have in my life. After Lucas, I never thought that I would ever find love again. But from the moment I met Jude when he walked into my café, with his thunderous face and his furrowed brow, he'd always been on my mind one way or another.

The love I have with him is different to the love I had with Lucas – and maybe each relationship is like that. You don't replace the love you had. You just find another different kind of love, and I know that this is a deep, meaningful and fulfilling one for us both. Two people bringing out the best in each other and living their best lives.

Instead of protecting myself from love, I had thrown myself into it wholeheartedly, and Meredith was right: if I hadn't been brave enough to step into this relationship, I would have missed out on so very much.

As I looked across at the shelf at the back of the bistro, which took pride of place looking out over the whole room, I smiled at the photograph of my mum. The lady who made me the person I am today and taught me everything I know. And as I looked around me now, I looked at the people who would make me the person I would be tomorrow.

You can't change the past, but you can use it to shape the future.

Family isn't always about the people you are related to by blood. Sometimes family is a mix of people you choose to have in your life for all time. Families are all shapes and sizes these days. However dysfunctional we may be, we are a beautiful, blended mix of old and new, good and bad.

If you are lucky to have all of that together, have people who you love and who love you right back, and for most of the time get on well with each other, then you are truly blessed.

I'm so fortunate that I've been able to find my family.

ACKNOWLEDGMENTS

I'd like to thank everyone at Boldwood Books for the work you've done in producing and championing my books. Your love for the publishing business and your author care shines through and is so refreshing to see in the crazy world of publishing x

To Sandra Ferguson and Susan Sugden for your fab edits and for making sense of my gobbledegook x

To Alexandra Allden for your fabulous cover design and for bringing Driftwood Bay to life x

To Nigel Adams for being on the end of a message to answer all my fire service- related questions. And for the pictures of firemen that you sent me for *ahem* research x

To Rachel Gilbey for being Queen of the Blog Tours! You're fabulous, thank you for all your hard work in organising and sharing x

To the writing and author community who have supported me and my writing. You make the writing world a better place and don't realise how much you make a difference. Thank you to each and every one of you x

To Sue Watson, Emma Robinson and Susie Lynes; my writing retreat buddies who make me laugh like no one else ever does and who encourage me to be a better writer x

To Emma Kirkham for motivating me, inspiring me and listening to me whinging and whining on a daily basis x

To Steph Wadlow for loving my books and being a stand-in

older sister. For the laughs and the lovely meals out and lovely sisterly memories made x

To Bev Salmon, for being my bestest friend in the whole wide world. Someone who never judges me, always supports me and loves me for who I am. Love you long time x

To my sister Lisa, for being an early reader and my biggest cheerleader. Love you sis x

To my son Ollie, for being totally awesome, hilarious and the most wonderful son I could have ever wished for. You truly are the love of my life x

ABOUT THE AUTHOR

Kim Nash is the author of uplifting, romantic fiction and an energetic blogger alongside her day job as Digital Publicity Director at Bookouture.

Sign up to Kim Nash's mailing list for news, competitions and updates on future books.

Visit Kim's website: https://www.kimthebookworm.co.uk/

Follow Kim on social media here:

 facebook.com/KimTheBookWorm
twitter.com/KimTheBookworm
instagram.com/kim_the_bookworm
bookbub.com/authors/kim-nash

ALSO BY KIM NASH

The Cornish Cove Series

Hopeful Hearts at the Cornish Cove

Finding Family at the Cornish Cove

Boldwood

Boldwood Books is an award-winning fiction publishing company seeking out the best stories from around the world.

Find out more at www.boldwoodbooks.com

Join our reader community for brilliant books, competitions and offers!

Follow us
@BoldwoodBooks
@TheBoldBookClub

Sign up to our weekly deals newsletter

https://bit.ly/BoldwoodBNewsletter

Printed in Great Britain
by Amazon